THE UNTAPPED
GENERATION

THE UNTAPPED GENERATION

DAVID & DON WILKERSON

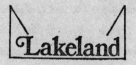

LAKELAND
BLUNDELL HOUSE
GOODWOOD ROAD
LONDON SE14 6BL

First British Edition 1972

ISBN 0 551 00258 1 (*Lakeland*)

Printed in Great Britain by
Cox & Wyman Ltd.,
London, Reading and Fakenham

CONTENTS

ACKNOWLEDGEMENTS

There are several to whom we would like to express our thanks for help in writing this book. Because of the variety and type of subject matter covered we have sought the ideas, suggestions, information, and advice of friends.

We are grateful to "mom" (Ann Wilkerson, our mother) for her help on the chapter on Rebels, Runaways, and Revolutionaries; to John Benton, Associate Director of Teen Challenge and Director of the Teen Challenge home for girls (Walter Hoving Home) for his help on the materials on prostitution; to Mary Earls, a former Teen Challenge CURE Corps worker, for her suggestions for the chapter entitled "The Trapped Generation".

And a special "thanks" to Lester Eisenberger, pastor of the Assemblies of God Church in Yonkers, New York, and Director of Counselling at Teen Challenge. Many of the counselling techniques covered in this book are the result of Mr. Eisenberger's work at Teen Challenge and from his personal counselling. Many young people, former addicts, and troubled persons, have been affected by his counselling.

We would also like to thank our secretaries, Margaret Colao and Naomi Garcia, for the many hours of typing on the manuscript.

We are grateful to Jim Reapsome, the writer, who has taken our rough draft and put it together in the form which you will read.

DAVID and DON WILKERSON

FOREWORD

This book was conceived in the struggles, throes and frustrations of ghetto counselling. Developed through years of trials, errors, and testings, the approaches mentioned here have proven their reliability to my brother and me.

The problems spoken of are not confined to the ghetto alone—they are consuming youth at large: a troubled generation from every social class who are seeking peace in dope, sex, perversion and ultimately in death. They are found in the large city ghettos, the upper echelons of suburbia, peaceful rural areas, and the "typical" American town. They vary from religious to secular backgrounds, from divorced and broken homes to close family relationships, from wealthy to poverty-stricken homes, from different races and intelligence levels.

We have tried to set down many of the basic tenets for hitting this generation's "vibrations"—to be "straight" in order to win them to a revolutionary life in Jesus Christ.

In the changing age in which we live, *The Untapped Generation* assumes a terrifying relevancy. These days could well be our last chance to reach this dissatisfied, unfulfilled yet extremely intelligent generation. Therefore it is important that our counselling make use of the most effective tools possible.

In *The Untapped Generation* these tools are revealed in a lasting tribute to the work here at Teen Challenge, and to all those working in the ghettos, small towns, rural areas and every variety of American life where youth is found.

We feel that this book will prove a valuable sourcebook to the pastor, Christian worker, and layman who find occasion to counsel *The Untapped Generation*.

DAVID WILKERSON

THE STREETS WHERE
THE LONELY WALK

The streets where the party is
  Where lights blaze and glare.
The gang and the debonair from this thoroughfare,
  Amid all the gaudiness and much seeming bliss.
Loneliness stalks its prey,
  And in death finds its way.
Oh Holy Spirit, this is my prayer,
  Make me a blessing to somebody there. . . .
                                    GLADNESS JENNINGS

The Streets where the Lonely Walk are Calling to Me

Every Christian worker and counsellor must travel the streets
where the lonely walk. And like Nehemiah of old who walked
and viewed the ruin and decay of a fallen Jerusalem, the Christian worker must view the decay of humanity and the untapped
generation. And again like Nehemiah, he must take it to heart:
"I sat down and wept, and mourned certain days, and fasted,
and prayed before the God of Heaven" (Neh. 1:4).

The Christian worker must also understand the places where
the lonely walk. The gay bar, the pot party, the heroin addict's
shooting gallery, the scum of the local skid row or Bowery, the
sexual market-place where pimp, prostitute, and pick-up gather,
the sex orgy den, and the teenage gang hideout.

Come with us along a few of these lonely streets and into
some of the places where the lost and the lonely satisfy their
craving.

Where the Grass is Not Greener

First we go up three flights of stairs to the "pad"—a lower East
Side Manhattan tenement house apartment. A pot party is
about to take place. Inside is Mark, a twenty-one-year-old college drop-out; Frank, a nineteen-year-old runaway from New

9

Jersey (usually only a weekend runaway); Sue, a twenty-year-old hippie runaway from Michigan in her second year in the Village; and Clarence, a twenty-five-year-old Negro musician from Harlem.

Like many similar gatherings they had not planned a "tea" party. They had just happened to meet on the street and decided to go to Mark's apartment. Pot is usually not planned among such groups; it just happens. Though the four comprised a relatively small group for the usual pot gathering, they decided to "groove" anyway. Mark's apartment was well-known by a select number of East Villagers and used frequently as an overnight crash pad. Others would have been welcome had they come.

The smell of incense filled the room. The small living room contained a couch, a non-matching chair, a bench, and a large mattress in the centre of the floor—and a record player. The sound and music of The Loving Spoonfuls also filled the room. The conversation (there was much of it) ranged from "What have you been doing lately?" to more serious interaction on Vietnam, Cambodia, and other feelings about the establishment in general. Frank told about a confrontation with his father over the marijuana question and asked what he should have told his dad when asked if he was smoking pot. Sue and Clarence said, "Tell the old man," but Mark felt "What he doesn't know won't hurt him." As they continued "rapping" Mark got up, went to his bedroom, opened a dresser drawer, and pulled out a tobacco can. Hand-painted over the can were the words Acapulco Gold. Returning to the living room he opened the can and took out a "joint" which was lying on top of the loose marijuana. It was approximately two to three inches in length and about three times larger than a regular cigarette. "Wow, you really like roaches (a large pot cigarette)," commented Frank.

Soon each was puffing on the stick. Although there were other sticks in the can, only one was lit. Each inhaled carefully and deliberately, taking one or two puffs at a time. There was little talking now. As the stick burned down each smoker appeared more anxious to smoke it. They knew it got better at the end. (The resins in a marijuana cigarette build up towards the end as it burns, and the effect is greater.) Each grabbed for the end of the butt. Mark pulled a clip out of his pocket to hold the small butt, and to get the very last puff. Clarence was last. "Ahh, good to the last drop," he said.

As they continued talking at first the pace of the conversation was very slow but it soon picked up again. There was a noticeable difference in their voices—they were hoarse and high-pitched yet the words were clearly understandable. As talk continued they got deeper and deeper into each subject. However, they became noticeably more relaxed. They explored some subjects on a deep psychological level, each adding his own ideas and insights. In between there were laughter and expressions of delight. Each seemed to agree with the other's point of view. The meeting continued for about two more hours as conversation was mixed with some eating, more records and music, and some pacing back and forth through the apartment. Clarence fell asleep on the couch, Frank finally left to meet a friend, and Mark and Sue continued talking together. They all felt as if they had been to a great conference to discuss a most pertinent issue, and feeling that the matter had been settled and solved.

*   *   *

The above scene could have taken place in any number of other places. A plush upper East Side penthouse, a middle-class suburban home, a small Vermont farmhouse occupied as a hippie commune, or in a campus sorority house. Regardless of where it is, thousands of bored and lonely youth, and an ever-increasing number of middle-aged, walk into such pot gatherings hoping that the grass is greener—or browner—on the other side of the fence.

The streets where the lonely go are sometimes travelled by car. In this case we are going north of New York City to a small town just off the New York State Thruway. The place is a bar—better known as a "gay bar". At one time it was for straights, but when business became poor the proprietor started catering to non-straights (homosexuals). In such an area gay bars are not as prevalent as in a large city and thus the word spreads quickly through the gay underground. And soon *The Swan* had a new clientele.

This night there were approximately twenty patrons. Two women and the rest men, perhaps all homosexuals except for a few strangers who may have been driving by and stopped for a quick drink unaware that unofficially this was exclusively for gays. Also, occasionally the bar was patronized by "fruit flies" – women who for various unknown reasons like to associate with male homosexuals.

The homosexuals themselves ranged from ages eighteen to forty-five or fifty. Some were married with families. Those who were and held executive type jobs had travelled some distance

11

to get here for fear of being found out if they stayed in their own locality. The difference between a homosexual bar and a regular one is the conversation of the patrons. At a regular bar the talk is usually lengthy and the interaction between groups of twos, threes, or fours is generally involved. Not so with the "gay" crowd. There is much milling around or standing alone, and the conversations are short. What talk there is is very superficial—and cheap. Also there is much waiting. What they are waiting for no one knows. It is as if some lost friend is about to come, or that long-looked-for lover who is going to make them live happily ever after is going to come prancing in. Homosexuals are always looking for that ideal sexual object. Often they play cat and mouse games with each other, fearful of making contact, not knowing if they do approach someone whether they will be accepted or rejected. Homosexuals have the same problem in asking for a date as young men have inviting a girl out—there is always the fear of being turned down.

One might think by evening's end in the bar that all would pair off and go away together. This is not always the case. Some sit all evening and go out as they came in—alone. Others do make contact.

The gay bar, although unknown to the great majority of American people, is one of the most lonely places on the face of the earth.

Where the Society is "High"

The place is a walk-in basement apartment of a Brooklyn brownstone house. Rachel, a thirty-three-year-old drug addict prostitute, lives there with her nine-month-old baby boy. The dark, musty-smelling, dingy four-room apartment is also the temporary shelter for approximately a dozen or two male and female addicts who use the living room as a "shooting gallery". A shooting gallery is any place occupied by a number of addicts where they inject the drugs into their arms.

It is ten p.m. as we enter. The baby is sleeping. Five addicts have gathered, each bringing his own "stuff" (heroin). The regulars have hidden their set of works (needle, eye dropper, etc.) in a corner of the room. Others take theirs out of their pockets. One addict has no works so he will share another's. Pabo, the oldest of the group, lays his "instruments of death" on the floor. The cooker, a small bottle cap, has a hair clip fitted around it to serve as a handle. Placing the eye dropper and needle in front of him he takes his home-made eye dropper holder—the edge of a

12

dollar bill approximately a quarter of an inch in width—and rolls it around the top of the needle and fits it into the eye dropper. The wet dollar bill edge serves as a sponge to secure the dropper and needle snugly together. Next he opens the five-dollar bag of heroin, licks his finger, then touches the heroin lightly. He tastes it to test its strength. He is asking himself, "Is it good stuff; is it garbage, or is it pure heroin?" If the latter is the case, this could be his last shot. Most heroin is only two to five per cent potent.

Occasionally, either by accident or design, pushers will sell stronger heroin and the result can be an OD (overdose). It is a quiet way of doing away with somebody. Pabo is assured this bag is safe. Now he puts it in the cooker, carefully scraping it to be assured that every bit is used. Then taking the eye dropper and needle he places it in a glass of water, fills up the dropper, then shoots the water into the cooker. Next he puts a match under it to heat and dissolve the white powder in the water. Taking the needle again, he draws the substance out of the cooker and up into the dropper.

Anticipation is written over his face. Quickly he removes his belt and wraps it around his left arm, making a tourniquet. Now he is pumping his arm—the veins slowly puff up. Balancing his left arm on his left leg he takes the needle in his right hand and slowly injects it into the vein. With the thumb and first finger of his right hand he squeezes the rubber part of the eye dropper. Slowly the heroin goes into his arm. But suddenly he stops and pulls the needle out. He has missed. Pabo's veins are very bad. He has been on drugs thirteen years, since he was twenty years of age. It is not uncommon for him to take two or three minutes to find a good vein. Again, he drills. Smack—"It's a hit", he says out loud. Quickly the heroin enters his bloodstream, warms his body, and once again he is "up, up, and away".

Now he feels like a new man. Taking a piece of brown wrapping paper, he puts his works inside and rolls them up and puts them back in his hiding place.

While the others complete the same ritual, he sits down in a chair to "goof" (experience the dreamy world of the heroin high). In two hours the heaviness of his high will taper off somewhat and he will go home to his wife (a non-drug user) and go to sleep. Tomorrow he will go through the same routine three times. In the morning when he wakes up, about three o'clock in the afternoon, and late in the evening. He will do it, that is, unless he gets "busted" (arrested) or takes an OD. Or he will stop if he finally makes up his mind to listen to the pleading of his wife and go to Teen Challenge. If he is fortunate enough to remain alive and does not find a positive cure, he will continue to be a member of the "high" society, and live on those streets where the lonely walk.

Where "Groupies" Group

The small basement discotheque vibrates with the pulsating sounds of electric rock. Spotlights—all of them white—hang from the ceiling and flash off and on in split-second timing and seem as though they are timed to do so with each beat of the music. The rhythm and beat of the rock sound, the loudness of the amplifiers, and the effect of the split-second flashing of the white spot lights bouncing off from black walls produces a simulated drug trip. A rock group calling themselves The Grass Stains provides the entertainment. The smoke in the small room is heavy and so is the odour, which is sweet-smelling. It is marijuana. About fifteen young people are dancing. The rest, about twenty-five of them, sit at tables talking, listening, smoking.

Dottie, a close friend of the lead guitarist, sits off to the side at a table. The music, as it always does with her, blows her mind a little. When she smokes pot in such an atmosphere she quickly gets stoned. Since she has plans with Mike, the guitarist, after the show, she trips out on the music and passes up the grass.

*   *   *

Dottie is a rock-away, which is an offshoot of the runaway generation. The rock-aways follow the various rock 'n' roll musical groups around the country getting high on the music or pot, or both. In the summer the rock-aways go to the out-of-town rock festivals and in the winter make the rounds of the rock concerts, discotheques, hippie coffee houses, or wherever the acid rock groups perform. Dottie, besides having been a rock-away for two years, has recently become a member of the "groupies"—a special group which has come about as a result of the whole rock scene. The phenomena and the popularity of rock 'n' roll music and its almost addictive influence over teenagers has created the groupies. The object of the average groupie member is to have sexual intercourse with as many members of as many of the rock groups as possible. The excitement and romantic aura that surround the life style of the young and hip members of rock 'n' roll groups lures the sexually promiscuous girl into such a group sex bag. Some girls even play the "group conquest" game which means she tries to "make it" with every member of a particular rock 'n' roll group. Groupie activity

14

may also include going on a travelling tour with the group, sharing motel or hotel room and bed or beds, or to become an "old lady"—the mistress of one particular member of a group. Some rock groups have an "old lady" for the whole group, she is known as a "mother groupie".

Dottie is a non-touring groupie, which means she does not go on tour but instead is "in" with about four different performing groups. When one comes to town she goes to the performance and afterwards participates in her own groupie performance—sex. She is eighteen years of age, a high school graduate who lives at home, when she is there. On this particular night she is dressed in long pants, and is wearing a braless blouse. Shining purple eye make-up is spread heavily on her eyelids and around her eye sockets. Black mascara covers long, artificial eyelashes—she has no other make-up. Her hair is brown and plain. When she first tried to break into the groupie scene, she wore her hair Afro style although she is white. She did this simply to be noticed. Once she got to know some fellows she didn't wear it that way any longer.

Her first affair took place when she started hanging out in the lobbies of the hotels where the rock groups would stay. The activities in hotel suites of rock stars on tour resemble an orgy, especially on the last night after a several-night stand. One night Dottie overheard several members of a group talk about a group gathering that was about to take place in one of the suites, so she decided to crash it. They allowed her in. She let two members use her sexually that night and thereafter became friendly with Mike. Every time he came to town she was his "old lady". Only she didn't tell him that she was the "old lady" for three other members of three other groups. She only hoped they didn't all come to town at once.

Where a Man Can Meet God

John sat in my office looking up with innocence written all over his face. "I don't know anything about that case, Brother Don. Honest, I don't. I am innocent." A detective had just called Randy Larson, the dean of our Teen Challenge Centre, and told him he had found out from John's mother that he was at Teen Challenge. The detective stated that he was on his way to arrest John on a charge being held against him for receiving stolen goods. We asked the detective if rather than coming over to arrest John, he could come and turn himself in. Having John arrested within the premises of Teen Challenge would not go down too well with the other young men in the programme who

15

usually have a great resentment against the police. As we further questioned John he insisted that he was not guilty. "Really, I don't know what this is all about," he said most convincingly. I finally convinced John that it would be best for him to go turn himself in and if he was innocent, I said, "God will get you out of this situation."

Another staff worker drove him to Manhattan. Once before the detective, John continued to insist that he was innocent. He spoke of the change in his life and gave the detective a rundown on the Teen Challenge programme. After hearing the full story the detective, a narcotics agent, said, "Wait here. I'll be right back," and disappeared. When he returned, he told John that he had spoken to his supervisor and that the case would be dismissed. They shook hands and John and the staff worker walked downstairs to get into the car to return to Teen Challenge. As John was opening the door he looked at the staff worker and asked, "Should I tell the man the truth?"

"What do you mean?" asked the surprised staff worker.

"I'm guilty," answered John. "I really do know what that case is all about. I lied to the man. I don't know why I did. But the Lord is convicting me now. I know I can't go back to Teen Challenge and live a lie. Let's go back up and tell him the truth."

Slowly they walked back upstairs and found the detective again. "What's the matter?" he asked. As John made his confession, the gentleman became visibly upset. He began pacing up and down the floor. Angrily looking at John he said, "What are you trying to do to me? Do you know something? I just got assigned to the detective squad and you're one of my first cases. I don't know what my supervisor is going to say. You're going to make me look awful bad." Finally, after pacing the floor trying to figure out how to handle John's confession, he went back to find his supervisor. When the two returned the supervisor came over to John and said, "Let me shake your hand. I admire you for doing this. You've restored my faith in humanity. I've never seen anything like this before. I respect you for the courage you had in coming back to confess this. We'll have to process this case and you'll have to go to court, but in the meantime you can go back with these people until we call for you. I wish you a lot of luck."

John walked out of the office proud of himself that he had faced this important crisis in his new Christian life. He knew now that Christ had really changed his life. It had only been a few weeks since John's conversion. This was not to be the last crisis that he faced in his new-found faith. He had been an addict for many years and his steps from the needle to the cross are not easy ones. But this was his biggest crisis and the fact that God had given him the strength to face it gave him hope for the future.

John is twenty-six years of age, white, from a European background. He is single, received his high school diploma in a penal institution, and also learned a trade there. In counselling sessions, when asked why he came to Teen Challenge, he simply answered, "I want to face life without drugs. I'm sick and tired of jail. I want to live a decent life."

John's trouble started in the second grade when he began to play hooky. Through subsequent years, his parents were called to school but he was always able to talk his way out of it. When he was twelve, he said, he began to drink. "In my neighbourhood the fifteen-year-olds were drinking. It was the thing to do. It so happened I hung around the older fellows. They let me drink with them because they thought it was funny." At eighteen he was sentenced to a house of detention for larceny and unlawful entry. After serving twenty-one months he was released on parole as a craftsman's helper at $60.00 per week. He felt his employer took advantage of him in paying this small amount but he was reminded that it was this job that got him out of prison. This caused him to have a considerable amount of resentment. Then he was picked up by his parole officer while he was on the job. At the time he was high on pills. He was returned to the penal institution where he remained until he was twenty-one. Then he started using heroin, cocaine, speed, and even experimented with LSD. The latter experience he said, "was a good trip but I didn't take any more because I was afraid I would blow my mind". When he finally became hooked on heroin, he spent time in two different hospitals trying to kick his habit. But both times he was back on drugs a few days after his release.

John was introduced to Teen Challenge one day when he heard some fellows talking about it on a street corner. Two of the fellows were former users he had known. He asked one, "You look pretty good. You must have just gotten out of jail. How long was your rap?"

"I haven't been in jail, man. But I was arrested. The big Man got me—God. I went to a programme and there I accepted Jesus Christ into my life. You are looking at the result." John went away from that street corner thinking that it was incredible that these two fellows had been cured. Later a woman gave

17

him a tract from Teen Challenge but he didn't read it. He said, "I put it in my pocket. I remember thinking that something must be going on. First I met those fellows who had been cured and now a strange woman gives me a tract. I felt afraid, yet glad that God was after me."

A few months later when his drug habit was getting bigger and bigger, and getting the money together was becoming more and more difficult, he pulled the tract out of his pocket and called Teen Challenge. He was told to come for an interview and was accepted. "I split (left) after the second day. The religion was not for me. All that praying and Bible reading. It was too much for me," John stated. But after staying on the streets, shooting drugs for a week, he came back to Teen Challenge again. This time he stayed for one day. Then he split again. This time he said, "I stayed on the streets a day and a half, then called Randy and asked if I could come back again. God must have really been on my side 'cause Randy let me in for the third time, and when you split like I did usually that just doesn't happen. When I returned I still felt strange in the chapel services, but for some reason I started to feel good inside. You know, it's like they say. When they feed you God in the morning, Jesus Christ in the afternoon, and the Holy Ghost at night—you start getting 'hooked'. The Spirit revealed Himself to me one day, and I don't remember just when it was but suddenly one day I knew that I was different. I just knew I was converted." From this time on John said, "This place was simply beautiful."

John's parents were glad that he was off drugs, but they weren't happy about his being at Teen Challenge. He had come from a good section of the city, and his father had a supervisory job in a good establishment. He has two brothers, one older and one younger. John states that he got along well with his father, but there are other indications from the counselling sessions that give a different relationship. His father never disciplined him, and all discipline was handled by his mother with whom he got along very well. His relationship with his siblings was poor.

His parents are devout Roman Catholics and consider Teen Challenge strictly a Protestant organization. John told them, "Would you rather have a dead Catholic drug addict or an alive Protestant?" Later John stated, "Actually no one ever spoke to me about what religion Teen Challenge believed. I see now that it was not a church but the Bible and Christ that was most important."

18

1

THE UNTAPPED GENERATION

During a Sunday evening service an alcoholic drifted into a church in New York's Bowery district. He staggered to the front and sank into a pew. It wasn't long before he leaned over and dozed off, then suddenly he popped upright.

Much to the speaker's consternation, the drunk's unsteadiness soon distracted the congregation. No amount of preaching could overcome the man's bobbing and weaving in the front row. Finally, the speaker, a Teen Challenge staff man, ended the service and went to the alcoholic's side.

At that moment a deacon also arrived and admonished the Teen Challenge staffer, "Don't waste your time. Get the bum out of here!"

Was it a waste of time? The fellow from Teen Challenge didn't think so. Just a week before, outside the same church, he had stopped to talk with an alcoholic who was doing a little panhandling. The upshot of that conversation was a new man in Christ. After a period of time at Teen Challenge Inn he had been converted, reunited with his family, and started on a new job.

What made the difference in attitudes? The one Christian saw the alcoholic as a bum to be disposed of; the other saw him as a potential member of Christ's kingdom, part of the church's untapped resources. Perhaps the deacon was guilty of what I call the sin of the Jericho Road.

Remember the story of the Good Samaritan and the man who was robbed and beaten on the road to Jericho? The priest and Levite passed by the unfortunate victim. They saw his bleeding wounds and heard his groans of agony, but they didn't really see him as a man who needed their help.

It is possible for Christians today, seeing and hearing the awful effects of sin in the lives of people, to pass by on the other side.

Do we have an eye to see the potential in the untapped generation? I recall the time I was travelling through an African game reserve. The underbrush was thick and it was hard to see any animals. But by careful observation I was able to point out some of the monkeys, lions and zebras to others in our party who couldn't see them.

That's something of the way it is when you look at the youth of today, when you peer into the juvenile jungles of our society. Some Christians have an eye for the game and some don't. In the parable Jesus told, the Good Samaritan had an eye that penetrated the surface. He saw the possibilities of rescue.

Whether the church reaches the so-called unreachables among young people depends on whether or not Christians have an eye to see them and reach them for who and what they really are. Are they attractions or distractions? Blessings or burdens? Are Christians willing to work with them, love them, pray with them, accept them and counsel them until they become blessings?

What do you see walking the streets, sleeping in gutters, shooting heroin? Immoral vagrants? Disobedient children? Unclean loafers? Yes, all that, but what else? Do you see the possibility of chosen vessels for the Lord Jesus among them? Is there among today's street people a future soul-winner, a man of God, a great evangelist, a teacher of the Word of God?

At the 1969 U.S. Congress on Evangelism at Minneapolis I gave a seven-minute response to Leighton Ford's paper on "The Church in an Age of Revolution". I asked the 6,000 delegates from a hundred different denominations how they would feel if a smelly, unkempt hippie came into their church and sat in the front pew. Little did I know then that two nights later something like that would actually happen at the Congress.

During a musical programme two hippies came into the auditorium and sat on the floor at the front. When asked to leave by the ushers, they refused and so they were picked up and removed bodily. The audience booed. Later on the speaker for the evening remarked, "I must get this off my chest. We've just thrown out of this auditorium the two people who look more like Jesus Christ than anyone else here."

While the crowd cheered his statement, the two hippies were escorted back into the auditorium. The delegates stood and applauded. Then the speaker said to the hippies, "I'm talking about phonies in the church, and I'm sure you'll catch on real quickly."

Jesus said, "Ye have not because ye ask not." It is also true, "ye have not because ye *want* not". The church has already lost too many young people because it doesn't *want* to be bothered with them. By its actions the church shows that often it caters only to preferred types of people. Former addicts and former homosexuals, for example, aren't welcome.

Such an attitude denies the fundamental nature of the church. "Surely you know that the unjust will never come into possession of the kingdom of God. Make no mistake: no fornicator or idolater, none who are guilty either of adultery or of homosexual perversion, no thieves or grabbers or drunkards or slanderers or swindlers, will possess the kingdom of God. *Such were some of you.* But you have been through the purifying waters; you have been dedicated to God and justified through the name of the Lord Jesus and the Spirit of our God" (1 Cor. 6:9–11, NEB, italics mine).

What a crowd made up the church at Corinth! Former thieves, adulterers, homosexuals, alcoholics, slanderers and swindlers—hardly a desirable group.

Of course, you can say, "And look at all the problems they caused." But who is to say the problems would have been any less, or any different, with a sophisticated, refined church? Unfortunately, today, the church prefers to have its pews filled with nice middle-class people.

The issue is not whether Christians should reach up-and-outers *or* down-and-outers. We must not go after one group to the exclusion of the other. The Lord Jesus Christ came to give His life as a ransom for *all*: the pretty and the ugly, the refined and the uncultured, the good kids and the bad ones.

Some types that we wouldn't go out of our way to help, He deliberately sought out. Take the woman of Samaria whom He encountered at the well, for example. Jesus crossed ethnic lines and social barriers to talk with her. She had had five husbands and was not married to the man she was then living with. Yet Jesus took time to sit down and talk with this outcast, one who definitely was not "our kind".

Remember the crook, Zacchaeus? He was hidden in a tree, trying to get a glimpse of Jesus as He passed by. But Jesus looked up and saw him. Even more astonishingly, He invited Himself to stay with the man who had milked the Jews out of their money for many years. That was the day salvation came to this unlikely candidate for church membership.

Or, there was that sceptic Nathanael. When told about Jesus, he replied sarcastically, "Can anything good come from Nazareth?" We might have rejected him on those grounds, but not the Lord Jesus. He called Nathanael to Himself and said, "There is nothing false in him." Jesus saw the real Nathanael through the façade of his scepticism.

Christians are often deceived by appearances. They are impressed by how bad the young generation looks and assume that this hard appearance means hardness of heart. This is a definite hindrance in reaching the untapped generation for Christ. We cannot assume anything by appearance, either hardness or indifference.

One night I was speaking at a street meeting in Brooklyn. A young fellow right in front began to put on a little show of his own. He told jokes, did tricks on his bicycle, and generally disrupted things. He was having a good time entertaining himself and the audience.

Then I spoke up and said, "Friends, you notice the young man making all the noise. Out of all who are here, he's the one who is the most insecure and the one who needs this message. That's why he's making all the racket."

I looked right at him. "Young fellow, you're not fooling anyone. *You* are the chicken. *You* are the fearful one. Why don't you stop and listen? You need help," I said.

He stopped his antics and started to listen. After the meeting, he was one of the first to ask for prayer and help. He told me, "You cut me down, preacher, and you were right. I was afraid. I just put up a big front, but the only one I'm fooling is myself. I need God. Pray for me."

The challenge of the untapped generation is all around us, not just in the slums and ghettos. Young people are in trouble everywhere, in the posh suburbs just as well as anywhere else. Most Christians feel inferior when it comes to working with addicts, prostitutes and homosexuals. They think they can only work with middle-class people, housewives, businessmen. Somehow the church must break down this emotional barrier; new approaches must be found; practical training must be given.

The purpose of this book is to help Christians reach, counsel and rehabilitate the forgotten, the overlooked, the forsaken among us. You will find hints and guidelines here that will give you the know-how and confidence you need to work intelligently and compassionately with young people with all kinds of problems.

Much of our problem is fear of addicts and alcoholics. I had to learn to overcome fear when I first started to work with Teen Challenge. I was afraid to go out on the streets and talk with gang leaders, addicts and militants. This preconceived fear was a barrier to my witness for Christ.

But I soon found out that apart from drugs, apart from the

pull of the gang, these fellows were lonely and insecure. Most of all, they wanted love and attention. I did not have to be afraid of them.

Of course, you learn not to take unnecessary risks. Addicts in pursuit of narcotics and gang members heated up for a rumble can be dangerous. You have to find the right kind of atmosphere and setting for counselling.

Further, we do not assume that these young fellows are not interested in what we have to say. Many of them put on a front; they appear to be hard, tough, indifferent. They try hard to maintain the image they have constructed for themselves. Our job is to penetrate that façade and find the real person underneath. The counsellor must probe through layers of habits, attitudes and characteristics to reach the youth's mind, heart and will.

The same thing must be done in what seems like an untroubled suburban situation. I often make the mistake of looking at the faces in congregations and thinking that these people seem to be happy and well-adjusted. Later, I find out that the neatly dressed business man is an alcoholic; the innocent-looking housewife is on pep pills; the sharp teen-age girl is getting ready to run away from home.

The Christian worker has to be a spiritual detective, wherever he is, to catch the signs of need.

One night a group of drug addicts stood outside a church. Inside, the Christians were singing enthusiastically. Soon the addicts started to dance around the street to the tune of the hymn. One of them said, "You know, those people inside have something to sing about. We're out here dancing and we have nothing to dance about."

The Now Generation, the youth of America, are dancing to Satan's beat and lyric: drugs, sex, the Playboy philosophy. They are dancing, but deep inside many of them know they have nothing to dance about.

At the same time, Christians in the church do have something glorious to sing about.What we must do is build a bridge, or a pipeline, and get what's inside the church plugged into the needs of people outside.

Too often those inside wait for those outside to come into the church. This rarely happens. Instead, the Christians must go to those outside, those who are lost, those who have no hope without Jesus Christ. The "outs" may never come in, but the "ins" can go out.

2

TAKING AN X-RAY

The most important person in counselling is the counsellor. I say to all our new staff counsellors, "The most important thing you'll learn here at Teen Challenge is how much *you* need to change."

One of our staff was asked, "How's Billy doing?"

He replied, "He's doing all right. I think he's making some real progress, but I think I'm making more progress."

Billy was teaching the counsellor lessons about himself and his own need to grow and adjust to the situation.

Before entering a counselling ministry, and during the process of counselling, the counsellor must diagnose himself. He may need to make personal and spiritual adjustments; he may need additional maturity; he may need to resolve emotional conflicts.

One of the most difficult things to do is to tell someone they are not prepared for working with addicts and distressed people on an in-patient basis. A person may be well-trained theologically and academically, yet lack personal qualities necessary for working on a one-to-one basis with troubled souls. They may love, and have a burden to reach those in need, but they do not know how to relate to them.

What are the special spiritual demands on a counsellor?

Carrying the burden and weight of another person's problems; personally confronting problems in depth; discerning the problem and presenting the answer; trying in faith to lift a person out of his distress and despair. A counsellor must have the spiritual resources to bear up under this strain. If the counsellor is in a "live-in" situation, the problems and resulting tensions are compounded.

If the counsellor is not able to carry this load, he can unintentionally do more harm than good. As will be pointed out in a later chapter, the counsellee is usually a person who needs someone of strength to look to for guidance and confidence. If he is let down, he may never recover from the experience.

One of our counsellors was asked to drive some resident clients to a camp where we were holding a spiritual retreat for them. "Will you drive some of the fellows in your car?" we asked him.

"No," he answered curtly, "I want to get them off my back."

The supervisor replied, "They should be on your heart, not on your back."

If the counsellor does not have a strong enough heart for the task, he cannot carry them. He will always feel as though they are on his back. The weak, the weary, the wounded cannot only break a counsellor's back; they can get on his nerves. Many a Christian worker in the field of rehabilitation has broken under the strain of the ministry. It is one thing to say you have a burden to work with people in trouble; it is another thing to have the qualities necessary to fulfil that burden. Few who respond either emotionally or spiritually to the need for counsellors, realize what it takes to qualify.

Some may feel that if God has called them to this work, He will equip them to do the work. It is better to say, "If God has called me to work with the addicted generation, I will—with His help—prepare myself and try to learn everything that is necessary to fulfil His call."

What are some of the qualities necessary to be a good counsellor?

1. *The counsellor must know God.*

A minister came to me and asked, "I want to help. What do I have to do to get started?"

I said, "Be convinced of your own personal relationship to Jesus Christ. You have to know where you stand with God."

Unfortunately, he had great doubts about the fundamentals of Christianity as they applied to him. He had a seminary training; he was a well-educated man; he was sincere; he was willing to help in any way he could. Yet he was not qualified. He did not know God. Deep inside he was aware of his doubts, but he hoped by working with addicts and others whom he felt were less fortunate than himself, he might find some answers to his doubts.

Many qualities are necessary to be an effective Christian counsellor, but the foundation stone upon which all other qualities are built is a vital and growing relationship with Jesus Christ as Saviour and Lord.

A young college graduate asked me, "I have a degree in sociology. Would you hold that against me if I were accepted in the work of Teen Challenge?"

"No," I said, "as long as you were first of all trusting in

Christ, rather than trusting in your training and in your technical knowledge."

Her education and training would be great assets, if used properly and kept in the right perspective. On the other hand, it is possible to look for answers in secular training rather than trust in God.

2. *The counsellor must know himself.*

The counsellor must have insights into his emotional needs, as well as his spiritual needs. Self-understanding is important. The counsellor must know his weaknesses, and not let them hinder the counselling process. His own feelings, attitudes, even his prejudices, can throw a smokescreen up between himself and the counsellee. If the counsellor knows what his weaknesses are, and if he asks the Lord to help him overcome them, they need not be a hindrance.

A counsellor must ask himself, "Why do I want to help someone? What are my motives? Am I trying to work out some personal hang-up? Am I trying to fulfil a personal need only?"

Everyone needs to be needed. Christian ministers and workers do not have a sense of fulfilment unless they are helping others; that's why they feel they have been called by God to Christian service. Yet the counselling process can be used simply to serve one's own needs and not primarily those of others. A counsellor can be using it as a tool to work out his own feelings of frustration, or rejection by his peers, or for other personal reasons.

A certain counsellor kept questioning a client about his sexual life. Although this was not the real problem of the counsellee, it was the real problem of the counsellor. He was using the counselling sessions as an X-ray to diagnose his own problem. He was projecting his problem—a major one—on to the counsellee, even though it was only the counsellee's minor problem.

A noted psychiatrist warned counsellors, "You have to be careful you're not writing a contract in which you want something back from him [the client]." The counsellor must not have, without his being aware of it, a need to be needed, a need to cure someone, to be important to someone.

3. *The counsellor must know how to relate to others.*

He must not only *have* love, he must know how to share it. A person may be sincere, well-adjusted and compassionate, yet not have the ability properly to relate his love to others. Tom Skinner calls this process "fleshing out Christianity". The old cliché applies here: "It is easier to preach sermons than to live them."

How do you show love? How do you relate to others who don't want you to relate to them? How do you relate to those who want you to relate to them, but don't know how to accept your love? The greatest obstacle the counsellor must overcome is bridging the problem gap. How do you bridge the gap between the person with a problem and the one trying to help?

The counsellor, especially if he's a clergyman or someone closely identified with the church, will have the hardest time bridging this gap. He will be viewed as giving advice from his pulpit position as a professional.

The counsellor must talk across the table, shoulder to shoulder, not with an "I'm up here, you're down there" attitude. The counsellor's interest, sincerity and love must be conveyed, not through his ministerial position, or with religious jargon, but with a soft voice and simple words. Often a counsellor will talk *at* the needy person, rather than *with* him.

Counselling must not be done from a superior position. The counsellee must be accepted as a person of worth. He must not be given the impression that he is inferior.

The counsellor-counsellee gap can originate in the mind and attitude of either. On the one hand, the counsellor can be so dignified, so aloof, so unable to relate that he is the cause of the barrier; on the other, the counsellee may feel that because of his problems he isn't worth listening to.

Regardless of who creates the barrier, the counsellor must learn to break through it and relate to the counsellee. One of the greatest comments that can be given to a counsellor is, "You're coming through, preacher."

Role changing is important in knowing how to relate. The minister must move from his preaching role to that of a friend. The parent must change from his role as an adult to that of a companion of youth. The teacher must change from the role of instructor in the classroom to that of a concerned Christian friend outside the institution.

Some people find security in remaining in their one role. They seek respect, or demand it because of their position, but they do not earn the respect of others by relating to them as a friend on a man-to-man basis.

When clients come to live at Teen Challenge, there is a certain amount of respect they give me and I can request it because I am the director. If that is the only right I have to be heard, if that is the only basis on which I can ask for a hearing, then I have become glued to my director's role; I have created a wall of dignity, professionalism and position around me. I may never get through to my clients.

In my book *The Gutter and the Ghetto*, I wrote of my experience of coming from Bible college to the streets of New York. I did not know how to relate. I was comfortable in the pulpit within the confines of the church, but I was like a fish out of water on the streets. I had to learn to be accepted for who I was—apart from the church and apart from the fact that I was a preacher. I had to learn to accept each individual for what he was—alienated from God, the church, and myself.

There is another extreme to be avoided in relating to people. It is possible to go too far. This is the opposite of the "I'm up here, you're down there" attitude. It is the counsellor's loss of respect, dignity and leadership, caused by his going too far in trying to identify with a client or prospective client. There is a difference between being accepted and being so aggressive the counsellor turns off the client. The outsiders, the sinners, run away from zealous Christians who force themselves on them. In trying to break down alienation, the counsellor can make the gap wider.

A certain counsellor made the mistake of developing the attitude, "I'm one of you fellows. I'm with you." He felt he had to get into their clique. But they didn't want him to become a member of their gang. The moment he went too far, he lost their respect.

In our resident programme, counsellors are warned against developing a buddy-buddy relationship with clients. It is a matter of learning how to identify, how to relate without getting so close that the counsellee no longer sees the counsellor as a counsellor, but just as a buddy. The counsellor must win the client as a friend before he can lead him to Christ, but no progress has been made if he has *only* gained a friend.

Too many well-meaning counsellors, or those who are trying to play the counselling role, have been fooled by clients who were friendly to them, but did not actually make any progress towards changing. There comes a time in the counselling process when the counsellor must say and do things he would hesitate to do to someone he considered a close friend. This is the reason why identification must be maintained, but not at the expense of losing the proper working relationship between counsellor and counsellee.

In the close relationships that develop between counsellor and client, many disheartening things have resulted. Male counsellors have been emotionally, romantically, even sexually involved with a female client. Even in a man to man or woman to woman situation, there can be an emotional involvement that blinds the counsellor to the counsellee's real problem.

A further problem is overdependence of the client on the counsellor. The client needs a shoulder to cry on, but not a crutch to lean on. The counsellor can become the client's substitute saviour. As long as the counsellor is around to lean on, the client can function; when the counsellor is removed, the client goes to pieces.

The counsellor must know when to maintain close identification and when to remove himself. Clients must not be spoiled. Counsellors must not have pets or special cases.

In learning how to relate to a counsellee, the counsellor must come off as a person sincerely interested in his client. He must not appear to be counselling out of a sense of duty or obligation.

A counsellor can act as though people with their problems are an intrusion of his privacy. If a client suspects the counsellor is serving out of a sense of duty, and not because he has a real and actual interest in the client, the client will withdraw from the relationship.

We have a saying in our Teen Challenge resident treatment programme, "Are you serving from the schedule or from the heart?" The counsellor's duties must not appear to the client to be just a job. Drug addicts can spot a phony. They are keenly aware of the difference between those who are interested in them as persons and those interested in them as addicts.

Counsellors must not use clients for their own ends. Some counsellors simply want to gain some experience. Others are looking for a story, for some excitement and glamour, or just for a good case history. They may be totally unaware of the individual's inner feelings and struggles. Such counsellors may throw scripture at a client and show him a superficial love. This kind of counsellor will only try to keep his client on the hook until he gets his story and his own ends are met. This kind of exploitation has been the pattern of many counsellors in the past. If the client senses that the counsellor, too, is only using him, it can be an experience from which he will never recover.

4. *The counsellor must know how to react properly to the counsellee.*

It is possible for a counsellor to be able to relate and to get inside his client, but not be able to react properly. An x-ray of a person's physical, psychological and spiritual make-up can help the counsellor formulate a right reaction. There are reasons why people act the way they do. Behaviour is not a matter of chance. We've all heard the familiar excuse, "Well, that's just the way I am. That's just me." The counsellor's task is to find out *why* a person acts the way he does, in order to try and change that pattern of behaviour.

Developing a right attitude towards the person being counselled and accepting him as a person of worth is important. This means accepting him with all his sins, hang-ups and problems. I have seen counsellors spend much time trying to win someone, trying to relate to him, but when they got inside the person they were quick to judge him. They reacted in a way that prevented them from properly understanding their client.

What are some improper reactions to clients?

1. "This person doesn't want help." This may be true, or it may just appear to be true. In most cases it is a matter of trying to understand the client's reactions. He may show the opposite actions and attitudes from the average person. He may be hostile just to see how the counsellor reacts to his hostility. He may act indifferently as a cover-up. All of his actions may be deliberately calculated to test the counsellor's reactions.

Rather than deciding the client doesn't want help, the counsellor might better say, "He does not know how to accept help." Everyone wants help. It may be a matter of not wanting your kind of help. Or the client may not see that the kind of help the counsellor is offering him is the kind of help he needs.

2. "He is just no good." I've driven guests down the streets of New York where groups of men have been standing on street corners in the ghetto, and someone has remarked, "Look at those lazy bums; they just sponge off the taxpayers' money." There are spongers, but there are also young people who stand on street corners because no one has given them reason to do anything else. No one has tried to understand their lack of motivation. There are reasons why men stand on street corners and wait for their welfare cheques, why they drink, and why the young men wait for the narcotics pushers. These reasons have nothing to do with laziness, the taste for alcohol or drugs, or the fact that they are "no good". If a counsellor has such an attitude, it will affect his approach to the individual and his problem.

3. "I think he's a nut." Some people do have mental disorders. Often a client will ask me, "Do you think I'm crazy?" Or, they will comment, "I know there's something wrong with

me." The counsellor must react in a way that will ignore the client's feelings about mental disorders, but at the same time he must keep in mind the seriousness of the person's problem. He might be a mental case, but he should not be treated any less cordially because he is.

Answering Some Questions

The following questions are related to the material above. These are some of the questions most often asked by those wanting advice on how to deal with the untapped generation.

1. Is it necessary to have been an addict to reach one? If you have been a runaway, rebel or hippie are you better able to reach others with the same problem? If you are a middle-class white, can you effectively work with blacks in the ghettos?

It is not experience alone that qualifies a person to work with those in trouble and distress. Training and experience are necessary. Training in understanding a person's spiritual, emotional and psychological needs is most important. There are many so-called experts in the fields of drug addiction, juvenile delinquency and other related problems who can tell you all about drugs, addiction and misbehaviour of all kinds, but they are not qualified to work with the individuals afflicted by those maladies.

Former alcoholics, drug addicts, prostitutes and homosexuals often have an advantage over others who have not had such problems, in that they can understand the feelings, attitudes, weaknesses and hopelessness of those who have problems. But unless they have the ability to counsel, to relate to people in need, and to react properly to those with such problems, their understanding alone will not qualify them to be successful counsellors. Often former addicts do not have the maturity and spiritual depth to stick with persons involved in problems.

In a residence programme converted addicts, if properly utilized, can be of great service. They can detect problems in the new cases that other counsellors cannot. The convert-counsellor can detect insincerity more quickly. He cannot easily be fooled. He knows the ropes. The counsellor who has never been an addict is often too soft, too trusting and more easily fooled.

Convert-counsellors should not be used as such until they have had sufficient time to develop in their Christian walk. While a counsellor who is a recent convert may be able to relate immediately to a new client, he may not know how to react. That's because he may be struggling in his own spiritual life.

The new client will listen to the recent convert who has had his same problem. But when the going gets rough, if the recent convert-counsellor reacts improperly, all his good relating will go down the drain.

The convert from drug addiction, alcoholism and so on must take time to get Bible training and to prove his Christian testimony. However, any Christian worker, regardless of his background, can overcome the counsellor-counsellee gap.

2. How do you bridge the cultural, social, ethical and religious gap between the counsellor (especially one raised in a middle-class Christian atmosphere) and the client?

My own background could not have been more opposite to that of those with whom I work. This is true of many who want to reach the untapped generation. Bridging this gap is possible, but difficult.

The first step is to get the picture. The counsellor must get out where the sinners are. The first thing we do with new staff workers is get them on the streets, out into the neighbourhoods and communities where all the trouble starts. No counsellor can be effective until he has been exposed to the scene. He must see the sights, hear the sounds, smell the odours of the ghetto, the gutter, the skid row, the hang-outs. How do you do this?

If you are a pastor, take a day or night and go into the problem areas of your town. Find someone from that section to to take you on a tour. Call the police department and ask if you can ride in a cruiser on a night tour. See humanity at its worst. Meet the people, talk with the children, the teens, the parents. Get into the homes, the apartments. See how the other half, the have nots, live. Let some of the atmosphere soak in.

Go through the flophouses, visit the jails—go everywhere or anywhere so that you can develop the full image of their distress and difficulties. See addicts and their addictions. See the gay bars where the queens hold sway. Watch the hustlers make their contacts for the prostitutes. Such a tour does not turn a person into a qualified worker or counsellor, but it's a place to start.

Assuming the counsellor knows God, that he knows his own weaknesses and has submitted them to the Lord, and that he is seeking to counsel for the sake of others and for the glory of God and not for his own ends, here are some other characteristics he should possess to make a go of it. He should:

1. Not be given to anger.
2. Be able to accept criticism.
3. Not be given to prejudice (racial, religious, social).

4. Not be subject to moods of depression.
5. Have a sense of humour (ability to laugh at himself).
6. Not be given to over-optimism.
7. Not be given to pessimism.

3

THE CONQUEST OF
INNER SPACE

The counsellor must determine his goal. What result does he hope to achieve? Jesus said, "According to your faith, be it unto you." The same may be said for the counsellor and counselling. What he thinks, or believes he will accomplish, that he most likely will achieve. As a Christian, the counsellor must see that the ultimate will of God is for an individual life, and let this be the goal he hopes to help his client obtain. Anything less might be commendable, but still not be the attainment of his goal.

To accomplish his highest purpose, the counsellor must understand the crux of everyone's problem. The problem is basically one of the heart. The Scriptures say, "Keep thy heart with all diligence; for out of it are the issues of life" (Prov. 4: 23). Also, "Out of a man's heart, come evil thoughts, acts of fornication, of theft, murder, adultery, ruthless greed, and malice; fraud, indecency, envy, slander, arrogance, and folly" (Mark 7: 21, 22, NEB).

This is what makes the Christian counsellor's approach to all problems different from the non-Christian counsellor's approach. The Christian sees all problems as starting with the heart. The problem of the heart is sin. The non-Christian counsellor may give it other psychological names, but Christ calls it sin; as sin it must be dealt with. If the counsellee's problem is viewed in this context and properly dealt with, there will always be the potential for success.

Sin has various manifestations. Sometimes a person's problem is caused not only by his own sin, but by the sins of others inflicted upon him. Regardless, the basic problem is still individual and personal sin. The outward manifestations of sin might be drug use, alcohol consumption, sexual perversion, delinquent behaviour, violence, etc. But these are only the signs of deeper problems. Underneath may lie rebellion, bitterness, hate, anger, fear, loneliness, depression, etc. The outward acts of misbehaviour are only the top of the iceberg.

I do not believe a man is fully qualified to counsel until he views a person's problem morally and spiritually. State and federal institutions have failed in criminal rehabilitation and in the rehabilitation of the addict because they do not provide for dealing with spiritual needs. I believe in the separation of church and state, organizationally and institutionally, but you cannot separate a person's bodily and mental needs from his spiritual needs. Therefore, every institution should provide the opportunity for a spiritual ministry.

If there is a religious worker on the staff, he is seldom on the same level with the psychiatrist, the psychologist, the social worker or the vocational therapist. A person's religious therapy is left up to him; other forms of therapy are not. Other therapy is a regular and required part of the so-called treatment. The chaplain may be there. But when he is, he is shoved so much into the corner that he cannot instil faith into his clients. The relegation of religion and God to the lower rungs of the treatment ladder results in the failure to get to the core of the patient's problem and need.

Teen Challenge has been successful because we deal with individuals as sinners who can be delivered by the power of God through Jesus Christ. We have learned that drug addicts are not sinners because they are addicts, but *they are addicts because they are sinners*. We have been accused of over-simplifying the problem. But the results speak for themselves: approximately 70 per cent of those who graduate from Teen Challenge remain clean from drugs and continue to live a productive Christian life. No other programme or organization can make such claims. We have found the key. Christ can conquer the inner space of the heart. Since "out of the heart are the issues of life", treating the heart first, or along with treating the body, makes sense. The way to solving a man's mental, social and physical needs is through his heart.

The counsellor must aim for the heart. He must seek to lead his client to the knowledge of Jesus Christ as personal Saviour. Christ has power to conquer and defeat the sin nature of the heart, the nature that causes the specific acts of sin. If the counsellor does not aim to do this, there cannot be total success. In many cases there will be complete failure, or at best, only limited success.

There are multitudes of ideas about the problem and its solution. When one person talks about "helping someone", he may have one goal in mind, while the next person may have an entirely different concept. New programmes appear every day with new approaches.

The problem of drug addiction puts this into focus for us. There are various approaches to this problem. At one time the medical profession was thought to hold the key to a cure. One doctor stated, "It's a medical problem and the layman should stay out of the field of drug addiction treatment." It was felt that the addict's problem simply was drugs, so the answer was to get rid of the drugs in the body and the addict would be cured. However, it was soon discovered that addicts left the hospital only to shoot up dope within hours, even minutes. The hospital became a place for the addict to get rid of his physical dependence on drugs. He knew he would not find a permanent cure. Drugs were taken out of his body, but his craving remained. Furthermore, the reason why he used drugs was not found.

Psychiatrists have attempted to deal with the drug problem too. They take into account the emotional, psychological and sociological factors that contribute to the use of drugs in the first place. This approach has produced only fractional results. The psychiatrist can diagnose but he can't deliver. He can analyse but he can't provide the inner strength and motivation needed to overcome the problem. A problem that has been effectively analysed and brought out in full view of the afflicted person, without the hope for change, is double trouble.

One fellow told me, "The psychiatrist told me about problems I never knew I had before. So when I came out of the hospital, I left with all the problems I carried in with me, plus all the new ones I picked up from the head shrinker. I ended up with twice as many hang-ups, and still no solution to my situation. I went deeper into drug addiction as a result."

I have seen this happen all too often. The despair immeasurable for the addict who has been made aware of what is wrong with him, but is bereft of the influence of hope, faith and love! Such despair adds to his addiction and plunges him into deeper anti-social acts and self-reflecting behaviour.

Another fellow said that after many counselling sessions with a psychiatrist who had helped to pin-point some deep-rooted feelings of hatred towards his brother, he finally came to realize that such feelings did indeed exist. "What should I do?" he asked the analyst. The answer was simple: "Start trying to find some love for him and show it whenever you get the opportunity." The young man returned later to talk to his psychiatrist. "I've got another problem now," he complained. "Where do I get that love I need to show my brother? I know I need it, but where do I find it?" One problem had led to a further one.

His dilemma serves to illustrate a point. Unless the person in need finds something outside himself, or finds some outer force to enter into him and provide the strength to overcome his problem, then the psychiatric approach is more harmful than helpful. Many come out of the counselling session confused and confronted with knowledge about themselves and their problems that they are totally incapable of doing anything about.

* * *

Another popular method of treatment for addicts and alcoholics is the self-help method used by various non-professional groups. There has been some measure of success with this approach. The key to it is addicts or alcoholics helping others who are hooked. Each has a chance to talk about his problem. Some treatment programmes use a group therapy method known as "encounter sessions". In these they "tell it like it is" about each other. No holds are barred. Everyone's attitudes, feelings and behaviour are scrutinized by the rest of the group. No one is allowed to hide or play the phony role. Each person is brought face to face with himself and with the truth about what he must do to recover. A certain standard of behaviour is maintained, such as total abstinence from drugs (for addicts) and alcoholic beverages (for the alcoholic). Certain other disciplines are also strictly enforced.

This approach incorporates some good elements, but it has loopholes. No inner controls are provided. There is no acknowledgment of God; the standard of moral behaviour is left open to question, since each group establishes its own. What if a small group within the larger group should vote a different standard? What happens when the addict is away from the group?

Sometimes leaders exert undue influence on the group. Such was the case with the Synanon group in California. The leader started viewing himself as the messiah of the addicts; everything revolved around him. The treatment programme turned into a cult of leader worship.

What can be learned from these groups is that the addict needs to find a relationship with a higher being to find a standard of behaviour to pattern his life after, and a motivating force to give him the strength to make the difficult journey out of the deep hole of addiction, depression and perversion.

The most important element is left out of the counselling in all of these programmes. The counsellee is not led to the conquest of inner space. Each programme denies the dynamics of a spiritual encounter with supernatural power. The psychiatrist or counsellor becomes a substitute god or saviour, rather than the agent to lead the one in need to the God and the Saviour. The patient-helping-patient approach means they are using one another as priests and lords. The client must always have the support of the group; otherwise he is left alone to work out his problems and face the obstacles involved.

If the counsellor cannot present a way of life that enables his client to be born anew from above, then at best he is only going to lessen his miseries. A girl who was under treatment by a psychiatrist was asked if she was doing any better since her visits to him. "Well," she said, "I'm not better, but I'm less sad." If the counsellor knows God, and if he can present the truth about the Conqueror of the ages, Jesus Christ, there is every hope of a lasting recovery for the client.

The conquest of inner space must go by various routes. The journey inside man, to deliver light and life through Christ and by the Holy Spirit, must be done in various stages and through such routes as the physical, psychological and sociological aspects of the client's problem.

When I said that the counsellor's goal and highest task is to lead his client to a saving knowledge of Jesus Christ, I did not mean that we are to by-pass his physical or material needs. Spiritually speaking, the way to a man's heart may be through his stomach, or wallet, or family. The client's temporal needs dare not be neglected. We must not be so concerned with souls that we forget lives. There is a balance and we must find it and minister accordingly.

I am greatly concerned about those who relegate the mission of the church to feeding the hungry, aiding the poor, binding up wounds of the body—involvement in temporal needs—and then call it quits. Such social involvement is commendable. The Christian humanitarian with a social conscience is often hard to find, especially in evangelical circles. The Bible backs up the social activist. It speaks of giving "cups of cold water" in Christ's name. Jesus warned, "When I was hungry you gave me nothing to eat, when thirsty nothing to drink . . . when ill and in prison you did not come to my help" (Matt. 25: 42, 43, NEB). The world suffers today because the church has often failed to see this as part of its mission.

However, the Christian counsellor dare not limit his calling to meeting social needs. Does the man to whom you've given the cup of cold water have the living water in his soul? Will you leave him with a full stomach but an empty heart? Does the one you have visited in prison know about the One who broke the prison bars of sin and death? If I had to choose, I would rather go to heaven on an empty stomach than to hell on a guaranteed annual income. This is not to say I oppose or approve of guaranteed wages; it is to say something about priorities.

A drug addict told me, "I went to a minister to ask for help. He gave me five dollars, and sent me on my way. I could understand that he might not know how to treat an addict, but he could have at least prayed for me. He didn't even tell me about Jesus." I wish my liberal, social activist friends would hear and heed this message. Perhaps the word is written to them.

We have had many come to Teen Challenge and say, "I want to help. I want to work with addicts." The sad part is that they have not been rehabilitated themselves. They do not know how to pray. They do not know how to lead a soul to Christ. They would gladly wipe the sweat off a brow, carry cups of cold water, or soup, but they do not know how to minister to the heart. In the absence of a mission to save souls, they have taken up the cause of saving lives. Again, I admire and commend such a commitment. Its only fault is it does not go far enough. It is a commitment more to earth than to heaven; more to the body than to the soul.

Perhaps one reason our liberal friends have forsaken the gospel to "wait on tables", so to speak, is because some evangelicals bathe themselves in the sunshine of God's love, while millions of people are suffering the bitter pains of human existence. I believe in the rehabilitation of men's bodies, minds, marriages and work habits just as strongly as I believe in the salvation of their souls. The evangelical can be so hung up on reaching men for Christ that he fails to see that the man he is trying to reach might be out of a job, need an education, and be the object of discrimination.

Man's spiritual and material needs are not two different bags; they are one bag and the counsellor has to get into that bag by whatever means he can. We cannot compartmentalize man and his needs. The secular world acts as if the soul does not exist; the sacred world acts as if the body does not exist.

One man, commenting on the strong evangelical approach taken by Teen Challenge, said, "I'd rather give a drug addict two slices of bread than a gospel tract." It so happens that we give them a tract along with the two slices of bread.

Sherwood Wirt in his book, *The Social Conscience of the Evangelical,* said:

> Why does the move towards social involvement seem to require a rejection of Biblical Christianity, why must the one accompany the other? What is there in the present age that seems to make it mandatory for a man to move from orthodoxy to atheism before he can be taken seriously in his quest for the good of humanity?
>
> Some people who are concerned to affirm social change are also inexplicably denying the reality of spiritual change in persons. . . .
>
> Jesus never for a moment believed that his kingdom would be rung in simply by an improvement in the external conditions of human life. . . .
>
> When a man becomes a believer he does not retreat from his responsibilities as a member of society.[1]

Bill Milliken wrote in *Tough Love:*

> We have to change our cities. We need to replace rotten buildings. We must bring education to ghetto people. But if we aren't giving equal rights to their hearts, if we aren't giving them ourselves as well, the problem will never be solved. Nice, big, new houses don't answer the cry of the hurt heart. Any look at the statistics on the number of alcoholics behind expensive suburban doors will show that. Better clothes, better homes, better schools don't give the complete answer. People want more than material things, they want more than eight hours of your day, or a job, or analysis. They want your heart. But we have to give our hearts with no strings attached. We can't say, "I'll love you if you'll come my way, if you'll believe what I believe. If you follow Christ, then I'll love you." We must remember He loved even those who did not love Him.[2]

We must meet people in need where they are. If they are socially or materially well, and their need is basically spiritual, then the counsellor can get down to the business of conquering inner space. But if the client has immediate external needs, then the counsellor must begin there. If he is destitute, we must minister to his destitution. If he is hungry, we must feed him. If he is in prison, we must visit him. And we must not turn him off, regardless of the circumstances of his destitution. We cannot ignore someone because "it's their own fault". We dare not take

40

the attitude, "Well, he made his bed; now let him lie in it". It is not ours to judge or condemn his failures.

A young man came to us in dire physical straits. Among other things, he suffered from hepatitis, a common problem among drug addicts, contracted by using a dirty needle when injecting a shot of heroin into their veins. We helped him get admitted into the hospital, which turned out to be a difficult project in spite of his apparent suffering. Later he returned to Teen Challenge to enter the rehabilitation programme. But while he was in the hospital various staff members visited him, took him slippers, newspapers, candy, reading material and other things. The fact that he was being treated kindly even before he had come to Teen Challenge, and even before he had accepted Christ, was more than he could understand. He said, "I've never had anyone do anything like that for me—ever—in my whole life. You people were total strangers, and you treated me like an old friend."

Another young man, after being at Teen Challenge for two months, stated, "What really touched me was when this white fellow came to my room and when he saw that I was not feeling well asked if I wanted a back rub. Here I was, a dirty, greasy dope addict, and this fellow was soothing my back with rubbing alcohol."

Such simple acts of kindness are often the wedges into a man's soul. Even the most simple deeds can mean so much. Sherry, a girl who had just come out of prison, was greatly affected one day when a counsellor came to her room while she was making her bed and assisted her in this chore and chatted with her. Sherry said, "She didn't preach or counsel with me, she just treated me nice, and this impressed me so very much."

Sometimes a person's external problems are serious. They may be pressures that weigh on the individual or they may be road blocks hindering him from finding the spiritual help he wants and needs. Providing assistance may mean the counsellor has to give up a day of his time to help the counsellee take care of some business. It may mean a difficult confrontation with a parole officer, with an alcoholic's wife, or with a drug addict's family, or persuading the loan company not to press charges until the person is rehabilitated enough to assume his personal debts again. It can also mean a personal financial investment in this person's soul. At Teen Challenge it has sometimes meant arranging child care for a girl addict's baby.

Whatever the external problem, we must use this as the point of contact to get through to the client. These are the routes we

41

must travel to conquer inner space. You may have to go via the stomach, the wallet, the mind, or various other routes, whatever is necessary to get to the heart. Whatever is necessary, as Bill Milliken comments, to "earn the right to present Christ".

This point of contact is the launching pad; that's where we launch our conquest of inner space. In some cases, if you are a minister or in another position where you are recognized as a counsellor, the client will come to you. Your office becomes the launching pad. By his coming, you already have the point of contact. (The psychiatrist's couch is another example of the launching pad.) But few who need counselling will come to the church or the minister. The counsellor will have to establish his own launching pad. He will have to meet the person on his level, amid the external elements of the client's problem.

This is where social assistance serves its highest purpose. This is where the church must get into the mainstream of human need. By any and all means, the counsellor will have to get out where the sinners are and get involved with all their problems.

I am mentioning here only a few examples of launching pads; there are many more.

1. *Teen Challenge Centre*. This is our residence for addicts, alcoholics and other habit-bound persons. In the home a bed, food, shelter, clothing, recreational and educational facilities are provided. Medical treatment is also provided whenever necessary. Whether the client accepts the spiritual cure or not, he is still given this material aid. What if he continues to refuse the spiritual cure? He is allowed to remain, as long as he keeps the rules and regulations of the home. (Only a small percentage are dismissed.) However, it is not easy for one to remain in a Christian atmosphere, living under biblical ideals and principles, without accepting Christ. Those who refuse to accept usually leave on their own. However, no one is left out in the cold. Those who leave are referred to other agencies where they can receive treatment without the religious element.

2. *Coffee houses*. These are points of contact with hippies, runaways, tourists, students, and anyone who wants to talk. The programme is the person. As the advertising circulars state, "Come for a unique experience in religious conversation." But always more than religion is talked about: politics, war, sex, the church, whatever. Everyone who comes in has his or her own "bag". Each has his own philosophy of life. Conversation must begin on the person's level. The counsellor must show an interest in that person as an individual. He must show an interest in his interests. He must listen long and carefully. By

listening in sincerity and showing a genuine interest in the humanity of that person, the counsellor earns the right to talk and to present Christ. It is not always easy. But listening must come before preaching. Human interest must come before heavenly interest.

Coffee houses all over the world have become excellent launching pads for Christians to carry on a limited form of counselling. Often the Christian can only touch on the spiritual problems of the one to whom he is witnessing. However, the counsellor can do a little probing and thereby make his witness and counsel more relevant to that person's particular need. At other times the Christian witnessing purely on a spiritual and biblical level may be helping the person with some psychological, emotional, or fleshly problem—although without being aware of it. Regardless of how far the counsellor is able to get on the journey to deliver the message of the Gospel to inner space, the coffee house situation is an excellent launching pad.

3. *Bible clubs and children's schools.* Christians in each locality must evaluate their own situation and establish points of contact accordingly. Different approaches are necessary for different situations. In order to reach the ghetto child in the inner city, Teen Challenge has used the school approach. The schools, called New Start Schools, are patterned after the government's anti-poverty Head Start schools. Conducted by vista-type volunteers, these schools are staffed by qualified teachers. The Gospel is presented to ghetto children who will become the addicts, alcoholics and muggers of the future, unless they receive now the instruction and counsel of God's Word from compassionate Christians.

For the teens there are small group Bible clubs. A full round of activity, both sacred and secular, is conducted. The Gospel is presented to lead the teens to Christ and to make disciples out of them. Most of these teens already have been involved in delinquent behaviour. Patterns have already been established. Slowly but surely, they are travelling on the road to addiction and other problems. Others can still be reached. Inner space can be conquered. The club and its activities are the points of contact. If the worker knows in what direction he needs to go with each youngster, the point of contact can lead to conversion. Again, the goal must always be kept in mind.

At the same time, the counsellor cannot forget that he is ministering to the whole person. He must always be aware of the struggle for survival the teenager may be going through in

43

his home, school and community. If this is kept in mind, the counsellor will understand the lack of interest or understanding the teenager may have in responding to the goals of the counsellor and the organization, and his lack of response to the love of God.

Another effective method is to have staff live in the community and become fused with the people. This has been a good way to earn the right to be heard. This method has been used with good results by Bill Milliken and his Young Life group in their work in the ghettos of the Lower East Side of Manhattan. This I am convinced is *the* most effective method of reaching inner city youth, and conquering inner space amid the slums, garbage, vices, poverty and frustrations of the outer space of the ghetto. (See chapter 10.)

4. *The church and launching pads.* The reason I have chosen to list the church last is not because I view it as the least effective point of contact. I do so to stress its importance and to show how it has been an unnoticed centre for counselling and rehabilitation. Many problems are solved within the church, although unnoticed by the pastor and the people. Many have been rehabilitated through a dramatic conversion experience and through the follow-up of a minister in Bible teaching sessions, in private counselling, and in small group situations which, though not particularly structured as such, still result in a therapeutic, problem-solving ministry.

The church has been under severe attack for its failure to solve many of the problems in our society, and rightly so. When we decry the corruption in our society, we must always come back to the church and its failure to be a strong influence in stemming the tide of immorality and iniquity. But I fear that while the church is being attacked, we fail to notice the good that it is doing. If we think things are bad, they would be much worse if the doors of the churches were closed.

Long before special programmes such as Teen Challenge and others were established to conduct specialized ministries, the church in various degrees was reaching the same type of individuals and preventing addictions. I think of many alcoholics who have been made "new creatures in Christ Jesus" by going down the sawdust trail, by making a decision in a gospel crusade. I met a man in Canada who, while sick and in misery from an alcohol binge, heard a gospel preacher on the radio. That started him on his search for God. Through a further point of contact with a Pentecostal church, he now enjoys, after fifteen years, freedom from alcoholism. This same story can be repeated over and over, in church after church. In days gone by it was common for people with severe problems to come into the church and find an answer simply by receiving the Gospel and being helped by the follow-up programme of the church.

The church is and ought to be a "Society for the Prevention of ——". The blank stands for whatever the situation calls for. It has been the prevention of divorces, broken homes, suicides and addictions of various forms. It has also been the prevention of poverty, prejudice, perversion and a number of other problems. True, it must do more of the same, but let us not forget the prevention it has already provided for multitudes of people who find refuge and help within its walls.

It must also be pointed out that opportunities for the conquest of inner space are often lost in the church. Tragically, many potential points of contact are missed. For various reasons good contacts are unnoticed, ignored and unwanted. The addict or the troubled soul cannot make a point of contact, or be launched into the kingdom, because he is different socially, economically, racially. He cannot find counsel or refuge in God's house because *he doesn't fit into the pattern of the type of sinner that church is looking for*. He may be an "unrespectable" sinner, whereas that church has developed a ministry to "respectable" sinners. Perhaps inwardly the members say, "Get the bum out of here", or, "he's the wrong kind of bum. He doesn't fit into our counselling category."

Consequently, many people like this attend church, sit regularly in the services, and never have a point of contact established with them. Furthermore, some of them who do outwardly seem to fit the ideal of that church may have serious problems, but they are never given the opportunity to reveal their problems, to talk about them, to receive counsel for them. Many of these same people come to the altar, have a prayer said over them, and are sent on their way still fighting battles for which they have no answers—and for which they may think there *are* no answers.

My brother Dave established an effective method in his crusade ministry by counselling every young person who comes forward. Even when there are several hundred, he takes time to let each young person make a confession of faith, briefly relate a problem, or request prayer. Each one is given a brief word of counsel by my brother and afterwards he prays with them. Then the one who has made a decision is assigned to a personal worker who gives further scriptural counsel.

The altar has always been one of the best points of contact

45

and launching pads for lost and troubled souls. They should not be shoved through the altar as if it were an assembly line. I have made it a practice, no matter how many or how few come to the altar where I am the speaker, to ask each one why he has come to the altar and what he would like me to pray about. Use the altar service as an opportunity for counsel and guidance. It is often the only place where certain people will open up to relate problems and listen to advice.

5. *Preaching and teaching.* Through preaching and teaching a minister or Christian worker can establish an indirect point of contact by presenting the Gospel as it relates to particular problems. When I speak in church, often young people will come afterwards to confess drug use, promiscuity, homosexuality, and other problems they would not dare to mention to others. They do so, perhaps because they know I am only there for a day or evening and then I'm gone, but also because they know I will not be shocked by their problem and will understand the difficulty they are having, because of my experience in working with people who have similar problems. Any pastor or Christian worker who is in a place of leadership can establish similar points of contact and counselling launching pads. For example, a pastor might speak on the dangers of drug use and the Christian approach to the problem. This will open the door for young people in the church to come and talk about their temptation with drugs. Or the pastor might speak about homosexuality, presenting not only the scriptural warnings against it, but also expressing a compassion towards those who might be involved in it. Such speaking will in time bring out of hiding those who have such problems.

NOTES

¹ Sherwood Wirt, *The Social Conscience of the Evangelical* (London, Scripture Union, 1968).
² Bill Milliken with Char Meredith, *Tough Love* (London, Lakeland Paperbacks, 1970).

4

LIGHTING FIRES

Counselling has been described as a dynamic relationship between two people who are approaching a well-defined problem with consideration for each other so that the less mature or more troubled person is aided to a self-determined resolution of his difficulties. The outcome from counselling should be that the client should make some constructive helpful action on his own behalf.

How do you get the counsellee to do something? How do you light the fires within him that will produce hope, action and change, so that the one who has been doing wrong will begin constructive action that will lead him towards recovery and healing?

One of our Teen Challenge counsellors came to me, concerned about the progress and attitude of one of our resident clients. "He's got to do something," the counsellor stated firmly. "No," I said, "you've got to do something. The problem is yours and ours as much as it is Freddy's at this point."

"What do you mean?" he asked.

"We have to ask the Lord to show us how we can spark the right action in him," I said. This is the counsellor's great challenge – lighting fires, sparking that ray of hope within the troubled person so he will begin to take constructive action for himself.

When someone walks out of our treatment programme we must ask ourselves, "Did we fail to light the fire?" A match must have a sulphur tip before it can spark into a flame; in the same way, the counsellee has to be lightable. He must have an underlying desire to be changed. If he has that desire, if he is ready, we must ask ourselves, "Did we fail to scratch the surface of his desire and spark him towards a new life? Did we fail to understand his problem, so we could show him the way out of darkness and into light? Did we fail to get him to do something?"

Gregory was another one who thought about going out the door. I had taken a strong interest in him for a number of reasons. To begin with, Gregory was a Negro who had come

47

to us during the time of some of the worst riots in the Bed-ford-Stuyvesant area, where he had been living. Since this section is just a few blocks from our Centre, I felt that if Gregory could find a solution to his problems at Teen Challenge, then others from that neighbourhood might be encouraged to come to us too. We had done a lot of praying for Gregory, knowing that his short stay with us had not yet been productive. It was unfortunate that at the time he was with us there happened to be several boys at the Centre from the deep South, one of whom had made things rather difficult for Gregory.

All our efforts seemed to have been in vain, though, for one day Gregory came to me and said, "I can't make it here. I haven't made any progress here and I don't feel the Lord has done anything for me. It's time for me to go." I knew Gregory had sincerely been trying.

"Give God one more chance," I said. "If you go into the chapel with me and pray, I guarantee you that God will do something for you."

As soon as we got to the chapel, I prayed for Gregory, asking God to come to his rescue at that very moment. Gregory didn't stir, didn't say a word. I thought to myself, *Don, now you've really put God on the spot. You promised Gregory that something would happen.* I closed my eyes and prayed a little longer. Still, Gregory did not react in any way at all. I began to think that perhaps I had overstepped my bounds by insisting that God would take hold of him. Then I looked at Gregory and I saw the tears rolling down his face. . . . He began to sob. Then he began to pray out loud. When he arose, he told me, "I feel that the Lord has touched me." During the remainder of his days at the Centre, it was evident that the Lord had touched Gregory and it was a pleasure to watch him grow in Christian stature.[1]

Many clients the counsellor deals with will have been in other treatment programmes, and will have spent time with other counsellors. They may come to you having suffered the bitter disappointment of past failures. They have sincerely tried to change, but in the end found themselves worse than before. They may have been told by other counsellors, "You don't want help." One of our clients had been told by a social worker in a previous programme he had been enrolled in, "The only way you'll get out of your trouble is if, when you leave this place, you run in front of a truck and get killed."

The client may not have had any motivation, or little motivation, in past attempts to find help. In most cases the fault, however, lies at the doorstep of the programmes in which the client was involved. The client found no one to light his fire. He found no power to connect with his own will to produce true and effective will-power. The difference between the counsellor-counsellee relationships developed by Christian councellors and non-Christian counsellors is that with the Christian there is a Third Party present in all his conversations and sessions with his client. The Christian counsellor allows the power of God and the power of the Holy Spirit to help the client believe change is possible, and to show him that God will supply the power to get behind his desires and his will to help him to do all the "some-things" necessary for full recovery.

From the moment the counsellor-client relationship develops, the counsellor must look for the opportunity to strike a chord of hope—to light the fire—in the client. As the client reacts to the counselling sessions, the counsellor must find that "some-thing" somewhere during the course of the exchanges, to signal him to throw out the challenge to the client.

Have you ever struck a match that wouldn't light? You may have kept striking it and striking it, but it just wouldn't light. Then finally you gave it that one last effort and out came the flame. Counselling is similar to this simple experience. The counsellor must keep trying to rub the counsellee the right way. He must keep the counselling process flowing along until the client reveals the true nature of his problem, which may be just the point where contact can be made and the fire lit.

In reasoning with one client I tried to convince him that Christ would free him from the misery-go-round of arrests, jail terms, hospital visits, and the daily hassle (the addict's life routine of stealing, purchasing drugs, injecting the needle, etc.) of the drug addiction life. He was not interested in spiritual things so I sought his response on a human and social level. He could not see himself as a Christian. "Do you want to be a dirty dope fiend the rest of your life?" was the theme of my counselling. This however didn't arouse his interest. There was no response—I wasn't making contact—no flame or even a flicker was evident.

The next time we were together I began on a new line of counselling. "Christ will make a man out of you," I said. Then he told me that he had a daughter. I further explained how God would give him the power to be physically and spiritually cleansed from dope and sin so he could get a good job, support his

49

daughter, and assume his role as a father. This he very much wanted to do. He began to take a new interest. When I explained Teen Challenge has a job training programme he was even more interested. A spark had been lit. In further counselling I kept feeding this flame of his interest in rehabilitation based on his desire to improve himself.

What was the difference in his reaction to the two lines of reasoning? We hadn't rubbed him the right way. The first way we hadn't reached the level of his real interest and need. When fear of suffering from drugs did not spark an interest, a challenge to a better and fuller life did.

Sometimes a person's problem may not be only spiritual. It may be a serious emotional one. We find in some counsellees who respond spiritually yet are having difficulty that perhaps something in their mind is "bugging" them. One young man feared he could no longer behave fully as a man sexually. (Years of drug addiction help make the addict incapable of functioning normally sexually.) When he was able to express his fears freely, he was reassured by the example of others who had been drug addicts yet after their conversion had gone on to live a happy married life, that he could do the same. He felt relieved and was able to grow faster spiritually from that point on.

"This programme just isn't working for me," an alcoholic client said one day. "Nothing is happening to me. I still feel the same as I always have," he further bemoaned. He was in my office with coat in hand ready to terminate our counselling relationship. "Do me and yourself a favour before you go. Go downstairs to the chapel and tell God what you just told me," I suggested. At first he hesitated, then said he would. About an hour later I ran into him. "I'm not leaving," he said. "God just told me to be patient and to wait on Him. I'm going to do it." He learned his first lesson in "doing something". He found that God does help those who help themselves.

One young man walked out of the Teen Challenge centre having made up his mind to return to drugs. While standing waiting for a subway to take him back to the pusher and the cooker, he felt the spark and flame of God's love well up within his soul. He felt free from the craving of drugs. As the subway train pulled in, he walked out of the station and back to the centre and got on his knees to thank God for revealing Himself. After eight years the flame still burns.

Sometimes a fire is lit in a client, and it looks as if he has begun to do something to seek change. Then the light quickly goes out. Perhaps the fire was lit on the wrong surface. Perhaps

50

the counsellor struck only the top level of the problem. There are usually several levels to a person's problem; the fires of change must be lit on the right level. The right level is the roughest level. It's the most difficult level for the counsellor to talk about and to expose, but the lowest, roughest level of the client's problem provides the best surface and opportunity to spark change. When Jesus spoke to the woman at the well, He began on the surface level, her need for water. Then He got to the core of her problem, her five husbands, which symbolized her thirst for living water. Had Jesus not reached that level of her problem, she would have gone away still carrying that secret and that problem—only to face it again without help.

So the counsellor's great task is to challenge, to motivate, to get the client moving in the direction of a cure. This is not easy when the person feels he has no reason to change, no strength to change, and when he is addicted to drugs or alcohol.

Our problem at Teen Challenge is that although our home is full of clients, often they have a very low level of motivation. Their bodies are present with us, but their thoughts and desires have nothing to do with God or a new life. Referring to this problem one day, in chapel, I asked them, "How many of you are present this morning?" They looked at me quizzically. "Some of you are here," I said, "but many of you are not. You're walking the streets of Harlem looking for the pusher, or you're up on a roof preparing a set of works to shoot it up. Maybe someone else is in bed with a prostitute." That got their attention. "Bring your mind into chapel," I continued.

The point is, how does the preacher, the Christian witness, and especially the counsellor, capture the mind, heart and will of those who may be different, unwilling and rebellious prospects? Every case deserves a chance. No one is beyond reach. There is nothing or no one "too hard for the Lord". Many people with whom we have dealt seemed at the outset impossible to reach. Without the hope of the Gospel, without faith in the power of God to change and transform people like this we would never have tried to light the fires.

The counsellor must have faith, dedication, patience and compassion to keep trying to light the fire, and once it is lit, to keep throwing coals on it. Some clients have worn out, more than one preacher, Christian worker and counsellor. I have seen many once zealous Christians give up on "impossible" cases. Policemen, doctors, social workers and others in various professions have thrown up their hands in despair and have become indifferent to the needs of the addicted generation. "I think we should do what Hitler did and build furnaces to put them in," one policeman told me as I was walking the streets making contact with drug addicts. As sorry as I feel for the addict, I feel more sorry for that policeman and others who have no hope for the hopeless. Perhaps some are incurable, but only from the standpoint that they do not want to be cured. However, the counsellor must maintain a positive conviction that every client is curable.

Suppose you are now ready to light the fire. You have made contact with a prospective client. What steps do you take? This book does not deal primarily with making the initial contact; it is primarily about how you help your client find "newness of life". We shall discuss the steps towards that end under three headings: (1) the pre-counselling period; (2) the counselling period; (3) the post-counselling period.

The Pre-counselling Period

1. *Determine readiness.* Is the client ready for the kind of help you have to offer? Some are ready for recovery; others must go through a process of pre-counselling to be made ready. Many Christian workers and counsellors are ready, but their prospects are not. You can be too eager and thus scare off your would-be client.

Some of the signs the counsellor should look for and question regarding a client's action, to determine readiness, are the following: Does he appear interested in help only to please someone else? Does he appear to want *only* temporary assistance? Is he looking *only* for material aid? Does he appear to be in a "tight spot" because of a pending trial, jumping bail, being AWOL from the service, or neglecting child support? Is he a travelling hippie, runaway vagrant, or a travelling alcoholic mission tourist? If any of these signs appear, the chances are this client is not ready.

Readiness can also be measured by positive signs. Is the client willing to be inconvenienced to obtain help? An alcoholic called me and wanted an interview. "I'm really desperate," he said. "Can you come tomorrow (Wednesday) at ten o'clock for an interview?" I asked. "Can we make that Friday instead?" was his reply. It was apparent he was not that desperate for help. The counsellor should ask himself, "Is the client ready to accept a plan for recovery?" The client may question, express doubts and fears, and be somewhat resistant, but is there a basic willingness to at least try? Most of all, is there a basic spiritual desire to commit his life to God?

The counsellor may also set up various appointments with the client. If the client keeps them, he is showing readiness. A pastor called me and asked, "An alcoholic is coming to my church. How do I know if he is really sincere? I've been stung so many times by these fellows, so I want to be sure." I suggested that he have the gentleman attend various church services, and that the pastor request him to attend private counselling and prayer sessions at other times. After one month he called me back to say that the client had done all of this, what should he do next? We invited him to come to Teen Challenge where he became established in his faith. Later he returned home and is now a faithful member of the same church. The pastor had waited for the client to turn from a nibbler into one who took a solid bite.

Don't play the "ready or not, here I come" game. Another version is "ready or not, you're going to have to seek help". That game is played mostly by parents, husbands and wives, and relatives of the person who needs help.

Some counsellors are the way I am when it comes to fishing. As soon as I get a nibble, I yank up my line and I lose the fish. I have not learned to let the fish nibble the bait long enough so I can set the hook. The counsellor may think he is getting a hook in the prospect's jaw, only to find out there was no real bite. The prospect may have been only nibbling, asking a question or two. There is a difference between "nibblers" and real "biters". One is a prospect, the other is a client. One is still in the pre-counselling stage, the other is ready to be counselled.

We get many nibblers at Teen Challenge. They come to us shopping around for a cure. They are not at the point of desperation and are not really motivated to find a cure. They feel they can be choosy at this stage of their problem. They listen to our offer. Some even think it's a sales pitch. They want to know if it's easy or hard to be cured by our methods. How long does it take? Do you give a "money back if not satisfied" type of guarantee?

The nibblers often talk like they want help. They may be courteous, acknowledge God and make promises. From all outward appearances, they seem ready. "I'm sure he wants help" is often what ministers, parents and new counsellors say when they bring someone to us for help. Experience, however, tells us that most likely this person is not ready for help—yet. But it's hard for the inexperienced counsellor to detect this. "I thought it was just terrible when you turned down this one fellow," a staff counsellor recalled as he reflected on his early days of becoming a fisher of men. "I thought for sure this fellow really wanted help. It's not Christian to turn him away. But then I learned that I was ready to help him, but he wasn't ready for my help. It was a valuable lesson I had to learn, but it wasn't easy."

Parents sometimes bring a son or daughter to me and say, "Talk him into staying at your place." Or they will say, "Tell her what she's doing to herself." Sometimes they will come with the pronouncement, "My son must stay. I insist." One father told his son, "You stay here or I'll kill you."

Such action on the part of parents or relatives only creates a wider division between them and their children, and makes their children more determined not to seek help or accept it. They hope to spite and punish loved ones by their refusal. In the same way, the counsellor can widen the gap between himself and his prospect by over-eagerness, by forcing the counselling, and by not knowing when the person is ready.

2. *Keep the lines of communication open.* Often the counsellor will get angry when the prospect does not respond. The anger may be prompted by the counsellor's feeling of rejection and by frustration over his seeming inability to get through. Such anger shuts the door to future relationships. The door must never be shut completely. It should always be kept open, even if only a crack.

At Teen Challenge we tell those who are not ready, "Whenever you make up your mind you want help, we'll be ready to offer it." No matter what the circumstance of their rejection, we try to maintain a Christ-like spirit towards them, so they will know that at some future time they will be welcome.

There are reasons for a prospect's refusal of initial offers of help. He may be embarrassed. Perhaps he was high, drunk, or in a state of deep anxiety, and did things for which he was later sorry. If those who dealt with him during this difficult and tense moment acted in anger or hostility the lines of communication could be permanently damaged. Jesus said we are to forgive "seventy times seven". That does not mean that the church, the Christian worker, or counsellor must be a doormat for a prospective client to walk on, but it does mean that the counsellor has to deal with the situation with TLC (tender loving care).

The father who says to his teenager, "Get out of the house and don't come back until you change," is not an example of keeping the lines of communication open. Parents of rebellious and addicted children must try to maintain some form of communication with them. Even when drastic measures have to be taken, the action should be done with the most possible kindness and understanding. This is easier said than done. How can you be understanding and kind when you have to commit your child or relative to a correctional institution? It can be done; I have seen it happen. The family keeps in contact and expresses an interest in the child during the correction period. Committal sometimes must be made for the protection of the child, society, and other members of the family. When family, parents and friends refuse to visit, write, or call during this period, this cuts the line of communication.

A former addict recalled his early days of drug addiction, when he would come home high on drugs. His mother would always scream, cry, lecture, and plead. Sometimes he would listen, sometimes he would ignore her. One night he came home and his mother looked at him and said nothing. It happened the next night, and the next, and the next. He became very depressed and finally one night he went to his room and cried. He thought his mother didn't love him any more because she didn't yell at him and lecture him any more. He felt secure as long as his mother said something about his addiction. When she stopped saying something, he felt he had lost contact with her.

I don't advocate such measures to keep in contact. There are better ways to maintain those lines of communication. The counsellor should let the prospect know that the door to his home, office, church, youth centre, and his heart will always have a welcome sign hanging outside it.

3. *Don't give up.* The moment of readiness may come at any moment, at the most unexpected time, and often through the most unusual circumstances. Don't give up hope. If the counsellor gives up, the moment of readiness will go by unnoticed. The counsellor's faith, patience and compassion will be tested to the breaking point, but he must not give up.

The Jerry McCauley Mission in New York City is named after a converted alcoholic who, while on New York City's Bowery, went to a mission altar eighteen times and made a profession of faith and a start towards a cure. Eighteen times he went back to the bottle. Some people gave up on him, but others did not, and finally the nineteenth time he made it. Later he started a mission to help others. He made it because someone didn't give up.

The continual resistance, hostility and failure on the part of a prospect can throw the counsellor off course. He can become indifferent, hardened and blind to the evidence which may later appear to show that the prospect had changed and was ready to be helped.

What do you do about someone who abuses your kindness and interest? What do you do about someone who is "conning" you? The counsellor must not allow a prospect to take advantage of him. He may have to tell the prospect outright that he feels he is not being honest. This may break down the relationship, but it does not mean the case is forever lost. If the counsellor does not give up, the prospect may change his attitude later and come back seeking help on the right terms.

Not giving up means the counsellor must be *available*. The cliché, "Where were you when I needed you the most?" applies here. Circumstances can change overnight, especially for the prospect who is addicted to certain habits. On the other hand, it may take months or years for a prospective client to be ready. Regardless, the counsellor must not give up and he must be available and accessible. Those who are addicted to serious habits live dangerous lives; they run the risk of getting into trouble at any time. This works against them on one hand, but it works in their favour on the other, in that their trouble can wake them up to their need for help and provide the proper degree of motivation towards seeking it. The counsellor and Christian worker must be there when that person wakes up to his need.

4. *Strike when the iron is hot.* Keeping the lines of communication open, not giving up, and being available are important in the pre-counselling period because the counsellor is then ready to light the fire and to strike when the iron is hot. Here, too, it is important to determine when the client is ready to move out of the pre-counselling stage and into the counselling stage. The purpose of the pre-counselling period is only to set the stage for the all-important process of getting the client to "do something". During the pre-counselling period what the counsellor does is most important, but in the counselling period the most important thing is the client's action in taking concrete steps to help himself.

5. *Let the Holy Spirit prepare the prospect.* The counsellor can hinder matters by being more ready than the prospect and by doing too much. Certain measures must be left to the Holy Spirit. The Spirit leads into all truth and convicts of sin. Don't try to do what only the Holy Spirit can do.

I asked a young man in our Teen Challenge programme why he came to us. "Because my parents made me," he said. He was honest, but his answer showed he was not ready. Because he was with us against his will, he resisted counsel and became even more belligerent.

I recall a new convert witnessing at our Greenwich Village coffee house. One of his friends, whom he was trying to win to Christ, did not appear interested. Finally the new convert grabbed him by the front of his shirt and said, "Look, buddy, don't get smart with me. You need Jesus Christ and you better accept Him, if you know what's good for you."

That is not what Jesus meant when He said, "Compel them to come in"! Many honest and sincere personal workers use the wrong methods and thus turn off prospective clients. There comes a time for "do or die" tactics, when the counsellor feels his prospect is the hottest he will ever get, but this must be done prayerfully and by the leading of the Holy Spirit. No one should be badgered into the kingdom of God or into accepting counselling. Badgering is certain to meet with failure; conviction is done by the Holy Spirit and is met with success.

6. *Be alert to "mooders", "conners", and sympathy seekers.*

a. "Mooders". Two staff workers came to me quite upset. They said they were disturbed because "every time we bring a drug addict or alcoholic off the streets, they are turned down by the staff. They are told to come back the next day, and when the next day comes, they are no longer in the same mood for help."

"You've answered your own complaint," I said. "You said the next day they were no longer in the mood for help. If they really wanted help, don't you think they would have showed up?"

There are those who for various reasons go through moods when they want help, but when their mood changes, they no longer respond. The "mooders" are those who on certain occasions, either when under the influence of drugs or alcohol, or when depressed, say they want help, but when their mood passes they are no longer motivated to find help. It was only a mood and nothing more. The mood that motivated them in the first place must be strong and deep enough to make them really want to quit their habit and get away from their problem. They have to stay in the mood long enough to do something.

We have devised methods to test "mooders". We call these methods the "mood testers". In the case of an addict, we may ask him to come back the next day or call the next day. Depending on the case, the counsellor can do other things to test the "mooders".

A young, attractive airline stewardess came to one of our

57

services and sought counsel. One of our staff girls spoke with her. The stewardess expressed a desire to serve the Lord, but the counsellor could only go so far with her; she did not seem to want to go any further in the counselling process. Later, I found out why. She was in a state of temporary spiritual openness. She had been carrying on a secret affair with a married pilot, who had just informed her that their relationship would have to stop. She came to us during the shock and depression brought on by this experience. She was in the mood of love—spiritual love and the counsel of others. Her interest, however, was a rebound from the bump the pilot had given her. Perhaps that was the thing she needed to draw her to Christ. Or, it could have been just a mood, and she might have gone on to another lover to fulfil her needs.

b. "Conners". They turn on the tears, tell the sad story, or tell the counsellor, just about anything they think the counsellor wants to hear. Their purpose may be to get a free meal, a bed to sleep in temporarily, money, or just a little attention. A key phrase counsellors should look for to spot "conners" is: "I need a place to stay." Chances are he is a touring panhandler who frequents mission after mission preying on the compassion of the Christian for three hots (meals) and a cot (bed). Another thing to watch for is someone who comes seeking your help on Tuesday and on Thursday informs you he must appear in court on a criminal charge and would like you to go with him. Nine times out of ten it is all part of a plan to make it look good before the judge. In another case a young man came to the altar for prayer. When I asked him why he had come forward he said, "Do you think Jesus can get me a new pair of shoes?" The "conner" is different from the "mooder". The "mooder" usually is sincere during his mood. The "mooder" does want help when he says so. The "conner" on the other hand, knows just what he is doing and usually plans what he is doing. He plays it cool and slick. The experienced counsellor learns to pick out the "conners". But in the process of gaining the experience, the counsellor may lose time, money and effort.

c. Sympathy seekers. These people do not want help, only attention and sympathy. They will do anything to gain attention, and after they get it, they go on to someone else. They will take the counsellor down the road of their sorrows and miseries, delighting in them. They may even be proud of their failures. They are happier when they are sad. They find security in their hopelessness because their problems have become their identity and they fear losing that identity. They can be helped, if they want to be and if they are willing to admit that their problem is that they enjoy their difficulties.

My brother Dave found a teen-aged addict living in the basement of a tenement house. The young fellow took care of the furnace and in return slept on a bed in the basement. He was a greasy, dirty, skinny dope addict. My brother was so moved by his condition that he compelled him to come to Teen Challenge for help. He stayed overnight and then left. Later my brother went to visit him and asked him why he had left. The boy replied, "Preacher, you did a mean thing to me."

"What do you mean?" Dave asked. "Why do you say that?"

"Preacher, you took me out of that basement; you took away my security. I don't know how to live where you live."

Not only was this boy hooked on drugs, but he was also hooked to his misery. Perhaps something he had done in his past made him feel he deserved to be in that condition, and somehow he felt he was working out his sins by being in that state. He found happiness in his misery.

The Counselling Period

Once the counsellor has determined that his client is ready, the counselling process can begin. Some who counsel are unaware of any techniques or procedures to follow and thus they stumble along doing more harm than good. Others, who may have had no training but who look to the Lord for insights into themselves and their clients, and look to the Holy Spirit for guidance, use the right techniques even though they are not aware of it.

The Lord has revealed many things to us in the Teen Challenge work. He has shown us how to do the right things, even though we were untrained. The Holy Spirit gave wisdom, discernment, and knowledge when they were needed. But we have made mistakes out of ignorance. The fact that some of our clients became converts, in some cases, was not because of our counsel but in spite of it. God overruled our mistakes. We were sincere, but sincerity is no substitute for truth and for proper training.

The counsellor should seek all the technical training he can get. This does not mean training is a substitute for trust in the Lord and the guidance of the Holy Spirit. The counsellor must know by the wisdom of the Holy Spirit when and how to apply any training he may have. At the same time, he must realize that only the Holy Spirit can, in the final analysis, provide the solution to problems. This is the unique difference between the Christian and the secular counsellor. The secular counsellor looks at a client's needs from a psychological and emotional perspective. The Christian views the problem also from a divine perspective. In many cases, the solution to the problem will be through the meeting of the client's spiritual needs. If the spiritual need is met, and the client still has problems, then the counsellor's knowledge of emotional and psychological needs may be just the key to getting to the root of the problem. This is why the Christian counsellor should be the most qualified to deal with the needs of the untapped generation.

What are the important procedures to follow during the counselling period?

1. *Be a good listener.* A counsellor is usually noted first for his ability to talk to his client, but listening is more important than speaking. In normal conversation few people really know how to listen. Jesus said He knew many people who listened but did not really hear. The great sin of the church is that it looks, but does not see; it listens, but does not hear.

Listening is done on several levels. The first level is when we listen for just the words that are being said. What is heard is taken at face value. The second level of listening is when the hearer concentrates on the words he hears and tries to understand the deepest significance behind them. That is listening with thought. The third, and most important, level of listening is to listen with the ears, the mind and the heart. While the client is talking, try to get into his mind.

A popular song talks about the "rivers of the mind" and the "back roads of the mind". While the client is speaking, the counsellor slowly walks with him along the "back roads of his mind", trying to understand the deepest and fullest meaning of what the client is saying. Sometimes the words of the client are misleading; they are detours around the real problem. The counsellor must try to find this out, and learn the feelings, attitudes and needs of the client that are *behind* his words.

Bill Milliken in *Tough Love* says, "It's so easy just to listen at the first level. We strip off the first layer of the onion, and then we don't want to smell any more, we don't want our eyes to water any more, we don't want to feel any more deeply. Therefore, we condition ourselves to listening only superficially to what people have to say. What happens then? We miss what they are really trying to tell us. We come up with the wrong medicine, the wrong answer. We give answers to questions that aren't even being asked."[2]

60

The counsellor should not be shocked by anything he hears. If the one being counselled is a close friend or relative, the counsellor should not make judgments or exclamations of surprise, such as, "John, oh no, how could you do that?" Or, "John, no, not you, don't you know that's wrong?" At this point such judgment and expressions of shock will cause the client to withdraw. He will be afraid to relate any more of his problem, feeling the counsellor will not understand.

Proper listening helps build a bridge between the counsellor and counsellee. If the counsellee senses that the counsellor is listening (third level) and is trying to go hand in hand with him through his problem, confidence and trust will begin to build up between the two.

In the counselling process there is the "marriage of problem-solving". That is when the two—counsellor and counsellee—become one. The counsellor walks with the client into "the deepest chambers of his soul".

Some professional counsellors call this empathy. It is "feeling into". It is derived from the Greek word *pathos*, which means a deep feeling akin to suffering. It is identifying with the sufferer and his problem. It is trying to enter into the person's problem as if it were your own. Empathy is the key process in counselling.

When a client was sent to the office of our director of counselling, Lester Eisenberger, he went most reluctantly. The client felt the counsellor was only doing a job and had no real interest in him. As the young man sat in the office, he answered all the routine questions as to his name, address, and other personal data. In the course of such questioning the client mentioned that he had polio. Mr. Eisenberger then asked the client how he had contracted polio, how it affected him physically (the client walked with a limp), and how he felt about his problem. From that point on the client became very open and talked freely. When he left the counselling session the client said, "You really are interested in me." Had the counsellor not been listening, he would not have been able to empathize with him. As soon as the counsellor heard the client mention polio, he left what he was doing to travel with him into the back roads of his mind, allowing him to explore his polio problem which, as it turned out, had created a severe emotional hang-up.

One psychiatrist described this process as becoming so identified with the other person and his problem that the counsellor "gets rid of himself". If the merging process is successful, both the counsellor and the counsellee are changed. Rollo May in his book, *The Art of Counselling*, says, "We might even, in fact, judge the merit of a particular conversation by asking how much it has taken us out of ourselves."[3]

It is also through the listening process that the Christian counsellor gets what we call a "burden" for his client. This is the marriage, or falling in love in a spiritual sense—of the counsellor and the counsellee. When this has been accomplished, the process can go on to the solution of the problem.

2. *Get the client to talk.* It would seem that getting the client to talk should be listed first, but it is listed second for good reason. Getting the client to talk is not usually a problem, but getting him to talk about the right things is. That is why listening is most important. The counsellor must be a good listener, on the deepest level, so that he can pick out certain key phrases and themes that are coming through—and then try to get the client to talk about those themes.

Much territory might have to be covered before you get to the client's real problem. The counsellor will have to do a great deal of listening—and let the client do a great deal of talking until "the real client stands up" and says, "This is me; this is my problem." In this process the client will take the counsellor down the rivers of his mind—back into various tributaries and detours, getting stuck (if the counsellor lets him), in a lot of muddy non-essentials. The counsellor will have to pick out the important things and bring the client back into the main river of the problem and keep rowing along that course.

Tony came to me and said he felt like leaving Teen Challenge because he couldn't read. "I'm very embarrassed about this," he said. We prayed and then I said, "Is there anything else bothering you, Tony?" I had the feeling he hadn't come out with the real problem. Then he related another problem, but I didn't react or say much to him about it. Again, I had the feeling he hadn't come clean. Finally, he admitted having difficulty adjusting to other people who were different from him. He had been running away from the normal adjustments of life, be it family, friends, or the people on the job. In the process of talking it out, he also realized that others were getting used to him as well, and that he hadn't done his best to help them get adjusted. It took time, but after a few detours Tony had finally admitted what was really bothering him.

When the real problem is coming out, the client may not want to talk about it. It may be painful for him to do so. The counsellor should carefully and tactfully get the client to talk about his painful experience. It must come out. Like a surgeon with his knife, the counsellor will be cutting into the client's very being—but it is a hurt that will heal. And it will only heal by going through the painful experience of talking about it.

3. *Pin-point the problem.* A counsellor asked a new client, "What's your problem, young man?" To which he answered, "That's why I came to you. I want you to tell me what my problem is."

The purpose of the counselling session is not so much to tell the client what his problem is, but to guide him along so he will talk himself into a corner, and come to see his problem for himself. It takes time for the problem to emerge and come to the surface. The counsellor and counsellee will have to discover it together. The client may be "hung up" on the symptoms of his problem and still not know the cause.

Don't react too quickly. I've had clients leave my office, and after they were gone I felt that somehow we had not arrived at the real problem. The counsellor may react too quickly to a surface problem or a symptom and keep the client hung upon a major aspect of his total problem. Much time can be wasted by majoring in minors.

One client, Paul, pointed out his difficulty in relating to another Christian who was trying to help him. "What he did to me was not right. How can he be a Christian and do that?" Paul complained. I proceeded to "get to the bottom of this" by hastily defending Paul before the fellow Christian worker. When the worker told his side of the story, it revealed that Paul was having a serious problem in learning to relate to other people. "Paul," I said, "you told me what he did to you, but you didn't tell me why." As it turned out the Christian worker had handled the situation properly. The client had lured me into his favourite game of pin-pointing his own problem and getting someone to defend him. He lived a life of majoring in minors, and I was letting him play the game at my expense. After this we began to deal in majors—his difficulty in accepting authority and listening to the advice of others.

Majoring in minors is also done by dealing with symptoms rather than causes. A young teenager who may have a habit of marijuana smoking, or another who is being influenced by friends to do harmful deeds, cannot be told to just "keep away from old friends" or to change schools, neighbourhoods, churches, or whatever. What must be dealt with is why he is so easily influenced. What can be done to provide him with the inner resources to stand up against the crowd?

However, serious problems can be missed by the counsellor's brushing off a statement of a problem. Reuben came to me and said, "Brother Don, everyone keeps telling me I talk in my sleep and blaspheme Christ."

"Come on, Reuben," I said, "don't pay any attention to what others are saying. They're just trying to get you all upset."

But my quick reaction turned out to be wrong. He *was* blaspheming in his sleep. His subconscious mind was being revealed in his sleep. It was a serious problem and it needed to be dealt with.

Often in a family situation children will come to parents, or young people in the church will come to a minister, and relate what may seem to be an outrageous problem. They appear to be exaggerating; it's something you think Mary could never do. But in reality it's true and very serious.

If a client's problem is overstated or evaded, the client must work through the counselling process until he arrives at his real problem and pin-points it. If the problem is understated, then the counsellor must keep probing, that is, by allowing the client to talk until the more serious problem is pin-pointed.

In pin-pointing the problem the counsellor must determine if the problem is physical, psychological, emotional or spiritual. It may be all of these. All problems are spiritual in nature, but are they only spiritual? Is a person's emotional conflict due to a spiritual emptiness? The girl who goes out with any fellow who will have her and gives her body to him—is she expressing only a spiritual need, or has she been emotionally and psychologically damaged from something done in childhood? The young man who uses drugs—is it because he rebelled against God and the teaching of Christ that he got into the wrong crowd and out of curiosity used "stuff", or has he suffered from emotional conflicts brought on by a broken home and mistreatment from parents? Moreover, has he suffered brain damage from extensive use of drugs?

The non-Christian counsellor denies the existence of spiritual needs in the client, but the Christian counsellor can be just as wrong by denying the existence of physical, psychological and emotional problems. The counsellor must understand that whatever seriously affects one part of a person will also affect another part. Emotional and spiritual problems are twin brothers. Man is a whole being; the whole being must be kept in mind during the counselling process.

What should the counsellor do if he feels the problem is physical or mental? What should be done about referrals? No referral should be made until an effort is made to minister to the spiritual needs of the client. Ministers who turn clients over to a doctor or psychiatrist should not leave them in the hands of someone who is not providing ministry to the soul. This kind of co-operation is possible; more of it needs to be done in solving multiple problems.

Referral may not even be necessary. If the counsellor leads his client to a conversion experience with Jesus Christ, the total problem may be solved. The solving of the spiritual need may lead to the solution of the emotional need; the solving of the emotional need may be the solution to the physical need. Some churches are full of people who would have needed hos-pitalization, psychiatric sessions, or even confinement in another type of institution, but for the grace of God and the power of God to heal the total man. Through the ministry of physical healing, many side effects brought on by that physical problem have been solved.

This does not mean referrals should not be made. Some coun-sellors and ministers feel that to refer someone is an admission of failure and a lack of faith. Healing comes through many forms and the counsellor must not deny a client medical or other professional assistance. Again, if this assistance is provided not as a substitute for ministry to the soul but along with it, then the counsellor should feel safe in making referrals.

4. *Don't talk too much.* Most counsellors have difficulty with-holding advice and solutions. It seems strange to tell a coun-sellor not to counsel but this is vital to the counselling process. The counsellor will be tempted to pick up something the client says and go into a long, wordy, perhaps biblical explanation filled with religious jargon and nice-sounding solutions. There is a time for the counsellor to give advice, but only after he has worked with the client through a session or several sessions, and only after he is sure everything has come to the surface.

It is helpful for the counsellor to restate some of the client's problems or to lead him in one direction and away from what appears to be a detour. The client may come to a brick wall; he may be at the core of his problem and have difficulty getting everything out. The counsellor can help the client clarify, modify or redefine certain things to aid in his "coming out" process.

Don't cut the client off. An example of talking too much, too soon, is to say to him, "Oh, I know just what your problem is. What you need to do is . . ." The untrained Christian counsellor may brush off the person with, "All you need to do is get right with God." That may be true, but the person may never see his need for getting right with God until and unless he sees what his problem is, and why he needs to get right with God.

Edward came to my office with a problem. "I listen to jazz music all the time and go to dirty movies. I do this rather than read my Bible." He had presented his problem to several counsellors. They had immediately gone into a sermon about the evils of jazz and movies. He was dealt with on that basis only. When he came to me, I asked him, "What are the reasons you do these things?" It was evident that the things he was doing were only symptoms of a deeper problem. After several sessions the real Edward stood up. He had had several homosexual experiences in the past, and now that he had completed our residence programme and was out working, the problem had come up again. Jazz and movies were a smokescreen for his real problem. Those who had been dealing with him had talked too soon and too much.

Try to get the client to answer his own problem. Through the counselling process the client should arrive at the conclusions the counsellor desires, without the counsellor's having to state them. When the client asks a question, it is good to say, "What do you think?" A client may reply, "What do you think I should do?" In many cases the client knows what he should do and is trying to avoid it. He can be questioned in return, "But what do *you* think you should do?" In this way the counsellor has a chance to find out whether the client would accept his advice before he gives it.

While talking with our trained resident counsellor, Lester Eisenberger, I asked him about a particular case. "What did you tell Bob?" "I didn't say anything," Mr. Eisenberger answered. "Why didn't you tell him that what he was doing is wrong?" I asked. His answer was simple: "I can tell him what's wrong, but at this point he is not ready to accept it; so what good will it do for me to tell him? He has to arrive at this conclusion himself. I think with a few more sessions together he'll reach that point."

Many counsellors arrive at conclusions the counsellee himself has not reached. I've given, in counselling sessions, what I felt was an excellent diagnosis and answer to a certain client's problem. I felt pleased with myself for having given such an answer and counsel. The only problem was, my client didn't come to the same understanding of his problem that I had.

It might be that the client is looking for quick, simple

answers; to give them to him would be a dis-service. The desire to tell people how they should handle their problem is not an acceptable substitute for allowing the troubled to pour out their feelings.

5. *Involve the client in his own cure.* A common mistake of rehabilitation programmes is to try to perform a cure regardless of the motivation, attitude and co-operation of the client. One of the mistakes we made in developing the Teen Challenge programme was that while we were treating clients, we smothered them with our love, but we were not preparing them for the outside world. We were not getting to the root of their problems. Like many parents, we spoiled and babied them along, being over-protective, pacifying and sustaining them on our faith and prayer. We picked them up and accepted them at any time, under any circumstances, and in any condition. They were allowed to remain almost without any restrictions. They came into our programme carried along by our zeal and enthusiasm. They were given constant attention, often were pleaded with, begged and coaxed to remain when they wanted to leave. Some would stay for a time just because we asked them to. However, at night many did run off. We soon realized we were running a hotel, not a rescue station.

Our biggest mistake was in not allowing the addict or prospective client to involve himself in his cure by proving, to one degree or another, that he really wanted to receive help and overcome his problem. We therefore began to make some changes, so the person could show signs of wanting help. Screening was done more carefully, and other measures were taken.

Many addicts and alcoholics who came to us had in previous situations been given this same royal treatment. Everything had been done for them. They were given free drugs; they were never allowed to suffer pain. Every comfort for the body was provided. Nothing was done to give them a chance to exert their own efforts towards a cure. They expected this same treatment when they came to us. They called up and said, "I'll join your programme if you drive over and pick me up." They had developed an "I'm doing you a favour by coming" attitude.

To overcome our mistake, we first made it harder for a person to enter our treatment programme. We set up tests to determine a degree of motivation. If we met someone on the street who expressed a desire to be treated, we set up appointments for him to fulfil. If he came, we felt he had passed one small test. When addicted persons are involved, passing this small test is an accomplishment. Even for other more sophisticated people, keeping an appointment with a pastor, Christian worker, even a friend, can be a difficult thing. The counsellor should not run after a client. If there is no response, he should keep the lines of communication open, but other than that, he should make the prospective client come to him. This enables the person to express by an outward act that he wants inward help.

One young man who came to Teen Challenge said, "You don't know how hard it was for me to knock on that door. I walked up the block, looked at the door, then passed on. I walked around the block several times before I had the courage to knock." That simple act, which most people can do without giving it a second thought, is a difficult task for a distressed and troubled person. But if he is to overcome other difficult tasks, he must begin as soon as possible to tackle the immediate ones. Forcing or trying to persuade a prospective client into a counselling session or relationship is to deny that person the right to express his own will. Such denial robs him of his most precious asset—self-expression and self-determination. For one who feels robbed of self-respect and self-expression anyway, this is a tragic denial.

6. *Ignite hope and spark change.* Talking too much can be a mistake, but not talking enough or at the right time can also be a mistake. The right moment and place during the counselling process must be found, when the counsellor begins talking, advising, and counselling. It must not come too soon or too late.

After the counsellor has listened, interpreted and pin-pointed the problem, he must begin to speak words of hope and instruction to help the counsellee "begin to do something" to help himself. This is the real moment of lighting the fire. The counsellee must turn hope and desire for a change into action. Someone has said, "Feed your faith, and your doubts and fears will be starved to death." The counsellor's task is that of feeding faith, igniting hope, and sparking action in the counsellee. The difficulties he faces will dampen his hope; the flame will flicker; it may even go out temporarily or completely. The counsellor may have to "relight" the client many times over.

One great difficulty of counselling with those who are weak, struggling, and slow to progress, will be the visible disappointment and anger the counsellor may display before the counsellee. The temptation will be to terminate the relationship. "I can't do anything else for you, Andrew," I said to one counsellee. "I'm sorry to disappoint you. Please forgive me," he apologized as he saw my disappointment. Then realizing what I was doing to him—reinforcing his despair rather than helping him out of it—I went into forward gear in my counselling. "But God can still forgive you. He hasn't given up on you." After I put my arm around him, we went down on our knees. I asked him to pray and slowly he began to confess his weakness and to pour his soul out to the Lord. When we finished he was ready, as he said, "to go out and give it another try". A dying flame had been re-ignited.

The counsellor must never lose his faith in himself or in God. Also, he must not lose faith in the one he is counselling. This does not mean the counsellor should fool himself by thinking that progress is being made when it is not. Being realistic is important, but not at the sacrifice of faith and hope. The counsellor must by faith see the "evidence of things not yet seen" in the counsellee. He must keep throwing on coals of fire to keep hope alive, so that his client's "becoming" progress will continue.

This is the importance of the Christian counsellor. When the non-Christian counsellor exhausts every means of endeavour, all hope is lost. The Christian counsellor has a further hope. He has God on his side. As long as the counsellor and counsellee believe God is alive, hope for a solution still exists. The counselling process may seem to be at a dead-end, but as long as God and faith are alive, there is hope.

A word of caution. The counsellor should not make promises to his counsellee. Statements such as this should be avoided: "Give me a few sessions with you and everything is going to be all right." Or, "God is going to come down and take your whole problem away." Or, "Let's just pray about this; God is going to work everything out."

There comes a time for expressions of faith in God and His Word, but positive faith must be arrived at by the counsellee, not just the counsellor. Likewise, the counsellor should not tell the person he is making progress when he is not. He should be honest, yet positive about the future.

Theology and the Counsellor-Counsellee Relationship

The counsellor and the client must understand the place that God, faith, and salvation have in the counselling process. Proper understanding can mean a solution; improper understanding can mean a failure.

The client may be looking to God and the counselling session to remove the reasons for his distress and trouble by some magic or automatic force, rather than learning how he can by faith in God cope with the circumstances surrounding his problem. He must not run away from his troubles, but face them squarely and, by so doing, overcome them.

The client must be shown that God wants to give him the resources to face life, and that He works in and through his circumstances to find a cure. He cannot run away from himself or from his problem, but he can run "through the fire and not be burned". Salvation is an escape from sin, not from life. Christ saves from sin, but the client must realize he still has to be "in the world".

The proper theology of counselling is to help the client not to be confused about God's part in his recovery. God works in and through the client, but with his co-operation.

The counsellor must have faith that God can change his client; and he must try to spark that same faith in his client. Faith is that spark; it is not the end result. When the Bible says, "All things are possible if you believe", it does not mean one can just believe and immediately the problem is removed. It means that faith and belief make it possible to achieve the end result.

Harold Hass in *Pastoral Counselling with People in Distress* says:

> Man's essential problem is his alienation from God, which results from sin. Man's sinful nature and his sinful behaviour have separated him from God and worked havoc among men. Ultimately sin is at the bottom of all of man's physical and mental distress. It is also what prevents him from reaching his full potential as a human being. To alleviate distress at its source, the breach with God must be healed. To free man to be all the Creator intended him to be, that is, to realize his full potential, the results of sin must be remedied. The pastor's (counsellor's) unique function is to be about the business of mending this break by means of the gospel of Jesus Christ.[4]

The problem of the client does not end, nor does a solution begin, until Jesus Christ is accepted as personal Saviour. It may take much counselling before this decision is reached, or it may come at the beginning of the contact. Regardless of when the decision is made, only through this new birth experience is the person able to be healed. Everything before this is preparative counselling or "sowing the seed". When conversion takes place, a whole new dimension is added to the counselling process. The counsellor through the power of the Holy Spirit is the agent to light the fire; Christ is the fire.

NOTES

[1] Don Wilkerson and Herm Weiskopf, *The Gutter and the Ghetto* (Waco, Texas, Word, 1969).

[2] Bill Milliken, *Tough Love.*

[3] Rollo R. May, *The Art of Counselling* (Nashville, Tennessee, Abingdon Press, 1967).

[4] Harold J. Hass, *Pastoral Counselling with People in Distress* (St. Louis, Mo., Concordia Publishing House, 1970).

5

THE ADDICTED GENERATION

Tripping Out With LSD

"It's a groovy experience. Nobody can psych you out once you reach this utopia. You're immortal. You think you are God and can judge, or fly, or float, or condemn or all four. You're in a purple haze where red stars and blue moons cover your feet. At the same time tunnels begin to form. As they take shape, they loom larger and larger and whirl madly.

"Suddenly there are hundreds of them—dark, black, empty tunnels. You fall to your knees as they rush at you, pounding you into the red stars and blue moons.

"Then you're plunging head over heels through the tunnels, past snakes and cows and frogs with bloodshot eyes. You fall and fall. It feels like only minutes and yet eternities too. Then you see flames ... waiting for you, surrounding you. They begin to burn. *There is no escape!*"

*   *   *

"Isn't it true that drug addicts are mainly people of low intelligence, and that only certain kinds of personalities are addiction prone?" a high school student asked me.

"That is a tragic misconception," I answered. "While it is true that certain people may have more reasons to turn to drugs to fill a need in their lives, the drug addict population is made up of a wide cross-section of society. What you must understand is that anyone and everyone is a potential drug user and thus a potential drug addict."

If we have heard it once, we have heard it a hundred times from young people: "I am different. I can take drugs, but I can always leave drugs when I want to." Sadly enough, many who take drugs just to experiment, find later that they cannot stop taking them. Many are sincere in their desire only to experiment, or to take drugs for kicks. However, they find out that they are unable to make the proper judgment regarding further use of other more potent drugs, once they are in a drug atmosphere. The result is that the "now" generation is turning into the addicted generation.

Because of this rise in addiction, the church is going to have to find a new kind of youth worker. In addition to a Christian education director and a youth director, the church must enlist and train a full-time youth worker who can converse with those caught in the web of drug addiction. Some of the strongest churches in the country are facing the problem of drugs among youth from the best homes in the church. A book I have in my library, written in 1965 for pastors interested in counselling drug addicts, states: "Few ministers in the suburban churches will have occasion to counsel an addict.' That statement was accurate at the time it was written. But it must now be said that this is no longer true. In the last few years drug use and drug addiction have spread like a cancer into the tree-lined suburbs, those islands of what was thought to be safety and isolation from the problems of the inner city. Parents who moved out and bought homes at great financial risk to hide their children from drugs and other related problems, now find they must face the very same difficulties they sought to escape.

In the face of this rising tide of addiction, what basic facts does the Christian worker need to know?

Three Categories of Drug Involvement

The counsellor will meet three different groups of young people involved in the drug scene: (1) users; (2) abusers; (3) addicts. These three groups are distinct yet closely related. The counsellor must not mistakenly treat the user as an addict, nor should he treat the addict as a user. There is a difference between drug use, drug abuse, and drug addiction. Yet, the difference is often a very thin line. It is important to know where one type of drug involvement begins and ends, and where the second type takes up.

The drug user and the drug addict may be compared with the social drinker and the alcoholic. And the drug abuser may be compared with the problem drinker. The drug user uses the drug, but the drug uses the drug adict. The user can control the amount of drugs he takes, the addict cannot control himself or the drug. The user is an experimenter, the abuser is one who finds he has an ever-increasing need to experience the high or the euphoria it gives him, and the addict is one who seeks total escape from reality.

Addiction has been defined as a state of periodic or chronic

73

intoxication produced by the repeated consumption of a drug and involves tolerance, psychological dependence, usually physical dependence, and an overwhelming compulsion to continue using the drug which detrimentally affects both the individual and society. The World Health Organization (WHO) recently recommended that the term addiction be replaced by a single and more general term—"drug dependence". They described drug dependence as "a state arising from repeated administration of a drug on a periodic or continuous basis".

Programmes to help the users, abusers and addicts are more effective if they deal with each group separately. Mixing users and abusers with addicts may result in the addicts' influencing the others; users and abusers often look up to addicts and go on to more serious drugs to prove they know "where it's at" in the hard drug scene. Younger drug users learn about other drugs and the "tricks of the trade" from the more experienced. Addicts are proud of their drug knowledge and will show it off to others, in order to compete with their drug addict peers.

However, once the addict experiences a genuine conversion to Christ, he can have a most effective influence on the users and abusers, and on those who have never tried drugs but are facing the temptation to do so. Youngsters will listen to one who has been there. In Teen Challenge work we see the effectiveness of converted addicts who give their testimonies at high school assembly programmes and relate the problems they encountered through drugs.

The whole drug scene is often glamorously painted as an innocent "in" way of life. Many young people feel they are being left out if they do not indulge. Drug use has become fashionable. One of the reasons why accurate figures on drug usage—especially marijuana—are hard to obtain is that many kids claim to have used it when they have not. This is because they think "everybody is doing it". Teens get a one-sided view. They are told about the supposed harmlessness and the non-addictive aspects of pot, and about the mild high it causes. They are told that it is no worse than a cocktail. That side is only the street side of the story, the party atmosphere side of the drug question.

Young people need to hear and see the darker side. They need to be told the facts about what drugs will do and will not do. They can't be scared into staying off drugs, however.

After one school assembly, a young girl came to our group and said to us, "Thanks for coming. You told us about one side of the drug problem that the other kids never tell us. Now I'm in a better position to make the right decision about whether I will use drugs or not."

A student at the University of North Dakota told one of our Teen Challenge converts, "You said you smoked marijuana and then went on to heroin, but all I read refutes this. Research seems to contradict you." Mario, the converted drug addict, answered: "You read about marijuana in the paper, but I experienced it; that's the difference."

The high school and college marijuana users represent the type of drug user who emerged in our society in the mid-nineteen sixties. He is not an addict in terms of physical addiction. Some outgrow such drug use. Others do not. Unfortunately, wherever marijuana is found there are also hard drugs. In a very short time a marijuana user can turn to more frequent use of drugs and become an abuser. The abuser can become an addict almost overnight.

Young people who think that they will never become hooked on drugs are often sincere. But once drugs go into the body and mind, will-power, reason, good sense, and sound judgment all go out. We tell young people, "I believe you when you tell me you don't plan on getting hooked. But when you take drugs, you are in a certain atmosphere (the atmosphere of drug use has become just as important as the drug being used) and you become a different person in that atmosphere than you were when you first walked through the door."

A further danger is that a person does not know just how he is going to react to a drug. For example, when using marijuana the reaction can be different on any occasion. The initial effect of pot is often nil. First-time smokers usually get sick, some report no effect after several uses, some no effect even after ten times. However, eventually, the user will begin to experience mild sensations and perhaps get stoned. The effects come on slowly and smoothly. But after repeated use, and if the dosage happens to be stronger, the effect can be frightening. Marijuana is smoked, sniffed, or ingested. The mental effects include a feeling of euphoria, a dreamy sensation, or exultation. One user said, "I felt like the world had stopped and I had gotten off—I was in the twilight zone." In this state there is a free-flowing of ideas (good or bad, or both): senses of time, distance, vision, and hearing are heightened. Hallucinations may result from large doses. Some users are talkative, some giggle, some act silly, others become boisterous, moody, and drowsy. When such effects occur in an atmosphere of rock music, psychedelic lights and the gaiety of a crowd the net result may be a stoned young

75

lady or man who has no ability to resist other drugs or large doses of the same drug.

The step up or down from the marijuana culture may never happen, yet it does more often than the user will admit and more often than any authority will ever be able to know. When other drug usage takes place, it may be LSD (acid), a stimulant such as amphetamine, or meth-amphetamine (speed), a depressant or sedative (goof balls), or the direction may lead to heroin (horse).

The depressants cause intoxication similar to that experienced by the alcoholic. The abuser also exhibits slurred speech, his reactions are sluggish, he may be emotionally erratic and easily moved to tears or even laughter. Or he may become very angry. One client became upset with me when I refused to interview him because he was "goofing" so badly. "I'm not high," he kept insisting. He became very disruptive and created a scene in front of others. Then he started to laugh.

Those on stimulants become talkative, excitable, and noticeably restless. One young man said, "When I take 'ups' (a stimulant drug) I like to walk and walk and walk." Others experience insomnia, heavy perspiration, or tremors of the hands.

The LSD user experiences changes in perception, thought, mood, and activity. Time seems to slow down or even stop. There is also sometimes a sense of being detached from one's body. One user said, "I kept feeling like my fingers were falling off." The user may experience a free-flow of weird or bizarre ideas—including feelings of persecution. Trivial events take on unusual significance and importance. "A button can appear to be the most important image you have ever seen," said another LSD tripster. After a number of hours the effects of LSD begin to wear off. Sometimes fatigue, tension, and recurrent hallucinations (flashbacks) may continue long after ingestion of the drug. Psychological changes brought on by the drug may continue for indefinite periods.

The counsellor who meets on an individual basis those involved in drugs will have to determine the extent of the person's drug problem. (If the person is only a user, that may not pose too great a problem in the counselling process.) If abuse or addiction are involved, then the counsellor's task is to help the person to overcome both the addiction to the drugs and the reasons for it. The addict will first need help and strength to get clean from the drug, physically, and then to face up to the problem of overcoming the emotional and spiritual needs that led to his addiction.

76

1. *The curious.* Some young people are always curious about something that is mysterious, adventurous, dangerous, and illegal. But while curiosity is given as an excuse for having started a habit, it is often later found out that some character defect perpetuated the drug-taking.

2. *The weak-willed.* Some young people seek a simple, quick, magical solution to the problems of life and to their own character defects. Such young people need little urging to get them started and they find it difficult to put down the habit once it has been fixed. These include the severely inadequate, immature, and the lost and depressed.

3. *The social addict, or the social give-ins.* These are young people who take drugs because it is the sociable thing to do. In their clique, everyone is doing it. Not to do so would mean to be left out. Taking drugs is a prerequisite for belonging to some groups.

4. *The sense seekers.* These are made up of the more artistic types who are seeking break-throughs or a renewal of their creative power. They perpetually seek to spring free of their ordinary way of seeing or sensing the world around them.

Some users claim to have understood themselves better after taking the mind-expansion drugs. One boy said, "My mind opened up—I found out a lot of things about myself I didn't know—but I didn't like what I found. And I have no ability to do anything about the things I learned."

5. *The escapers.* These are young people seeking escape from boredom, responsibility, frustration and anxiety. Many are affluent youths who have become bored with blessings. They don't know how to get high on life. They cannot accept responsibilities or the difficulties that make a young person grow. Life turns them *in*, not *on*.

6. *The accidental drug user.* This is a young person who has been turned on to drugs by a friend, relative, or some older person. The young person taking the drug did not really know what he was getting involved in, and accidentally got hooked.

One fellow related, "My best friend gave me a marijuana joint. Although I knew it was dangerous, I trusted him and so I thought everything would be all right. I had a pleasant drug experience and so started smoking from time to time with him until I woke up one day and found myself hooked." Although in the latter case, the young man was not completely naïve to

77

the drug scene, he nevertheless became accidentally involved because he trusted a friend.

7. *The persuaded addict.* Related to the social and the accidental user are those who have been persuaded to indulge. A husband persuades his wife; a boy friend turns on his girl friend. The user may go along because of some misguided sense of love, or—in the case of some girls—because of some idea that if she were involved, she would be able to help her man with his drug problem.

8. *The prescription addict.* Some get involved in drug addiction through physical problems for which the doctor prescribed a certain drug. However, they find that while the drug alleviates their physical problem, it creates a worse one in that they develop a psychological dependence of which they are unaware. Prescription addicts are often people who started their drug use under extreme stress.

9. *Stone heads.* This is the type of young person who has found absolutely no meaning or value in life. He has come to the conclusion that anything is better than what he has experienced. He will take anything and everything, perhaps even a combination of drugs and alcohol.

10. *The religious seekers.* A growing number of young people use drugs as a religious sacrament. They seek personal insights or religious experiences. More frequently, they use psychedelic drugs (LSD and others). They are searching and believe that these drugs open up new levels of spiritual understanding.

With an estimated 250,000 addicts in the United States, there is of course a great challenge for the Christian to direct his efforts to this group. But there is perhaps an even greater challenge to reach the users and abusers who number in the millions. Some young people can be reached through their drug problem. The counsellor who is able to address himself to the counsellee's drug use, and then go beyond that to get into his mind and heart, can develop an effective ministry to the addicted and to the pre-addicted generation.

The Drug User

The users primarily are made up of marijuana smokers, the so-called "soft drug" takers. Included in this group are young and old from all walks of life: the teens, the young adults, students, musicians, doctors, lawyers, businessmen, actors, as well as the more commonly known users, such as the hippies, the runaways, and the inner city teen-age gang members and delinquents. There are no "typical" marijuana smokers.

In dealing with this type of person, focus should not be put entirely on the drug. The pot generation has made up its mind about the so-called harmlessness of their "thing". No argument based on facts or experience will convince them otherwise. There are definite and real dangers in marijuana use—apart from any other drug—but its effects have not been studied long enough to present the necessary proof. Even if this proof were available, it might not do any good—as witness the warnings about cigarettes and cancer.

The more serious aspect of marijuana is the person using it. For young people, marijuana has become a symbol of rebellion. The problem is not the pot, but the person. Parents and many authorities make a mistake by focusing too much attention on the drug and trying to prove its dangers, without dealing with the rebellion or other issues and problems that young people face. Marijuana is only a symptom; causes, not symptoms, need to be dealt with. The cause may be a serious personality disorder, or it may be just the severe growing pains of adolescence.

Threats, and scare tactics will not work with a pot rebel. This is not to minimize the problem. Marijuana is dangerous. It is dangerous because it is a drug and it can lead to the use of other drugs. The counsellor should be aware of the hazards of marijuana, but he also should know the difference between it and hard drugs. However, he should not spend his time trying to convince the counsellee of the risks involved. When the facts are pointed out, it should not be in an emotional frenzy, but in a calm, convincing manner.

The counsellee, on the other hand, may seek to lure the counsellor into the great debate on marijuana with such statements as: "It's not any different from alcohol," "It ought to be legalized; alcohol is legal," or "Prohibition never worked," or "Getting high is a way of life; why aren't young people entitled to a high?" Another excuse is, "It's my body; I can do with it what I want; no one has the right to stop me."

These statements and questions can and should be faced, but only after talking about the more important issues. In most cases of drug use, there are difficulties of young people relating to their parents; there are broken homes; there is a lack of discipline; and many other problems that have been common to all generations.

And then there are the problems young people have in making adjustments to life with all of its hang-ups and hardships. Those who have found a way (and *the* Way) to face up to these adjustments do not need the thrill of a cop-out through drugs. Through their faith in God and their faith in Christ, they have found the strength and the ability to grow, to mature, and to attack life—not to run from it. If the drug user can be made to see that the use of drugs is a testimony to his immaturity and inner weakness, he may be able to see a deeper reason why he uses drugs. Most users will not admit to themselves that there is anything more to their use of drugs than the desire to get high or to have a kick. This craving is a greater danger to them than the drug. Marijuana, unlike heroin and other drugs does not build a tolerance or physical craving, but the need or desire to turn to some harder drugs may become stronger.

Drug use is both a "high" (pleasure) and an escape. The pleasure may be good for your feelings, but it is not good for your life as a whole. Marijuana smokers must be brought to see that they are *copping out,* not *coping with* life.

Copping out comes in many forms. The marijuana smokers may actually represent the smallest group in our society who are on an escape route. Some escape through harmful means, such as alcohol. Others do it through legitimate means. But the overriding desire to escape is nonetheless harmful to their personalities. There are those who escape from life by changing from job to job; those who go from social involvement to social involvement, from one romantic and sexual association to another. There are a multitude of things that the average westerner does to relieve his frustration and find escape from life's difficulties. It is all part of the same thing—hiding from life's realities and trials, rather than facing them head on.

The greatest danger of marijuana may not be in what it does, but in what *it does not do* for the individual. It makes promises, but it cannot fulfil them. It may make the user think pleasant thoughts, but it's like putting the gearshift of your car in neutral—the mind is disengaged. It is not in drive. The user does not go forward. If the drug user can be made to see the loss of values, the destruction of character, or the weakness of his personality, he may be able to view his smoking pot as having an adverse effect on his total being, and thus be ready for help and to seek change.

The Drug Abusers

Drug users become drug abusers. Copping out can become a way of life. The more youth turn *away from* rather than *towards* life and its problems, the more they get used to escaping and the more it's necessary. Drug abuse comes as a result of

80

both the effect of the drug upon the mind and body, and the deterioration of the personality.

Users never intend to become abusers. But slowly and subtly the process takes place. Before they know it, it happens. When it happens, it is a blow to their egos and a frank revelation to themselves that there is something wrong with them. This shattering revelation usually means they need more drugs to alleviate the pain of this knowledge.

The drug abuser is in the process of becoming addicted. Most likely he will not see his involvement in drugs as a serious problem. Users and abusers see only the "high" side of drug consumption. All too often the abuser is at a phase of his drug-taking cycle when he is deriving satisfaction, euphoria, and release of tension from the chemical he is using. He is feeling no pain; what more can you as a counsellor offer him? The symptom is pleasant, the cure much less so. The low side, the side effects of his drug use that bring misery and suffering may not have appeared yet. Therefore, it is difficult for him to be motivated enough to examine himself and his reason for using drugs.

The abuser (who could be termed the pre-addict) usually withdraws from family and society, and will not come out of his seclusion unless the counsellor makes contact with him. The counsellor will have to work with him along the lines suggested in Chapter 4 under the heading of pre-counselling. The Christian counsellor's greatest task is to make contact and keep contact alive. Methods for making contact should be developed as launching pads. From the launching pad the counsellor can work with the abuser until the counsellor-counsellee relationship develops.

Users and abusers are saying by their drug-taking: "Please, help me." But they do not know they are saying this. Not until they see that drugs do not give answers, but instead rob them, will they be ready for help.

The Addict

Usually, the problems caused by drug-taking prepare the taker for rehabilitation: criminal arrest, sickness, physical weariness, family and home conflict, jail and hospital confinement, social stigma, the misery-go-round of hustling for the money to support his daily habit. Apart from the above reasons, addicts usually do not want help. Rarely will they submit to counsel or rehabilitation in the early stages of their drug use or addiction cycle. Jesus said, "They that are whole need not a physician" (or counsellor). The addict views his drug use as a cure and not as a problem. If the addict is on mind expansion drugs, he will have a feeling of superiority and wisdom. Not until he has had a few bad trips (they all do, eventually), and not until he suffers the related miseries of addiction, will he be a good candidate for counsel and rehabilitation. Therefore, don't play the "ready or not, here I come" game with the addict.

What can be done for the user, abuser or addict who has not been motivated to seek help? In some cases, nothing can be done but to wait for the situation to get worse. When it gets worse, we may be able to help that person. The challenge and task of the counsellor will be to watch and wait. The lines of communication (chapter 4) must be kept open. Periodic visits into the drug world are one way of keeping the lines open. Through the counsellor's Christian witness, the addict may recognize his spiritual need, and seek help. Through an experience with Christ his need for drugs will be alleviated. The best response we have found has been from those who have been motivated to seek a change in their life because of the conviction of the Holy Spirit.

On one occasion I was speaking at a church near London. A young man came to the altar, drawn by the Holy Spirit because he recognized his spiritual poverty. He had been on his way to London's Soho district to trip out on LSD. After making his decision, he turned to the Christian counsellor who had prayed with him and said, "I just discovered something. Now I don't have to go to Soho and shoot LSD. Now I have accepted Christ." He had come to Christ, not to get away from drugs, but because the Word of God convicted him of his need for a Saviour. But through his experience with Christ the need for drugs was removed.

One young girl addict who was converted said: "Well, this is just like getting high." That is not to suggest that receiving Christ is just a good feeling. Certainly Christ is more than a feeling; He is a way of life—but a way of life that is accompanied by good feelings of joy and peace. The Christian has his periods of euphoria that are far more powerful than a shot of dope.

One converted addict, who was tempted to return to drugs, said that after he took a shot of heroin he got the shock of his life when he found that he could not get high. He said, "Once you have felt the fullness of God's power, dope no longer has the same effect on you." Such Bible promises as, "I have come that they might have life and that they might have it more

82

abundantly" (John 10:10), and "Oh, taste and see that the Lord is good" (Psalm 34: 8), and "In thy presence is fullness of joy" (Psalm 16: 11) have an appeal to the drug generation.

The Drug Personality

Much has been said about the addictive personality, or those who are prone to become drug addicts. However, no one type of person becomes a drug addict. There are certain types who are fertile ground for drug addiction, but it is not the personality alone that causes drug use. Many young people with so-called addictive personalities are not addicted, and will not become dependent on drugs. They number in the millions. Once a person becomes physically and psychologically addicted—regardless of age, race, or social and economic background—he reacts to the drug craving like other addicts. Addicts develop similar behaviour patterns: dishonesty, deceptiveness, lying, stealing, and various criminal acts, in addition to not trusting other people. However, these patterns are usually brought on by the drug. Most addicts did not steal or commit crimes before their drug addiction.

Apart from the drugs, addicts are persons with individual problems and personalities. Each one must be dealt with according to his particular needs. A fifteen-year-old and a thirty-year-old may behave similarly on the streets and in their activities in the drug world, but in counselling and rehabilitation they must be dealt with on the basis of the particular personality.

Understanding the Addict as a Drug User and as a Person

It is difficult to counsel the addict while he is in his drug world and under the influence of narcotics. Contact and Christian witness can be done while the addict is high or sick, but it is best that *counselling* should not be done when an addict is in such a condition. When high the addict is another person. Judgments about his reactions cannot accurately be made when he is in such a state of mind. He may make promises while under the influence of the drug, tell lies, talk incessantly about meaningless problems, and relate other feelings that have been brought on by the drug.

There are exceptions, of course. One addict told me, "Look, I'm high, but I know what you are saying and I know what I am saying." However, it is still a good rule not to go into extensive counselling when the addict is under the influence of the drug. It takes a trained and experienced counsellor to know just how much the drug is affecting the user. Many ministers and other workers have been fooled because they passed judgment on an addict's decision made while he was under the influence of a particular drug.

The opposite condition from the above is when the addict has not had any drugs for a period of time, and is suffering withdrawal. He may not want to talk to you because he is getting low or sick, and only has a shot of dope on his mind. He may be irritable and hostile as a result. He also could be dangerous if he gets really sick and becomes desperate. He may act sincere and make promises of rehabilitation, but only to build up the counsellor for a "con" job. He may ask for money, or for some consideration that is part of fulfilling his need for drugs.

It is not advisable to try to lead an addict to a decision for Christ while he is under the influence of drugs. It never hurts to pray for him, but it is best not to have him pray for himself, unless it appears that the Spirit of God is moving upon him, which can happen.

However, when the addict is low or sick (if he is open and ready for it), it is a good time to minister to him from the Word of God and to pray for him and with him. In our rehabilitation programme at Teen Challenge, we find the withdrawal period an excellent time to reach the addict. If he is motivated, and if he is willing to submit to the withdrawal, he will become very sick. In his pain and suffering, he can be led to look to God for help and strength. We have seen many cases in which supernatural healing took place. Through His healing touch on their bodies, they have found that God does have power. Through this discovery they commit their lives to Christ. We have found that when an addict does not have pills, drugs, or any form of medication, it forces the issue with him. He has to do something to help him through the withdrawal. He usually does one of two things: he either runs away or he runs towards God and asks for His help.

Some would question the medical and theological soundness of this method, but it works for us. No addict at Teen Challenge has ever died during withdrawal. The pain does not leave them with any physical damage. We carefully supervise the withdrawal. If any complications arise, we immediately send the person to a clinic or hospital. A registered nurse is also in residence at Teen Challenge. The spiritual benefits of withdrawal through prayer far outweigh the physical hazards that accompany "cold turkey". As we tell the addicts, "What is five or ten days of physical suffering, compared to a whole new life you have waiting for you after your withdrawal is over?" The nights are long and the days are cold, but any addict who has gone through it and has experienced freedom from drugs and the new life in Christ will tell you, "It was worth it!"

We are not opposed to other methods of withdrawal. "Cold turkey" withdrawal happens to be a method that works for us. We recommend it to others.

The following is a brief outline of the important steps to take in counselling the hard-core, physically and psychologically addicted person. The addict, as opposed to the abuser and user, is one who has become physically and or psychologically hooked. The use of drugs has disrupted his normal pattern of living and behaviour.

1. *Establish the fact that the person is hooked* (*addicted*). If the person is physically hooked, this might not be difficult to establish. However, he may be in the early stages of his addiction. Some addicts will wait until they are "strung out", using five or ten bags of heroin a day, before they will admit they are hooked. The drug addict will delay this admission as long as he possibly can.

In the booklet, *A Positive Cure for Drug Addiction*, which we distribute to addicts on the streets and elsewhere, there is a section entitled "The Teen Challenge Message to Drug Addicts". It lists five steps to a cure. The first step is "admit you are hooked". The addict is told: (a) It doesn't matter whether you take off once a day or ten times a day, you are hooked, so admit it. (b) Quit talking about a big habit or a little habit. You are either hooked or you're not hooked, so be honest.

2. *Find out what kind of help or cure the addict wants*. The addict may want only temporary help, such as a physical cure (withdrawal). Perhaps he is a mooder, or a conner, who only wants attention and not the permanent cure. He must be told that there is no simple, painless cure. There are no sympathetic drugs or substitutes that can pull him out. He must be convinced that hospitals cannot help him on a permanent basis. A doctor can pacify him with some pills; a psychiatrist can tell him why he is on drugs; but neither can cure him.

He must also realize that places where group therapy is used as the only means to a cure cannot give him what it takes to stay clean when he is out on his own in a real crisis. If he thinks that other forms of therapy might work for him, he will not be ready for you and for a spiritual programme.

3. *Be honest with him about the difficulties he faces on the road to recovery*. He must be desperate and willing to fight for

85

his cure. Instilling faith, confidence and hope in the addict regarding the possibilities of a cure must be done honestly, objectively, and without being over-optimistic. He will want the quickest and shortest route to recovery—one that has no pain, no sacrifice, and no cost. He is used to quick answers to all his problems and to all pain—a shot of dope. He finds it difficult to have to wait for something and to fight for his answers.

Telling him that God will take care of everything might lead him to think he doesn't have to do anything for himself. He must realize that he can't be cured in three weeks or three months. It will take him at least one full year before he is able to assume all the normal responsibilities of life and be on his own.

In our *Positive Cure for Drug Addiction* booklet, step number two is, "quit looking for an easy way out". We tell the addict "Don't expect to be trusted or babied. You can't fool experienced people in the field of narcotics, so quit working angles. ... If you run around making connections, you can work for a cure. Get up off your seat and quit acting like a baby."

4. *Through prayer lead him to a personal experience with Jesus Christ.* The addict is also a sinner. Use the same methods in leading him to Christ as you would with anyone else. Get him on his knees before God in prayer. Pray with him and pray for him, and teach him to pray.

Quoting from *A Positive Cure for Drug Addiction:* "You must have faith in God. When you connect with a pusher, how do you know he is not giving you rat poison instead of H? You shoot it up without testing it under a microscope, because you must have faith that it is junk. If you can trust a pusher, why can't you trust in God? He never lets you down. You must come to Him like a little child and ask for His help. He has never turned anyone down who is sincere.'

The addict may be reluctant to accept Christ because of the possibility of returning to drugs and thus not being able to follow the Lord. Some addicts, like others with serious difficulties, will want to work on their problem first and then give their lives to Christ. They must be made to see that the way to overcome their problem is *through Christ*.

5. *Help him face his fears.* The fear of failure is stronger in an addict than in any other individual. He has sensed failure from the early stages of his life. He has probably failed at various attempts at rehabilitation. He is afraid to start again, and of perhaps having to face the pain of failure. He must see that

through Christ he can make it. He must realize that it is "not I, but Christ liveth in me" (Gal. 2: 20).

The new convert must realize he is not operating under his own will power alone; he is under new management, not in the hands of man, but of God. His faith will have to rise above his fears.

The convert also has fears of his past. The guilt from previous sins often haunts him. The teaching of the Word of God, plus personal prayer, will give him the assurance of sins forgiven, that there is "no condemnation to them which are in Christ Jesus" (Rom. 8: 1). Help feed his faith so that his doubts and fears will starve to death.

6. *Help him find meaningful activity.* For many addicts, the only work they have known is that of working angles. Normal work—household chores, handy work, cleaning up—is difficult for them to adjust to. Such work is not only important as a sign to show the addict that his life has changed; it is essential to his recovery because it keeps him busy and occupied so that the devil cannot play with his mind. Whatever work he is assigned to do, it should not be just busy work, but meaningful work in which he feels he is helping someone else or helping himself.

The counsellor will have to keep challenging and pushing the addict. He must try to understand the mental and emotional stresses the addict has lived under which have caused physical inactivity. Laziness starts with the mind. It takes the addict time to get used to using his body and keeping his mind on what his body is supposed to be doing.

Those who are making successful recoveries will soon learn the beauty and satisfaction that comes from seeing a job well done. Little things they could never bother about before—doing dishes, mopping floors—for the first time in their lives can become meaningful. Some of our converts volunteer for additional work besides that which is assigned to them, because they get a sense of satisfaction. They sense that they are working for the Lord, and are helping to carry their own work load.

Spiritual activity, when not balanced with work and recreation, may be harmful.

7. *Help him start planning for his future.* The addict has always lived for today; the only planning for tomorrow he ever did was to plan for tomorrow's dope fix. Through his conversion, help him to see that his future is not only in heaven, but also on earth. Encourage him to start planning his life all over again.

Some addicts started on drugs at an early age and thus they never had any ambitions. Some have never worked one day in their lives. According to their age and ability, help them to arrive at some practical goal for their future. Addicts who have got involved in drugs later in life may already have a talent or skill. Some may want to return to jobs they had before addiction started.

Beware of the converted addict's grandiose attitude about the type of work he plans to do. Suggest that he start with something small, yet meaningful. When he handles that, he can go on to greater things.

In *A Positive Cure for Drug Addiction* there are two important paragraphs regarding this:

"If you have no plans for your life, and if you are sure you can't help others, then mark down on a piece of paper five things you think you would like to do or be. Spend a few weeks investigating what is involved in each of these five things, then choose the one that appeals to you most. You must choose a goal. . . . Know what you want to do, then go after it.

"You must learn to love the things you once hated, and to hate the things you once loved. You can do the right things now because God gives you the power to do them."

How the Teen Challenge Centre Environment
Helps the Addict to Overcome His Addiction

If the drug addict is going to learn to grow—emotionally, mentally, and spiritually— he must be taught how to live apart and free from drugs or alcohol. He must also learn how to function without anti-social behaviour, without anger, hostility, immaturity, or in whichever way he previously reacted to reality. The addict must learn how to do this in a setting that to some degree is patterned after a home. It must resemble a normal situation. He must be in this environment of his own free will, and he must have the freedom to leave whenever he wants to. But he must also know there are consequences if he does choose to leave.

At Teen Challenge the addict learns behaviour by: (1) the example of other Christians; (2) the teaching of Christian behaviour through the Word of God; (3) direct confrontation of anti-social, unChristian behaviour through rules and regulations based on Christian concepts; (4) personal prayer through which the Holy Spirit reveals what Christ-like living is.

The result is that the addict is taught how to live and act. This teaching was the missing link in the addict's treatment in jails, hospitals, or other confinement programmes. In other programmes he was told why he must change but not how. He was told what he was, but not what he could be. At Teen Challenge, while he is learning *how* to live, he is also learning the *why*. The why without the how is failure. The why with the how is success.

Because at Teen Challenge we have chosen an old, tested, and proven method—the Christian faith—we have found the key to successfully rehabilitating the addict.

6

GUY OR GAY?

We were walking through a certain section of New York City when a fellow minister pointed to a person in front of us and asked, "Is that a guy or a gal? It's hard to tell, you know, nowadays."

"It's neither," I replied.

"What do you mean?" he asked with a puzzled look on his face.

"That's what is called a 'gay'," I said, further confusing him. I went on to explain the term "gay" which was not familiar to him.

"Gay" is the street terminology for a homosexual. There are various types of homosexuals, but gay is usually used to describe those who are obviously effeminate, flagrant, and who act and dress the part of the homosexual. The other kinds of homosexuals hide the indentifiable characteristics usually associated with the "homos".

The gays are becoming a prominent, activist minority group in our society. They are making their presence felt around the world. They are organized and open about their demands.

In large cities a whole gay world exists. There are gay bars, clubs, restaurants, theatres, cinemas and bookshops. There are beaches, holiday resorts, bowling leagues, computer dating services, campus fraternities and health clubs catering for homosexuals. There are apartment houses for homosexuals and even gay churches.

Homosexuals are found in all walks of life. Many famous stars of stage, screen, radio and television are notoriously "queers"; so are some top sports figures. A psychiatrist revealed that one of his homosexual patients was a world champion boxer. A substantial number of outstanding writers, artists, doctors, lawyers and business executives are known to be homosexuals. There is an unofficial but very powerful homosexual union. They look out for their own. When one gets into a position in a certain business, he will hire only homosexuals. They have literally taken over in some industries.

An off-Broadway actor my mother has dealt with in our Lost

Coin coffee house is an *actress* in the theatre. He dresses like a female and plays women's parts on stage. He, or she, comes to the coffee house beautifully dressed as a female with blonde hair and blue eyes and a very womanly shape. As a homosexual he plays the female role with male lovers.

Quite a few Hollywood homosexuals are married—purposely married—to present an image of normality. Most of these marriages, however, end in divorce. One famous star, a homosexual, was married for appearance sake, only to be divorced a year later. Some marry in hopes of overcoming their problem only to find out they are still attracted to males. One Hollywood wife of a male star suspected her husband was having an affair with someone else. He was—with another male star. Most of the Hollywood types of homosexuals are masculine looking, bulging with muscles. They walk, talk, and make love like a man but are males in looks only.

The problem is not confined to the stars. In Hollywood and on Broadway homosexuals are powerful as directors, composers, producers, playwrights, even backers of many productions. Since there is an unofficial homosexual union (one homosexual making a practice of hiring another homosexual) it is easy to see how many shows can have a number of homosexuals in predominance. Often those who do the casting will choose a homosexual, have an affair with him—and then fire him if the relationship does not work out.

There are a number of organizations promoting "gay power". "Civil rights" groups for homosexuals have sprung up in various forms across the country. New York and Los Angeles homosexual organizations banded together in the summer of 1970 under the banner of the "Gay Liberation Front". They staged "Gay Liberation Week" activities in those cities. On Sunday, June 28, thousands of homosexual men and women marched up Sixth Avenue, New York, from Greenwich Village to Central Park, carrying banners and wearing buttons with slogans such as "Gay is Good" and "Homosexuals are Human".

The serious thrust of such efforts is a demand that homosexuals be granted the same basic rights as their heterosexual peers to hold jobs, to wear military uniforms, to be free from embarrassment, and to gather publicly. Underlying this effort is the hope of homosexuals to overcome two main public attitudes towards homosexuality: (1) it is a sin, and (2) it is an aberration from the norm, a sickness that requires psychiatric treatment.

Homosexual "rights" literature says, "We will rally and petition our government. If necessary, we will bring a thousand drag queens to suburbia. We must encourage the entertainment industry to depict us as we really are. . . . Help bring about the day when we can openly love whom we choose."

The Mattachine Society, one of the oldest, best organized, and best known homosexual organizations, claims there are some twenty million homosexuals in America, with one million in New York City alone. These figures are, however, unrealistic. Homosexuals like to claim large numbers to promote the idea that it is normal to be a homosexual and that "everybody's doing it". The Kinsey Report states that ten per cent of American men have long periods of more or less exclusive homosexuality; only four per cent (two per cent of the women) are exclusively homosexual all their lives. These may be inflated figures also, but most experts do agree that there are about 2,600,000 men and 1,400,000 women who are exclusively homosexual in the United States alone.

From the above figures, and from the information that is available about the inroads homosexuals have made into business, industry, and the entertainment world, it is apparent that the Christian counsellor and the church must get involved in ministering to homosexuals. Until recently even the word homosexual was taboo in Christian circles. The mere mention of the word from the pulpit made people cringe. One prominent pastor in New York City, who dared to speak out concerning homosexuals, said afterwards, "A half a dozen men walked out of the service during my message on the subject."

The church must come out of the Dark Ages and recognize the existence of the problem; that many homosexuals have infiltrated the pew, the choir loft, the organ and piano bench—and even the pulpit. This is not to suggest that they must be thrown out. First, they must be counselled and pointed to deliverance from the evil. If that approach does not succeed, then the problem must be dealt with in another manner. Such conditions in the church must be reckoned with. But the greatest challenge is outside the church. The church and the Christian worker must make it known to the homosexual that there is help available, that they will help him with his problem and show him the love and compassion of Christ.

There are cured homosexuals in the church who have been helped through their conversion to Christ. But these are not many and they often live a lonely life, battling severe temptations, suffering in silence because they feel there is no one who

92

will accept them or understand them if they do share their problem. Counsellors are needed, therefore, in the area of follow-up witnessing and in prevention. Many young people on the verge of becoming homosexuals could be turned away from a lifetime involvement in homosexuality if a trained, alert counsellor were available to speak to them.

One of the reasons it is difficult to find male counsellors who are willing to work among the gay people is that homosexuality is so repulsive to the normal man. It goes against everything he feels and is as a man.

One of our workers rebelled when a Teen Challenge team was going out on the streets to distribute literature specifically to homosexuals. "Do I have to go?" he asked. When we asked him why he didn't want to go, he said, "I hate them." What he was really saying was, "I am scared of them." The homosexual whom the counsellor works with—or even talks with—may reflect something the counsellor sees inside himself. Perhaps he may have had some homosexual involvement in his teenage years and is afraid that it might break out again.

But most of all, there is the problem of finding the counsellor who has the patience, faith and the hope that Christ can cure the homosexual. This is a ministry that subjects the worker to abuses and exposes him to people whose personalities have often been totally warped by their way of life, and who often have temptations even after they are converted to Christ. There are minimal results, compared to the results of counselling other types of people. The road to recovery is terribly long. Yet the homosexuals represent a harvest field. Christ also died for them. The call goes out, "Who will go?"

In the book *I've Given Up On Parents* the author states:

It is not necessarily true that once a youth has become a homosexual, nothing can be done about it, but it is true that the rate of cure is very low. Everyone who has tried to help homosexuals—psychiatrists, psychologists, and pastoral counsellors—are in agreement that theirs is a very difficult pattern to change. But there are cases in which homosexuals have made adjustments that have enabled them to marry and have children, and, most important, abandon their homosexual ways. The chief difficulty we encounter is the large number of homosexuals who do not want to change. They like being the way they are. One cannot read their literature without becoming acutely aware that they feel theirs is a superior way of life.[1]

Those who have encountered homosexuals who want attention and not a cure find it difficult to develop a ministry and a
burden for them. They tend to ignore or openly refuse to help
the homos. Or they preach against the sin of homosexuality,
losing sight of the person behind the sin.

We have been greatly encouraged of late with regard to the
possibility of a cure for homosexuals. There was a time when
we felt it was virtually impossible—or that 98 per cent did not
want to be cured—but we are finding more and more who do seek
help and who are being freed from the habit. Admittedly the
numbers are small, but the point is: *homosexuality can be cured*.

The church must believe and preach that there can be hope
for homosexuals. As it does so, I believe more homosexuals,
will come forth seeking help. The reason they haven't, is because Christians have allowed the failures of the past to hold
them back from proclaiming the power of Christ to cure. If
only one in a million is cured, it means one thing: a cure is
possible. The odds are, of course, not that severe.

Many liberal churchmen and theologians are doing much to
"help" the homosexual—they are condoning the practice. This
helps those who are looking for justification and acceptance by
the church and society. One clergyman said regarding two
homosexual friends of his, "Both of them are very happy and
very much in love. They asked me to bless their marriage, and I
am going to do it" (*Time*, Oct. 31, 1969).

Homosexuals do need compassion and understanding. They
need acceptance, but not the kind of acceptance that says, "You
have a right to be the way you are; the church will condone
your practice." The homosexual needs acceptance in terms of
the counsellor's willingness to help cure him. There is a place
for the Christian in counselling homosexuals. The question is,
will we find a place in our hearts to love the person who practises homosexuality? Until the counsellor is ready and able to
make this commitment, the homosexual will continue to be
outside Christ and in bondage to his vice.

The Roots of Homosexuality

Homosexuals are made, not born. All males are created equal.
Most experts now agree that homosexuality is *not* the result of a
genetic or hormone predisposition. Male and female homosexuals do not constitute a "third sex"; biologically they are full
men and women.

What are the factors that contribute to the making of the
homosexual?

1. *The home*. Today the scientific consensus holds that homosexuality is largely conditioned by the environment in childhood, and most particularly by parental influences in the home. Sexual repression in the home is one of these factors. Children who are constantly being warned about the dangers of sex activity grow up with a grey if not dirty feeling about it. Natural sexual feelings in their teens are interpreted as unnatural and inspire feelings of guilt. Children may be taught to fear members of the opposite sex. Parents who have their own hang-ups about sex often reflect these, consciously or unconsciously, to their children.

Parents who raise their children in a sexually healthy home need not worry about raising a homosexual child; he will most likely grow up normally. In the sexually healthy home there should be a steady flow of impressions that will enable a child to conclude gradually and naturally that the heterosexual way of life is not only normal and right for him, but also productive and fun. Sexually well-adjusted parents know quite instinctively how to encourage masculinity in boys and feminity in girls; few adults require expert advice to determine what psychiatrists call "age-appropriate" behaviour in their own children.

Sex is not the only factor that contributes to homosexuality. Just as important is the ability of mother and dad to play their proper roles in the home. Studies show that homosexuals suffer from a lack of a solid identification with the parent of the same sex, and from deeply divided feelings for the parent of the opposite sex.

Mothers can contribute to homosexuality if they (1) are domineering; (2) are over-protective; (3) show preference; (4) play the son against the father; (5) have a poor sexual relationship with the husband which results in showering affection on the son; (6) are hostile; (7) reject the child; (8) have an unconscious desire to make a girl out of the boy, or vice-versa; (9) tell the child he was unwanted, or a "mistake"; (10) are puritanical; (11) demand to be made the centre of their son's attention; (12) make him mother-dependent; (13) act seductively towards the child.

Fathers can contribute to the homosexuality of their child if they (1) are weak persons; (2) are detached from their sons; (3) humiliate or belittle sons; (4) are cruel in punishment; (5) prefer one son over another, perhaps the son who is more like the father, or more masculine; (6) reject their son for other males. Psychiatrists agree that they "never saw a homosexual who had a good relationship with his father".

2. *Sociological factors also contribute to the making of a homosexual.* If some of the factors above exist in a home, it does not mean that the child will automatically be a homosexual. Usually homosexuality is the result of a combination of factors in the home and in society as a whole. It can result from the home alone, but studies show that experiences outside the home and in society at large also help make the homosexual.

Social factors which lead to homosexuality include: (1) the feminization of the male, masculinization of the female; (2) the high premium of male competition, along with female competition, (also competing with the male); (3) the diminishing importance of the parental role in the home; (4) the greater insistence on sexual "performance" or Playboy exploits; (5) the permissive attitude of the entertainment industry towards homosexuality; (6) the acceptance of homosexuality in society as a whole; (7) the demoralization of marriage; (8) the portrayal of sex as a game; (9) the American ideal which seems to equate virility with physical strength and prowess, and which leaves the less physically well-built male to be looked upon as a sissy.

3. *Experiences related to childhood may contribute to homosexuality.* Experiences can often create homosexuality in childhood, or they can help to develop a pattern that results in the outbreak of the problem later in life. Some young people may participate in occasional homosexual activities in childhood, yet make a satisfactory heterosexual adjustment later in life. It is usually only the combination of a poor relationship with parents, plus a bad experience outside the home, that results in the establishment of the homosexual pattern of behaviour.

Time magazine says that it is agreed by most experts that children will not become homosexuals unless they undergo many disturbing experiences during the course of several years. Also, while only one third of the confirmed adult homos can be helped to change, large numbers of "pre-homosexual" children can be successfully treated.

Types of Homosexuals

As with alcoholism, most homosexuality is hidden. That is, it is hidden to the average person. However, "it takes one to know one". It doesn't take long for two homosexuals to "make connection".

A favourite meeting place is the gay bar. It is fast becoming a social institution in America. Men go there, not primarily to drink, but rather to socialize with other homosexuals. The evening usually ends in pairing off and departing to one or the other's apartment. Those who do not make connections must resort to walking the streets, going to certain gay parks, or making contact in men's rooms or baths. The latter is almost as popular as the gay bar. It is sometimes referred to by the clientele as an "orgy room".

Most homosexuals go from one relationship to another. To find new partners, some homosexuals "cruise". They engage in gestures that immediately identify them to each other. Like the male girl-watchers, the male boy-watchers do most of their cruising with the eyes by making prolonged surveillance of the other man's body. It is also done by lingering in each other's presence, and over the shoulder glances. In men's rooms it may be done by a foot-tapping signal.

While taking a minister on a tour of Times Square one night, I decided to show him how such a possible contact could be made. We sat in a restaurant in the row facing the street and sidewalk. As crowds strolled by we started looking carefully at different individuals. One middle-aged man caught our eyes. He passed on, then came back and looked at us again. We returned the gaze. Then he disappeared. About three minutes later we turned and saw him taking a seat right next to us in the restaurant. We got up and walked out—and he followed. Soon, however, we lost him in the crowd. However, it was apparent he thought we were "cruising".

One client, a homosexual, came and said, "I quit my job." When asked why, he confessed that another worker on the job was giving him the eye. He confessed, "I tried to avoid him, but my old habits and homosexual gestures, I guess, are still a part of me and I think he knows I'm gay. I just had to get away from that place before I fell." Homosexuals seem to have that natural instinct for recognizing each other.

Although there are some homosexual marriages that last some time, most homosexuals go from one partner to another. Long term relationships between two males are notably few. This is one of the miseries of such a life. When the homosexual gets older, he begins to have less appeal and often he has to buy sex.

One thing is for sure regarding the life of the homosexual, it is far from gay. Most of them present a picture of an average life style of any male, but behind the scene is a life of transitory relationships, lovers' quarrels, jealousy, and romantic power struggles. There is also the fear of exposure—even black-mail—and for the more desperate there is danger of arrest, of making advances towards a non-homosexual and perhaps a re-sulting beating. Even those relationships in which the partners agree that they are married (it is of course not a legal marriage) rarely last more than several years. The Kinsey Report of 1948 found that "long term relationships between two males are notably few".

To help the counsellor better understand the different types of homosexuals, these are their main characteristics as given in *Time*.

1. *The blatant homosexual.* These include the catty hairdresser or the lisping, limp-wristed interior decorator, the hip-swinging waiter, and so on. His lesbian counterpart is the "butch", the girl who is aggressively masculine to the point of trying to look like a man. Blatant homosexuals also include "leather boys", who advertise their sadomasochism by wearing leather jackets and chains, and certain transvestites. Blatants often draw sneers from other homosexuals; many of them are only going through a phase. Having recently "come out"—admitting their condition and joining the homosexual world—they feel insecure in their new roles and try to re-create their personalities from scratch. They try to act the way they think gay people are supposed to behave.

2. *The secret lifer.* Ninety per cent of the nation's committed homosexuals are hidden from all but their friends, lovers, and occasionally, psychiatrists. They prefer subdued clothes and close-cropped hair. They may dress more conservatively than flamboyant straights. Many wear wedding rings and have wives, children and employers who never know. They range across all classes, races and occupations. To lead their double lives, these full or part-time homosexuals must pass as straight; most are extremely skilled at camouflage. They can cynically tell, or at least smile at, jokes about "queers".

3. *The desperate.* Members of this group are likely to haunt public toilets or Turkish baths. [One young man I dealt with, who was faithfully endeavouring to live a Christian life, would suddenly become tempted while coming home from work. He would run into a subway toilet and engage in a homosexual act. It was as though an evil spirit came upon him.]

The desperate homosexual may be pathologically driven to sex, but emotionally unable to face the strains of sustaining a serious human relationship. Or, he may be a married man who hopes to conceal his need by making contact as anonymously as possible.

4. *The adjusted.* For the most part, these homosexuals live

conventional lives. They have a circle of friends whom they meet at gay bars or at private parties. Often they try to settle down with one lover.

5. *The bisexual.* Many married homosexuals fake enjoyment of intercourse with their wives. Some researchers, however, have found a number of men and women who have a definite preference for their own sex, but engage in occasional activity with the opposite sex and enjoy it.

6. *The situational-experimental.* He is a man who engages in homosexual acts without any deep emotional motivation. Many drug addicts in prison will engage in homosexual activity while there, but return to normal sexual activity when on the outside. The same often happens in the armed forces.[2]

Developing a Counselling Ministry to Homosexuals

Few Christian workers are called to work exclusively with homosexuals. Several converted homosexuals work full- and part-time for Teen Challenge with homosexuals. Our workers distribute literature to homosexuals in Greenwich Village. Roger Dean, a converted homosexual, has written a tract for homosexuals, called "Gay", which we distribute.

The Mattachine Society sometimes sets up its literature table in front of our workers. When we give literature to homosexuals, some of them curse, or throw the literature in our faces; some walk on slowly after taking a tract and then tear it into little pieces. Homosexuals don't like to hear what the Bible says about their practices, nor do they want to hear that there is a cure. Admitting there is a cure means they should do something to help themselves. They would rather believe God made them the way they are, or that they have an incurable sickness, or that homosexuality is as natural as heterosexuality.

Christian counsellors are needed to work with homosexuals. It is true, most homosexuals need professional help, and the average counsellor may not feel equipped, but he can at least present the witness of the Gospel and give hope through Christ.

Christian workers should learn as much as possible about the problem. The counsellor who is alert to pick out the signs can find the hidden homosexual. Realizing that homosexuality may be hidden behind another problem can be most helpful in knowing how to proceed with certain cases. If I'm interviewing someone whom I suspect of homosexuality, I ask politely, "Have you ever been engaged in homosexuality?" If the answer is yes, I ask next: "Are you now a practising homosexual?"

Knowing the answer to this at the beginning of the counselling session saves a lot of time.

As alcoholics and others often do, homosexuals may come to the counsellor with a problem that is only a smoke screen to conceal a deeper problem. Usually the problem they present is the result and manifestation of homosexuality. If the counsellor does not know the primary problem, he will be trying to treat the symptoms and not the cause. It may be possible to help a homosexual without knowing he is one, but such help would be in spite of the counsellor and not because of his know-how.

How to Counsel Homosexuals

The following suggestions are for the counsellor who is knowingly treating a homosexual. If the counsellor suspects the person with whom he is dealing is a homosexual, he should either ask him directly or work towards the goal of uncovering the problem. Once admission of homosexuality has been made, the counsellor can proceed according to the following outline.

1. *Find out if the homosexual views his activity as a problem.* There must be motivation. Why did he come to you? Does he consider his homosexuality a harmful, self-destructive habit that must be removed? Does he want to become "straight"? These questions should be first in the mind of the counsellor. He should look for evidence of whether the homosexual really wants to change. The homosexual may be saying, "Make my life more comfortable and take away the pain, but don't change me." He may want the counsellor to help him get rid of his guilt, but not his pleasure.

2. *Expect strong initial resistance.* The homosexual is a difficult patient because he is ruled by the bundle of fears that made him a homosexual in the first place. He has an unconscious fear of discovering heterosexual wishes and feelings, and an even greater fear of acting on such feelings. He is afraid of discovering the inevitable emotional bankruptcy of homosexuality. He fears his inability to shift to heterosexuality.

Added to these fears is his resistance to the message of the Gospel. Some homosexuals are deeply bitter towards God for the way they think He made them, or for allowing the conditions to exist during their childhood which set the stage for homosexuality.

If the counsellor understands that resistance in the early stages of counselling is normal for this type of person, it will help him. One young man I dealt with would get angry, say

100

abusive things, even vulgar things, but he would always come back, and each time his resistance was lower.

3. *Find out what type of homosexual he is and the extent of his involvement in homosexuality.* I have dealt with those who were more homosexual in their fantasies than in reality. Often young people are in the early stages of homosexual involvement and can be saved from it. Their fear of becoming a confirmed, life-time homosexual is usually their biggest problem. They must be shown that just because they have engaged in mental homosexuality, it does not mean they are a confirmed homosexual.

A young man in his thirties came to see me and the first thing he said was, "I am a homosexual." During our first conversation he stated that he had never engaged in homosexual activity with another male, but he had dreamed about such a relationship and had lusted in his mind after other men. From childhood he had engaged in homosexual fantasies, but fortunately he had never actually practised it. He was helped by the reassurance I gave him that he was not an overt homosexual, but rather had latent tendencies in that direction.

The counsellor will meet many who have latent tendencies towards homosexuality and he should encourage them to talk about it. Pastors should encourage this by having frank discussions with young people, and by informing them about sex and sex deviations. If I were a pastor, one of the first things I would do is either conduct a sex education course myself, or bring in some person competent in the field to do it. The prevention of homosexuality is one of the most neglected areas of Christian counselling and teaching.

In short, the counsellor should look for homosexuality in all of his dealings with others. He may discover either a latent or an overt problem.

4. *Beware of false confessions and contrived contrition.* One young man we dealt with at Teen Challenge wept and cried every time we talked with him. He said he was sorry. Whenever he could, he put his head on my shoulder, or on someone else's shoulder who was counselling him. He was mentally and emotionally disturbed, but he is an example of some who will come to the counsellor with high-sounding confessions and emotional outbursts of sorrow. The counsellor should not allow himself to become over-impressed by mere confessions or even deep contrition. Both of these are normal reactions for the homosexual during counselling. Such confessions must be weighed against further actions and steps that the homosexual takes to help himself.

Some homosexuals want relief from the guilt of their deviation; they get a certain amount of release by their outbursts of confession. Often they go through a regular cycle of confession, reversion, confession and reversion all over again. We have had to stop some homosexuals from seeing us or calling us, because we sensed they only wanted to use us to unload some guilt; they did not want to change.

There is also the religious homosexual who says, "I love God. I feel God is with me." They have convinced themselves that God accepts them the way they are and that He understands them. They have no desire to change.

5. *Teach what the Bible says about homosexuality.* The homosexual will not be cured until he looks at the underlying root of his problem. There are surface and psychological causes of homosexuality, but understanding them is not sufficient to lead to a cure.

The surface cause is that homosexuals have a fixation for members of their own sex that prevents them from having satisfactory relations with members of the opposite sex. When we asked a homosexual why he was one, he said, "I just happen to like men. As long as I can remember, I have been attracted to other men. I can't help it—my flesh just cries out for another man's flesh."

Psychologically, homosexuality is an acquired abnormality. It can be caused by the pampering and petting of over-affectionate parents, by an unnaturally close relationship between a boy and his mother, by fear of normal sex, by childhood training that sex is dirty, sinful, vile, and by the bad example of promiscuous parents.

Homosexuals know the theories and explanations of their behaviour. They seek sympathizing psychiatrists who will try to help them adjust to a hostile society, or to rationalize and justify their behaviour. Psychology can blame phobias, compulsions, obsessions, fixations, parental failures and misguided childhood behaviour patterns for causing homosexuality. Consequently, the homosexual can blame God, his parents, society and bad breaks for his condition, but rarely does he accept any responsibility for it himself.

This is why it is so important for the counsellor to lay a biblical foundation for the root cause of homosexuality. The counsellor must help the homosexual look at the basic cause, which is *creature-Creator distortion* (Rom. 1:25). We base this on a simple outline of Romans 1:18-32. The counsellor should take the homosexual through this outline as he seeks to lead him to Christ. This will set the framework for a cure.

(a) Man's basic rejection of God's deity (21a, 23). Man refused to honour God and refused to give Him thanks. Instead, man humanized God.

(b) Man's rejection of God's revealed truth (19, 20, 21b, 22). What can be known about God is plain to men, that is, His eternal power and deity. But men suppressed the truth by their wickedness. As a result, man's wisdom has ended in futility and darkness. "Professing themselves to be wise, they became fools."

In the case of the homosexual, the truth of this is particularly evident. The homosexual practises his sin because he chooses and professes his own wisdom, contrary to God's. He has substituted futile thinking for truth and reality. Homosexuals generally tend to be full of answers, based on humanistic observations sprinkled with some psychology and even a little religion.

(c) Man's glorification of the creature instead of the Creator (v. 25). The Scripture attributes "dishonouring their bodies among themselves" and women's exchanging "natural relations for unnatural" and men's giving up "natural relations with women ... committing shameless acts with men" (RSV) specifically to this glorifying of the creature. Overt homosexuality can be traced to serving the flesh, rather than God. When a person no longer honours and serves God, he is susceptible to becoming a slave of the flesh. Before one can become a life-time homosexual, he must ignore the voice of conscience, his knowledge of right and wrong, and follow a premeditated course of disobedience and stubbornness. A homosexual is a victim of a mind and imagination given over to the worship of the flesh. The homosexual feeds on filthy literature, on dirty pictures and lewd novels. His dreams, thoughts and imagination have been taken over by the demons of lust.

A converted homosexual once said, "My whole life I sought for love. I was always looking for that one special lover. I wanted to nestle into another man. I wanted to get into his personality, to take of his strength, his virility, and make it a part of myself. Then I realized this was a bizarre distortion of the love I was actually seeking in God. The love of God and the love of man are two extremes on the pendulum of love. I rejected true love and accepted the perverted kind. It was hell's parable of heaven's reality. ... Homosexuality is the complete distortion of everything God promises.

"Only after I accepted Christ, and received the teaching of

103

the Word, did I realize I had distorted the concept of love. I was loving the creature more than the Creator. I now worship the Creator and I have finally found the true meaning of love, and the means whereby I can ward off the lust of the flesh."

6. *Be prepared for a long counselling relationship.* Next to the mentally ill, the homosexual demands the longest period of time for healing. The fact that a homosexual will submit to lengthy counselling and therapy is in itself a great accomplishment. only those who have found hope in Christ will stick with treatment, especially if the counsellor is trained enough to see whether actual change is taking place.

The counsellor should make himself available as much as possible, both by personal visits and by telephone contact. While trying to help one young man, I told him, "Here's my phone number; when you are going through a severe temptation, call me and we'll talk and pray." One of the biggest hurdles for the homosexual is to find a relationship of warmth, trust, and confidence with another person to whom he can turn in the moment of his most urgent need. True, he must turn to God, but he also needs a human instrument to assist him in his contact with God.

The counsellor must be prepared to help the converted homosexual go through his "burning out" process. Roger Dean said the first four weeks after his conversion his life was blessed and wonderful, but then he faced great temptations. "I thought Christ dismissed all my problems," he said. "He did take away the old habits, the hustling, and all the old practices, but he did not take away the temptation. I still got shook up when I saw a man walk by."

He went through what he calls the "burning out process" when Christ had to destroy him. During this time, he said he wanted sexual relations with someone, with anyone. His lust was being burned out. "I told God I'd rather die than go back," he said. Meanwhile, his Christian friends and counsellors faithfully stood by him. He did not want to be alone to battle the temptations.

Perhaps Roger's motivation was rare, but it was evidence of God's power to change the homosexual totally. The counsellor should always let the hooked homosexual know that others have made it and conquered the habit. Most homosexuals will ask, "Do you know one homosexual who has made it?" He should be told that many have, and that it is possible for him to receive the same cure.

There are some homosexuals who fear being cured. Homosexuality is their security. They are afraid of what would happen if they were to become normal. Their problem also gives them an excuse for other things they do, which may or may not have anything to do with homosexuality.

Some justify drinking by the fact that they are homosexuals. Another homosexual client would constantly complain that he was not being accepted by other people because he was a homosexual. However, in his case only an experienced counsellor would be aware of his problem. He used this as an excuse to cop out from counselling. He said, "Since nobody else will accept me, I'll just go back to my old friends—I know they will accept me."

The counsellor must do as Jesus did. He appealed to a man's desire for health, healing and wholeness. "Wilt thou be made whole?" he asked one man. The question was not, "Do you want to get rid of your sickness?" but, "Do you want health?"

7. *Learn how to handle the homosexual's periods of regression.* Most converted homosexuals do not have an easy time "burning out" their homosexual lusts and appetites. Deliverance from homosexuality is much different from deliverance from drugs or alcohol, because homosexuality is a problem connected with the sex drive. One minister who had recovered from homosexuality and had married and had children, suddenly was faced with the old temptation again after many years of freedom. Whether this had anything to do with a coldness in his spiritual life, I do not know, but his case points out the difficulty of long-term recovery.

The counsellor must be understanding when regression takes place. It must not be interpreted as the counsellor's fault. Angry outbursts, lectures, threats of breaking off the counselling, humiliating and belittling the client will do no good. His faith will need to be bolstered. A direct, biblical thrust needs to be made to build his hope. Then an effort can be made to see why he reverted. Christ is not only the cure for the homosexual's sin problem, He is the cure for his search problem. The homosexual has sought in a relationship with other men what can only be satisfied when he is "in Christ". One homosexual told me, "I sought for a lover. I was on a constant search for true love." This need for a vital relationship with a person is met in a saving relationship with God's Son.

Eddie sat in my office; a steady flow of tears ran down his face. "I don't want to live any more," he said. "I can't go on like this. What's there to live for?" The slashes on his wrist confirmed that he had tried to take his life the night before.

Eddie had fallen back into his homosexual habit once again. It was a discouraging blow to him. When I asked him what had happened, he said: "I was riding home from work on the train when my eyes met this other fellow. Before I knew it, I was following him to his apartment." This had been his sixth relapse in the year since he had accepted Christ. "I tried," he said, "the Lord knows I tried. I've done everything you've told me to do."

Just how much he had tried to avoid temptation was difficult to determine. Eddie's problem was that although he wanted to be free of his habit and serve Christ, he had not yet reached the point of total despair and hate for the kind of person his homo-sexuality turned him into. But the more he enjoyed freedom from the habit over a long period of time, the greater effect each new fall had upon him. Finally, after yielding to this last temptation, he was ready for the first time to give up completely his own ability to stay clean and yield totally to God for strength.

What should a counsellor do in such a situation? I wondered if I should condemn him or comfort him. I first thought of condemning him. Three or four times Eddie said, "I'll leave if you want me to." Then I said, "Eddie, if you had really wanted to end your life, I'm quite sure you would have done it. I don't think you have given up hope. I think you slashed your wrist because you felt you needed to suffer for what you did."

In spite of Eddie's seeming hopelessness, I was quite sure because he had come to see me that he had not given up hope. Once I was convinced of this, I began to try to feed his faith. Through prayer and the assurance to him of God's forgiveness, his sobbing turned to tears of comfort and assurance that the Lord had forgiven him.

This case shows what a counsellor may have to go through in dealing with a homosexual. The temptation will be to give up or to threaten him. This should be avoided until it appears that the last thread of his desire is gone.

NOTES

[1] David Wilkerson with Clare Cox, *I've Given Up on Parents* (London, Hodder and Stoughton, 1968).

[2] *Time*, "The Homosexual: Newly Visible, Newly Understood" October 31, 1969. Reprinted by permission from *Time*, The Weekly Newsmagazine; copyright Time Inc., 1969.

7

SOBER OR FREE?

One of the things I fear, is that in the midst of the attention drug addiction is receiving, we are losing sight of the terrible plight of the alcoholic. Is society hiding its booze addiction behind the youth drug problem? Is our concern for the dope addict a genuine concern, or is it an evasion of the alcohol problem? For many, it is an evasion. No parent can honestly lecture his child about the dangers of drugs while holding a whisky glass in his hand.

One of the arguments I find it difficult to contend with when I'm talking to young people about the dangers of drugs is: "If our parents drink, why can't we smoke pot? It's no worse, and even less harmful." Whether marijuana is less harmful than alcohol has never been proved, but the young people do have a point when they say, "You have your thing; why can't we have ours?" Of course, two wrongs don't make a right. The use of one poison does not justify the use of another. However, if marijuana is wrong, then so is alcohol.

Perhaps society's concern for drug addiction results from the number of teenagers involved; the cost of supporting the habit; the quick physical tolerance the body builds up towards it; and the ever-present danger of an overdose. Alcohol, on the other hand, is socially acceptable; part of our way of life; taken in moderation by millions of people. Alcohol deteriorates the body and mind more slowly than hard narcotics do. Alcohol addiction simply does not stir the same emotions drug addiction does.

From our experience in dealing with both types of addicts and addictions, we believe there is a greater potential for success with a hard-core drug addict than with the hard-core alcoholic. Both in terms of rehabilitation and in terms of recovery, the drug addict seems to fare better. Emotional conflicts within the two are often the same, but the physical and psychological craving for alcohol is more difficult to overcome in the long run.

Therefore, there is a great challenge for the church and the Christian counsellor to reach the alcoholic. Counsellors will come in contact with more alcoholics than drug users. Statistics bear this out. For every 100 adults in the United States, 4.2 are alcoholics. In Nevada, 6.6 out of every hundred are hooked, in California, 6.4. The number of alcoholics doubled between 1940 and 1966, from 2,600,000 to 5,000,000. Alcoholism is five times more prevalent than cancer. Every year in the United States 250,000 people become alcoholics, or 1,200 a day. The national family relief cost of alcoholism is $2,600,000. Alcoholism takes approximately twelve years off the alcoholic's life.

Alcoholics—Who Are They?

For many, the typical alcoholic is a skid-row bum. Often, this is the type pastors and Christian workers are most in touch with. This is the kind we have dealt with most often in our Teen Challenge programme. Many of them have become hardened to the gospel. They think of the church only in terms of soup and sandwiches. The gospel service is the penalty they feel they must pay for their meal. If they had money for food, they would rather pay for it than go through the gospel service. They also learn the language of Christians; they learn what to say to "con" well-meaning Christian workers and to panhandle from them.

We have had little success with the rescue mission conditioned alcoholic. Perhaps this is partly because the kind of alcoholic who ends up on skid row is in the worst condition and thus frequents mission halls out of desperation. Some of these alcoholics have been helped. We have seen some marvellous transformations at Teen Challenge. But I wonder if in one way the rescue missions have not helped to perpetuate the problem. Have the gospel missions inadvertently helped to keep the alcoholic in alcoholism? Have we—I include Teen Challenge in this, for in a sense we too are a mission—unknowingly allowed the mission to be used as a flophouse? Have we let it be used as a place for young preachers, or would-be preachers to practise or to satisfy their preacher's itch? Have we used the skid-row alcoholic as a "gospel guinea pig"? These are serious, probing questions. They have to be raised and answered. Those of us who work with alcoholics must especially answer them, as we try to develop effective programmes to help and cure alcoholics.

But the skid-row alcoholic is not the typical alcoholic. We must turn our attention to the "hidden" alcoholics. Outwardly, they seem to function normally in society. A survey in one city, taken by an organization which treats alcoholics, found that

108

among 30,000 who applied for a "cure", there were 600 medical doctors, 300 priests and clergymen, 170 dentists, 650 lawyers, 18 judges, and more than 1,000 tradesmen and heads of industries.

Following is my own analysis, including the research of others, of the different types of hidden or unnoticed alcoholics. Most of them do not see themselves as needing help. Later, I will discuss the question of how to help the drinking person see that he does have a problem.

Types of Alcoholics

1. *The working or social alcoholic.* The largest number of alcoholics are in this category. Such an individual works, does his best to provide for his family, and to some degree carries on the functions of father and husband. He may lose time off from work, but he manages to hang on to his job. Others at work may be aware of his drinking problem and protect him from losing his job. In so doing, they may also unknowingly be keeping him from seeking help, because of the sense of security his job gives him.

His wife may also sympathize with his drinking and protect him from the children, other relatives, and friends. She may enjoy mothering him or caring for him as a patient. I have seen cases, both with addicts and alcoholics, in which after the husband was rehabilitated, his wife no longer showed an interest in him because she no longer had a sick patient to care for. The fact that there was now a man in the house who could look after himself and the rest of the family meant that she had to step down from the throne, so to speak.

2. *The hooked alcoholic.* This is the alcoholic who is psychologically and physically addicted. "It is possible that some irreversible change in biochemistry gives the alcoholic a sensitivity or 'allergy' to alcohol, so that one drink sets off a chain reaction leading inevitably to a drunk. ... The phenomenon of craving which helps perpetuate a binge may be caused by one or more of several x factors of a physiological nature—depletion of chlorides in the blood, faulty elimination of certain waste products produced in the metabolism of alcohol, lack of vitamins in the brain, or some upsetting of the enzyme balance."[1]

The hooked alcoholic is the one who suffers withdrawal pains when he tries to stop drinking. He may be working; he may be the social alcoholic; he may be the skid row alcoholic. When and at what point someone turns into a hooked alcoholic, no one knows. There just seems to be a point at which those who drink steadily find themselves physically and psychologically hooked.

The hooked alcoholic reaches this condition by several progressive stages:

(a) *Social drinking*. Probably 98 per cent of all alcoholics start on the road to their addiction by social drinking. The social drinker may be compared with the drug user. Social drinking is the first link in the chain of alcoholism, but just as all drug users do not become drug addicts, so all social drinkers do not become alcoholics. But as with drug use, no social drinker is immune to becoming an alcoholic. Every social drinker is a potential alcoholic.

(b) *Steady drinking*. Social drinking leads to more social drinking, and the next step is steady drinking. The drinking may be alone or with others.

(c) *Problem drinking*. The problem drinker is the steady drinker who finds that he now has a physical craving. He may drink out of habit, or he may drink more when pressures and problems pile up on him. His drinking has become a problem either because he has started to use alcohol steadily, or because he finds it has become the answer to other problems. Or it could be a combination of both reasons.

(b) *Addiction*. The problem drinker is now hooked or addicted. The flame has gone out of control. He has a physical craving that can only be quenched by alcohol. The question from this point on is how he can control or manage his addiction. Can he work and wait until the weekend? Can he get through the day? He may become a nipper or a binger. One out of ten or fifteen end up on skid row.

3. *The nipper*. The hooked drinker may develop the habit of sneaking off regularly to take a nip: a nip in the morning, a nip at noon, a nip at night, and maybe a few nips in between. He usually is never drunk; he is the most hidden of the hidden alcoholics. Many housewives and businessmen are in this group. The housewife can easily nip during the day at home, and the businessman or office worker can pull a bottle out of the drawer and sneak a quick one.

The nipper likes to maintain a certain level of inebria all day, rather than drink heavily at one time. This is the reason the nipper is usually never drunk, or doesn't have the appearance of being drunk. Only someone who knows this person well can detect the mild drunkenness or inebria.

The nipper is the most difficult to reach because of the hidden factor, and because he is able to maintain normality. The work-

110

ing or social nipper goes to great lengths to get his nip and to hide the fact. He must lie, deceive, and cover up. No matter who he is, and how honest he may be in certain affairs of his life, when it comes to satisfying his craving for alcohol, he will go to any extreme to have that one swig.

4. *The binger.* Some alcoholics drink heavily at times, then level off, or they use none at all for several days. There are men who disappear for three or four days—out on a drinking binge—then return home and stay off the bottle for weeks or months. Why they go on the binge and how they are able to stay clean for such periods of time is not known. Often the binger suffers from deep-rooted guilt feelings that rise up periodically and thus trigger the drinking. Or, he may be a person subject to severe depression and moods, which also serve as a trigger.

5. *The skid row alcoholic.* It is estimated that only about ten per cent, at the most, of the alcoholics end up on skid row. Some working alcoholics, nippers and bingers may spend short periods on some skid row, but those who end up there permanently, fortunately represent only a small number of the total alcoholic population. Those who do become a part of the row do so not because they want to be with other alcoholics, or because it is a good place to go to drink; they go there out of necessity. They are homeless and jobless. The flophouses become home. Some drift into skid row, not because of alcohol, but to find a cheap place to live. But after being exposed to conditions in skid row, they develop a drinking problem.

Skid row alcoholics not only have an addiction to alcohol, but to the atmosphere found on skid row. In skid row the alcoholic finds friends and fellowship, held together only by alcohol. Some of them find it difficult to leave the friends and fellowship behind. Conditions on skid row, of course, are deplorable. Most skid row alcoholics who come into our Teen Challenge Centre suffer from some physical infirmity: malnutrition, liver infection, nervous and gastric disorders, stomach ulcers, and skin infections known as wine sores.

The Roots of Alcoholism

Where does alcoholism begin? Does it start in the person or in the bottle? Is the alcoholic sick because he drinks, or does he drink because he is sick? Is the problem physical, psychological, emotional, or spiritual?

There are those who teach and believe that it is the alcohol which causes alcoholism. Others believe it is caused by the alcohol along with inner conflicts that have nothing to do with the

111

physical or chemical properties of alcohol. My own beliefs lie somewhere between these two opinions. Some people seem to get hooked just because they drink too much. Their bodies build up a physical craving, then a tolerance, and thus the craving for more and more alcohol.

But what about those who drink and never become alcoholics? And what about those who take one drink and are hooked immediately? Does a lifetime of drinking in moderation prevent physical craving? Does a personality disorder or emotional conflict make a person ripe for addiction?

The cause of alcoholism seems to be both in the person and in the alcohol. There is no doubt that some people are addiction-prone. It is also a fact that alcohol itself creates additional psychological and spiritual problems that perpetuate its use. The problem for some is first in themselves; later, in the bottle; and later still, in the bottle and the person. With others, it may work the opposite way. There may be nothing wrong with the person. It is the bottle. They like to drink. The body builds up a craving. As a result of turning to the bottle, something goes wrong inside the person.

I think it is an oversimplification, however, to lay the blame on the alcohol alone. If this were so, then the solution would be to isolate the alcoholic for a period from all use of alcohol. Get the alcohol out of his veins. But the psychological craving would still be there. And the emotional disorder that either preceded or resulted from alcoholism would still be there.

"Repetition alone won't produce addiction. It only comes when there is a motive for repeating. Alcohol is not habit-forming in the sense that a drug like morphine is. Rather than calling alcohol habit-forming, it is more accurate to say that it is a substance that lends itself to those who form compulsive habits easily."[2]

It is a fact, however, that alcohol is addictive. It is a poisonous substance that can and does create habituation, craving, and addiction. The question then is simply this: Does the poison alone do this, or are there other factors that have nothing to do with the alcohol which either produce or add to the addiction? Probably, it works both ways.

What are some of the factors that can cause alcoholism, or cause social drinkers to become alcoholics? Persons who have inward disorders or conflicts do not turn to alcohol necessarily because of those conflicts. They first drink socially; then, because of the inner conflicts, they are triggered into alcoholism. Two people may have the same type of personality disorder and the one is an alcoholic and the other is not. Just because a person suffers from some emotional weakness does not mean he or she is going to become an alcoholic. It is true, however, that persons with distress, anxiety, guilt complexes, and so on, are more likely to become alcoholics than others are.

In examining the roots of alcoholism, or the roots of emotional distress that can make a person susceptible to alcoholism, one must first look into the family background and the home. What kind of parents sow the seeds of alcoholism in their children?

1. *The "iron fist" parent.* This is the parent who rules the home like a dictator. Father is the man with the iron fist. He is to be obeyed rather than loved. He is the first and final authority. Children of the iron-fisted father grow up hating him. They live in fear and react to discipline out of fear. The children can never identify with their father. They look for the day when they can leave home and be free. The child of the iron-fisted parent is a puppet. He learns that to be loved, he must obey. He has to learn love through obedience. He is not loved because he is the child; he is only loved if he is the good and obedient child.

The result is that the child feels emotionally rejected and has great feelings of inferiority. Such instability can make it impossible for this child in later life to function as a man, a husband, or a father. One client told me, "I hated my father with a passion. I couldn't wait till he was dead. One day somebody walked up to me on the street and told me that my father had died. I remember being so happy and laughing. But then I began to feel so guilty for hating my father. First I drank because I hated him. And after he died I drank because of the guilt over hating him."

2. *The "success ladder" parent.* One father said, "I'm going to make sure my children have all the things in life I was deprived of." For this father, the child became the reflection of his own ego. The goals this father could not achieve he wanted fulfilled in his child. The hippie generation is the product of the success ladder parent. The child grows up hearing over and over again, "Get the right job, go to the right school, get the right position", and so on. Why? Because it makes mother and dad look good.

The "got-to-succeed" child is smothered by those parental ambitions. He cannot find himself, or choose his own goals. He is a creature of parental ambition. He also learns that love has a price: success. The more he succeeds, the more he is loved. The less he succeeds, the less he is loved, and the less he gets in the way of material pay-off. When the child cannot climb the success ladder, when he cannot live up to the lofty goals mother and dad have set for him, he either rebels or withdraws into guilt feelings. Several alcoholic clients in our dealings have been only children. In such cases they seem to have had intense pressures put upon them to excel according to a mother's or father's desire. In one case when the client could not and did not wish to fulfil his parents' ambitions, he rebelled by finding acceptance among a peer group in which the popular thing to do was to get drunk. At home he could not be a success, but among his friends he was.

3. *The legalistic parent.* These are the strict disciplinarians; they take a legalistic approach to life. If son or daughter lives according to all the rules, they are termed good and they are loved. The parents are usually religious, or have come from a moralistic background. Children of such strict parents can't live up to the rules and thus feel insecure. They either give up or become obsessed with the desire to be perfectionists.

The above outline does not mean that all alcoholics are the result of their parents' mistakes. Surveys show that some alcoholics had a poor relationship with their parents, but one must not assume that because a man becomes an alcoholic, his parents are to blame. Often there are purely sociological reasons for the use of alcohol. The availability of it, one's circle of friends, social activities, and other factors can enter into the use of alcohol in the first place. Also, stresses often develop later in life and create inner conflicts that can make a person prone to alcoholism.

Further proof that sociological factors can cause a person to become an alcoholic is found in the fact that the same personality traits and conflicts which show up in alcoholics also appear among non-alcoholics. Why didn't the latter become alcoholics? Perhaps because of their religious or cultural upbringing. Sociological factors prevented the outbreak of alcoholism. Social conditions can cause its outbreak, whether the symptoms that sometimes cause it are present or not.

I have often said to parents and church people in rural communities, "Given another set of circumstances, if your children were raised in an urban environment, or in a situation where drugs or alcohol were more prevalent and available, they too might have become addicts." Some young people find themselves working and living in social and cultural circumstances where there is much drinking, and their chances of addiction are, of course, much higher than if they had not been exposed to such pressures. During the years of prohibition, the *per capita* rate of alcohol consumption dropped by 25 per cent compared to previous years. The result was that many alcoholics were checked during that period. However, the present rate of increase in alcoholism seems to coincide with the increased consumption of alcohol. Is there more alcoholism now because people are getting worse, or are people getting worse because the use of alcohol is growing? Regardless, one fact stands out: we have become an alcohol consuming society, and we are paying for it in the ruin of lives.

How to Counsel the Alcoholic

1. *Understand the difference between alcohol and the alcoholic.* In other words, separate the sin from the sinner. We must condemn the use of alcohol and detest what it does to the individual, but love the person who is an alcoholic.

The alcoholic will not come to the counsellor who cannot see the difference between the evil of alcohol and the person who is the victim of its use. Many evangelists and pastors are so obsessed with removing alcohol and other evils in society that they never have time to help those who are the *products* of the social evils. When they work or counsel with alcoholics, they are more concerned with preaching, lecturing, and moralizing on the dangers of alcohol than they are in getting through to the person with the problem. Such Christian workers get a reputation for being crusaders rather than helpers; the alcoholic will not come to them or respond to them.

2. *Uncover the problem.* Most alcoholics belong to the "hidden" category. They are not easy to uncover. One has to become a detective. The counsellor must try to remove the barriers that prevent the alcoholic from coming forth. This can be done by building up a relationship of trust. The counsellor's trust relationship will knock down the barriers and bring out the knowledge of the addiction. When the counsellor suspects alcoholism might be behind a certain problem, the revelation of it, or the mention of it, to the person being counselled can create a strain, even a disruption of the counselling process. Only if the person trusts the counsellor will he open up and face his alcohol problem.

How can the hidden alcoholic be uncovered?

(a) *Advertise.* Advertise your concern, compassion and willingness to help by pulpit sermons, by Christian witness, and by normal everyday conversation. Build up a reputation for helping people in general. Pastors can further show their interest by promoting seminars, educational programmes and rallies on the prevention and cure of alcoholism. All of these activities let the hidden alcoholic know that you are interested and want to help. He can come out of hiding.

(b) *Recognize the prevailing symptoms surrounding alcoholism.* By knowing some of these signs the counsellor in the normal course of church visitation, or on business activities might be able to uncover alcoholism. Often behind marital problems, financial or job problems there may also be an alcohol problem. By watching for some of the prevailing signs that precede alcoholism, the counsellor can help the person while his drinking is in the early stages.

(c) *Watch for alcoholism hidden behind other problems that a client or contact may bring to a counsellor's attention.* Part of the alcoholic's dilemma is to recognize and admit that alcohol is his real problem. The problem drinker will hold out as long as possible before making this admission. He may not see that his drinking has anything to do with his problem. Therefore, he will not mention it because he does not think it is relevant to his problem. However, the problem he wants help with may be the cause of the alcoholism, and it may be making it a more serious problem.

3. *Make yourself accessible to people in general.* Counselling alcoholics is like counselling anyone else. Some of the same general principles outlined in previous chapters must be used with alcoholics. The counsellor must bridge the problem gap. This can only be done if he attracts people to himself. People must feel he is approachable, accessible, thoroughly sincere, and sense that he really cares about them. Some ministers and Christian workers get the reputation of being professional and aloof. "He's just not the kind of pastor you feel comfortable about telling your problems to. He just doesn't seem to understand," a person told me when I advised him to see his minister.

The Christian counsellor who seeks to help the alcoholic must develop rapport with people, have a pleasing personality, allow other people to be themselves, and not be preachy and authoritarian in his manner.

There are many simple things the counsellor can do to become an accessible person. You have to let your concern be known. Take time for brief conversations with families in church. Ask short questions that do not make you appear to be nosy but show that you are interested. When you get a report about someone's difficulty with a certain situation, make a brief inquiry about it so that the door will be open for you to minister in that situation. Ministers, church workers and counsellors should never assume that people will know they are available to help; their availability must be advertised. People who desperately need help often cannot break the barrier to ask for help or to unburden themselves to others. Pastors must constantly make it clear that counselling is a part of their ministry—not a burden but a desirable part of the Lord's work. Some people assume a pastor is too busy, or that their problem is insignificant, or that the minister is not interested or doesn't understand.

A young woman stopped me one day in the hall of Teen Challenge Centre and asked if she could speak to me. "I'm quite busy right now; I'll have to see you later," I said. But later it occurred to me that she was my business. I had at the time been doing some paper work. I realized that I had been called to work with people, not paper.

4. *Be alert and sensitive when dealing with the alcoholic.* The counsellor must have eyes and ears alert to hear what the alcoholic is saying. Listening, more than talking, helps to build rapport and to bridge the problem gap.

Mannerisms also are important. It is easy for a counsellor to mumble, "Yes, I see," and yet have his mind on something else, so that his client knows he is not really listening. I have the habit of sometimes scribbling letters, or leafing through papers when someone is explaining a problem to me. It's a nervous habit. It distracts the other person. He needs the counsellor's undivided attention.

The counsellor should also look the other person in the eye. Most people, however, will find it difficult to look the counsellor back in the eye. However, by doing this the counsellor can get the other person's attention and show him that he is listening. The counsellor's mood, position and facial expression all have something to do with showing he is listening and being alert and sensitive.

Listening helps the counsellor to get into the alcoholic's mind and into his world. It helps him sense his feelings and conflicts. The only way the counsellor can get the picture is by the words that come from the alcoholic's lips. They are all the counsellor may have to go on, if he does not know the individual personally.

From the counsellor's alertness and sensitivity the alcoholic will feel his empathy. The process of building up a relationship of confidence and trust is essential as the counselling process goes on and reaches the stage when the counsellor gives instruction and guidance in recovery and rehabilitation.

5. *Let the alcoholic unburden himself.* The alcoholic may only want sympathy or someone's shoulder to cry on. However, the start of all rehabilitation begins with the release of pent-up feelings, inner tensions, and the talking out of personal problems. This spilling out of sour feelings is in itself therapeutic. Some of these feelings are buried deep within the alcoholic. It may take time for them to come out. With every drink, these feelings have gone deeper and deeper into the caverns of his mind. They cannot come out easily. They must come out and the counsellor must not only be a good listener, but also skilled in drawing out these feelings.

The unburdening process is essential for recovery, but it is like breaking open a boil on the neck. At first the poison is slow in coming, then it may flow profusely. When this happens, the counsellor should not be shocked, disturbed, or uncomfortable; rather, he should be encouraged by this sign of progress. He should use brief questions and comments to keep the unburdening process going until he is sure the alcoholic has been emotionally cleaned out.

Beware of drawing quick verbal conclusions from these poured-out feelings. That can stop the flow of words. Be careful not to apply a bandage too soon. The client must let all the infection out before you can apply healing counsel. Much of the information the counsellor needs to understand the alcoholic and to formulate instruction comes from this unburdening process. The alcoholic must feel free to express his feelings of anger, hostility and hate. That is one reason the alcoholic has been drinking, to suppress his feelings. To tell him that his feelings are wrong will not do him any good either. He must get those feelings out in the open so that together with his counsellor he can explain the reasons for them.

6. *Find out the degree of motivation.* As with the drug addict, the first step in counselling the alcoholic is to determine if he wants help and if so, how serious he is about getting it. The counsellor may be ready but not the alcoholic.

It is good to evaluate what is behind his desire to be helped. How much pressure are his wife, parents, or others putting on him? Is he just in the mood for love or attention? Does he just want to be consoled? Is he looking for sympathy? Has someone or some circumstance forced him to seek help?

118

One of the city sanitation workers who picked up garbage at Teen Challenge was brought to us one day by his fellow workers. They asked us if we could help him. He said he wanted help. He checked into our programme but soon left. We found out later that his job was in jeopardy and he was pressured into seeking help. He was not sufficiently motivated for us to do anything for him.

Sometimes external factors can motivate someone to seek help, but only if there is first a desire on the alcoholic's part. The first and most important motivation must be internal; other external forces can reinforce and support his motivation.

The counsellor must also find out what kind of help the alcoholic wants and how much. Is he looking for temporary relief, or a total cure? Does he believe he can be helped? He may have doubts about his ability to be cured, but does he have a degree of motivation—at least to start? Does he believe you are the right person to help him? Why did he come to you?

When interviewing prospects for Teen Challenge Centre, we ask who referred them to us and why they came. We want to find out how much confidence, if any, they have in us and in the type of cure we offer.

I find alcoholics are never ready, or motivated, as they should be. If the alcoholic is motivated enough to start, the motivation can be increased later through a conversion to Christ. The question is, is his desire to stop drinking stronger than his urge to continue drinking?

During the counselling process the alcoholic's motivation runs in streaks. One day he may be highly motivated, the next day he may have no motivation. He is pulled by opposing forces. The desire to quit and the urge to drink are two forces which both run through his mind.

He may want to stop because of the consequences of his alcoholism, but he may want to continue because alcohol has become the solution to pain and distress. Even after quitting for a while, he may forget the miseries of drinking when the temptation to drink becomes strong again.

In the twelve steps to recovery of Alcoholics Anonymous, motivation is essential to starting on the route to recovery. Step one is: "We admitted we were powerless over alcohol, that our lives had become unmanageable." The Christian counsellor must determine whether the alcoholic he is dealing with has admitted this.

7. *Through prayer, lead the alcoholic to the "new creature" experience of the Gospel.* The counsellor must believe that if

119

"any man (alcoholic) be in Christ, he is a new creature: old things (drinking, personal problems) are passed away; behold, all things are become new" (2 Cor. 5:17). The right moment must be found to present this message and to introduce the alcoholic to this experience. It must not come too soon or too late. Is it ever too soon to attempt to lead a person to Christ? In the case of alcoholics, yes. He must be ready for you, the counsellor; he must also be ready to give himself to Christ. You must first lay a scriptural foundation. You must discern his spiritual understanding and hunger. If he wants help, does he want Christ's help?

He may have a gospel hang-up or he may be hardened to the Gospel. If he is a mission drop-out, he may have become calloused to the Word of God. He may still be bitter about having had to swallow the bait (gospel services) that many missions offer before they will admit the alcoholic for meals and a bed. He may have had a previous emotional religious experience, but either had no desire to follow through, or he was never taught how to follow through. Thus he has lost confidence in religion or conversion. He may have a negative outlook on the Gospel—a set of dos and don'ts. He may never have realized that a person can "taste and see that the Lord is good". Find out what is behind his resistance to the Gospel. Is it based on past experience, misunderstanding, or rebellion against God?

Regardless of his past knowledge of the Gospel, the alcoholic must be presented the truth that can set him free. I like the way a group called Alcoholics Victorious approaches conversion. In its creed, step number one is: "I realize that I cannot overcome the drink habit myself. I believe the power of Jesus Christ is available to help me. I believe that through my acceptance of Him as my personal Saviour I am a new man." Step four is: "I can be victorious because I know that God's strength is sufficient to supply all my needs."

The counsellor who takes this strong evangelistic approach has the greatest potential for a cure and the most comprehensive type of solution to present to the alcoholic. Christ can change the alcoholic. He can be made into a completely new person. Such a transformation gets to the root of all of the alcoholic's outward problems—his alienation from God—as well as the manifestation of that alienation, his emotional and mental conflicts. Christ removes the need for the bottle by changing the person.

Howard was thirty-six when we first met. He had been a chronic alcoholic for eighteen years. "I had made up my mind even before I was an alcoholic that I was going to be one. I used to dream about it. I'd see pictures advertising whisky or beer, and would get a thrill out of it," he told me. His mother and father separated, and when she died he was left with an inheritance. At the age of fourteen he began drinking and by eighteen he was hooked. Within three years he had swallowed up his entire inheritance. "I've been in at least twelve different state hospitals in twelve different states. I'd stay for a few months to get dried out so I could go out and enjoy drinking better." He said he had too much pride to go to missions so he had little contact with the Gospel. However, he wandered into a storefront church one night in Brooklyn where some Christian people presented him with the message of salvation, and then took him to Teen Challenge. He went through his withdrawal, worked hard as a resident of the programme, and openly and outwardly responded to spiritual things, but he said, 'I only read my Bible and got on my knees and went to church because I was told I should. I learned to respect the people who were trying to help me." But there was never complete surrender to Christ. He began to question and analyse the Gospel. As many times as he was counselled, he refused to yield his life to Christ. As a result he was back on the streets and back on the bottle. And now he had found a new scapegoat to blame for his addiction—the Christian. He projected his failure on to those who had counselled him. When he was drunk he would stand outside Teen Challenge and vent his anger. Through later contact and later counselling, when sober, he displayed the attitude that the Christian owed a debt to him. He sought material assistance and wanted his Christian counsellors to be his errand boy to help him every time his drinking got the best of him.

Contact with him was lost for a period of time. Then one night in a hospital a staff worker met him. He was in severe withdrawal pains. "What are you doing, Howard?" the staff worker asked.

"Getting some formaldehyde. I am very, very sick," he replied.

"Why don't you come back to Teen Challenge?" the counsellor asked.

"They won't have me," Howard stated.

"But Jesus wants to heal you. Come on, we are going back to the Centre. That's where the Lord wants you," the worker insisted. In spite of the fact that there was no room for him and of our reservations about his sincerity, he was permitted entrance.

121

"I was so sick when I came into the Centre that time that I was drinking hair tonic. Besides that, I had a hole in the back of my head—don't know where I got it—somebody must have hit me with a bottle. When I was withdrawing I kept seeing colour television. The programmes were all hallucinations. A horse leaped out of the TV and started talking to me. I was so sick. I couldn't take the pain any more so I tried to walk out the door. But my hands were shaking so much from the DT's (delirium tremens) that I couldn't grab the door handle. Then I fell down on the floor in front of the door. A brother came over and started praying. I told him I was going to die. Then they took me to my bed. I was so sick I couldn't move. I remember it was December 27th and something told me, 'Howard, if you make it through this year, you'll make it all the way.' Thank God, I did make it through the next few days and the new year came. But still I was not converted. It wasn't until a few weeks later when I was filled with the Holy Spirit that I finally believed I was really cured and that Christ had totally delivered me. Before the night when the power of God came upon me, I still didn't enjoy reading the Bible or praying or even going to Church. It was a chore to me. But after that experience with Christ—and that in-filling of the Holy Spirit, it was like eating steak. I wanted to eat and eat and eat." Happily he is still eating spiritual food.

After the "new creature" experience takes place, is the former alcoholic *sober* or *free*? Is he a sober alcoholic, or is he a free and whole person? It disturbs me that some sober alcoholics have this philosophy: "I am an alcoholic. I shall always be an alcoholic. I live one day at a time and promise myself only to stay sober for one more day. Tomorrow I may go on the worst binge I have ever had." Such a philosophy certainly falls short of the cure Christ offers. It is faith in oneself to get through a day, rather than the faith in Christ which can cause the alcoholic to say, "I can do all things through Christ who strengthens me."

In almost every church where I go to speak, a former alcoholic will come up to me and give his testimony of freedom from drinking. Each one, through a dramatic conversion to Christ (most often as a result of one visit to church and the altar), has found a complete deliverance from alcohol. When they get up in the morning, they do not fear that perhaps this will be the day when they will go on a binge. They wake up with Christ on their mind, not the bottle. This does not mean they never have temptations. They do. But when temptation comes, they can look to Christ to deliver from the temptation.

Most of these men also testify to the fact that the craving for alcohol is gone. They may have temptations, but not because of a craving that has never left them. The devil comes back to examine "the house" to see if Christ is still the occupant. Christ came in and transplanted the old heart, with its craving for drink, and put in a new one with its craving for God.

The "new creature" alcoholic emphasizes the cure, not the problem. A sober alcoholic considers himself still to be an alcoholic. The only differences between him and other alcoholics is that he is not drinking. The only thing between the sober alcoholic and alcoholism is a bottle of alcohol. Between the free alcoholic and alcoholism, however, is Christ. The one seeks to stay away from the bottle, the other seeks to stay with and in Christ. It is much easier to "walk in the Spirit" and not fulfil the desires of the flesh (alcoholism). The sober alcoholic says, "Once an alcoholic, always an alcoholic." The free alcoholic says, "If any man be in Christ, he is a new creation."

Does this mean the free alcoholic can drink again? Of course not. To touch a drop would trigger his alcoholism. This is not because his alcoholism was always there and not manifested. Instead, it is because the devil would bring back seven evil spirits worse than before. For one who has experienced the new birth to return to alcohol means that the old symptoms that brought on alcoholism in the first place had returned. The craving for alcohol would be the result of his having failed to pray, to have fellowship with Christ and Christians, to read the Bible and perform other Christian duties. The relapse would not be because of the power of alcohol, but because of his loss of Christ's power. No freed alcoholic who has walked in the Spirit and continued in the faith has ever suddenly reverted to the use of alcohol. The problem is not with the alcohol, but with the person who fails to keep the faith.

8. *Help the freed alcoholic to bridge the family gap.* The tragedy of alcoholism is that for every alcoholic there are an average of three to five others who suffer because of it. The alcoholic's family must be involved in his recovery. This is not always easy. The damage and division brought on by the past years of drinking do not heal easily. The new convert may expect too much from his wife, parents, or children, too soon. He will want them to accept him with open arms. The wife may want to, but she may be afraid to believe in him. Usually, the family will want to "wait and see". The counsellor should advise the converted alcoholic to prove himself and give his loved ones time to accept him. Once they are convinced of his

123

sincerity and his deliverance from the habit, they can begin to bridge the gap. Both the convert and his family must forgive past sins. Old wounds and tensions should not be reopened.

If the wife or family will not accept the converted alcoholic, the counsellor should invite them in for private counselling and, if they are willing, talk about their feelings and problems. When the counsellor feels the time is right, he should bring the parties together to discuss their differences. Both sides must give and take. The converted alcoholic's family should not be brought into the counselling process too soon. By having a private session with the family first, the counsellor can better decide the best time to have a joint session with the new convert.

Pressure is often put on the converted alcoholic to return home and take care of his wife and children. In most cases, he can do this, but the wife should be instructed to give her husband as much time as possible—if he is in a treatment programme—before asking him to come home. Sometimes the wife may want her husband back purely for financial reasons. Usually, the wife of an alcoholic is being supported from other sources. The counsellor should encourage her to continue receiving such aid until her husband is strong enough to return and assume all responsibilities of support.

Another problem the new convert may face on his return home is opposition to his conversion. The wife of one of our converts told him, "I'll accept you as an addict, but not as a Christian." Often a converted alcoholic will get the same reaction when he returns home to live with his wife, children, parents, or brothers and sisters. They will say, "That was all right for you; you really needed the help. We don't have your problem, so we don't need that religious stuff." This can be discouraging, even shattering, to a new convert who is proud of his new life and wants to give Christ the glory. The convert will need counsel about his attitude towards this reaction from his family. He must understand that they may accept him, but be reluctant to accept his Saviour. He should be encouraged to live his testimony, carefully sow the seed of the Word, and pray about the matter. In time he may see some marvellous conversions take place in his home. We have seen whole families converted. The counsellor should inform the family that the only adequate way they can help the converted alcoholic's rehabilitation is to share his spiritual experience. The same Christ who made the alcoholic a new creature can make his family new also.

The counsellor should recommend the following steps for a

family seeking to help an alcoholic loved one respond to treatment: (a) don't force or threaten him to seek help; (b) make suggestions that he seek help; be firm but not pushy; (c) don't baby him; (d) if he is living away from home, keep in touch with him; (e) don't support his habit; (f) keep from getting bitter or hateful towards him; (g) ask others who are knowledgeable to speak to him; (h) through faith and prayer, never give up; (i) don't blame yourself.

Even if a converted alcoholic should revert to alcohol, quit the counselling sessions, or drop out of the rehabilitation programme, the counsellor can and should maintain contact with his family. They may start coming to church to bolster their own faith, as they endeavour to live with the problem of seeing their loved one continue in alcoholism. I think of one man who returned to alcohol, but later he was motivated to seek help again because the members of his family became Christians and showed a new love and understanding for him. All the hostility and reasons for his continuing to drink were removed by the conversion of his family.

Occasionally, when the converted spouse returns home, he meets an adverse reaction from the wife who formerly controlled him or treated him as a patient. She loses her domination of the home because her husband can now assume leadership. This situation is not common, but the counsellor should be aware that it can happen. Such cases will take lengthy, careful counselling to work themselves out. It is like starting marriage all over again. The marriage must be built on a different premise and relationship. It can no longer be tied together by the alcoholism and weakness of the husband.

9. *Help the rehabilitated alcoholic face his responsibilities.* Some converts want to go back to work, or even into full-time Christian service, too soon; others, not soon enough. The counsellor must know when the time is right. When the convert is able, he must—whether he wants to or not. He must be challenged and instructed to do so.

The family should let him "stand on his own two feet". Many are afraid to let him assume any responsibility, because they are afraid the pressure will cause him to fall. However, the family should be told that responsibility is essential for the convert's regaining his self-respect.

The counsellor must firmly aid the convert to face reality. He may make excuses, find fault with those he works with, complain that he can't find a job he likes—all of which are characteristic of past patterns of behaviour. The counsellor should

125

"lay down the law" and urge him to accept the programme of recovery that has been worked out for him. At this point in his rehabilitation he should have reached a certain level of victory to be able to take such firmness and "tough love".

10. *Begin to phase out the relationship with the recovered alcoholic*. The attachment and relationship so necessary for successful counselling in the early stages of contact with the alcoholic can be detrimental during his recovery stage. The counsellor must release him, emotionally and spiritually. During follow-up contact should be maintained, but the counsellor should not impose himself on his client, nor should he allow him to call or visit with every little problem. Encourage him to make his own decisions. Don't do for him the things he should be doing for himself. The responsibility for recovery must be the alcoholic's, not the counsellor's.

The converted alcoholic must learn that he can stand "on his own two feet". But he won't make it if the counsellor gives him the impression that the alcoholic needs him, or that he is making it because of him. If the alcoholic gets the impression that the counsellor needs his recovery to feed his own ego—and aid the counsellor's personal success—the alcoholic will feel exploited. In many cases, a pastor, layman or Christian worker will strive to get an alcoholic reformed just so they can prove something to themselves, colleagues, or others. The result is a "my convert" relationship, in which the counsellor babies the alcoholic, smothers him, and finds it difficult to release him. If the rehabilitation fails, the counsellor sees it as a personal failure; if there is success, it is viewed as personal success. This kind of attitude puts great pressure on the alcoholic, who senses that he is just like a guinea pig in an experiment, or that his testimony is needed by the church or by some organization to prove it is doing a good work. This is the worst kind of exploitation.

11. *Help him develop a strong spiritual life*. The recovered alcoholic needs a "brimful" experience of and relationship with Christ. He must be, as young people at Teen Challenge like to say, "on fire for God", and "up tight with Jesus". The ex-alcoholic must depend totally on the Lord for his freedom from alcohol, and to maintain his new life.

Three things are necessary for the development of a strong spiritual life:

(a) *Daily prayer*. Just as he took a nip of alcohol in the morning, a nip in the afternoon, and a nip at night, so he needs to learn to whisper a prayer in the morning and throughout the day. Alcoholics who have been a part of a resident re-

126

habilitation programme must learn to discipline themselves to pray when they are on their own. They may experience a let-down because they are no longer in a spiritual atmosphere where they were encouraged to pray. When they are working and facing responsibilities at home, they must set their own schedule for prayer.

(b) *Christian fellowship.* The rehabilitated alcoholic needs the fellowship of other Christians. Finding him the right church is important. The right church is one where he can sense the presence of the Lord and where the people are friendly and help-ful. Remember, the alcoholic previously spent much time in bars and taverns where he found fellowship, friends and an atmosphere that meant a lot to him. The church must be every-thing, and more, that the local bar was. The recovered alcoholic also needs the friendship and fellowship of other Christians in his home. Because he does not drink any more, and because all of his old friends were drinking people, he needs new friends. Pastors should introduce couples to the recovered alcoholic and his wife, people the pastor feels would understand him and be compatible with him.

(c) *Christian service.* Alcoholics are notorious receivers; they never give out. After conversion, almost always they naturally want to give. They need to know when and how. Help them to find a place of service that is within their abilities. Take them to evangelistic services, on witnessing ventures, to retirement homes, jail services, and so on. Let them give their testimonies; that will help to strengthen them. A word of caution: too much activity, too soon, can do more harm than good. The converted alcoholic must be ready for Christian service. Don't try to make him an example until he is ready. He may want to take on more responsibility than he can handle. Involve him in Christian ser-vice gradually, and keep a watchful eye on him to see that he is maintaining his prayer life.

NOTES

[1] Howard Clinebell, Jr., *Understanding and Counselling the Alco-holic* (Nashville, Abingdon, 1968).
[2] ibid.

8

REBELS, RUNAWAYS AND REVOLUTIONARIES

THE END OF THE REBEL

Man Dies in Train Leap

A 21-year-old man was killed late Wednesday night when he fell or jumped from a Baltimore-bound Penn Central train a mile north of here.

The dead youth was identified as Richard Lee Beers, who is believed to have lived most recently in Greenwich Village, New York City.

Maryland State Police at North East said they found LSD, "speed", and other drugs on Beers' body and also on his travelling companion, Sandra Santana, 17, also of New York City.

A police spokesman said yesterday the girl told them Beers had taken LSD before the incident. He said that she claimed she saw Beers jump from the train, which police said was travelling through a wooded area at 60 miles per hour, and reported it to a conductor. Police were notified by Penn Central personnel in Baltimore.

Beers was pronounced dead on arrival at Union Hospital, Elkton.

Miss Santana, described by police yesterday as being "incoherent", is being held as a material witness.

Beers' father, Lee, a factory worker in Philadelphia, said his son left home three years ago, shortly after the death of his mother. The elder Beers said his son, an only child, "just wanted to be on his own".

The elder Beers said his son was a talented guitar player who, the father said, "expected to make it big right away".

According to the father, the youth played with the Wissahickon Folk Singers, a group which made one record and appeared on the Ted Mack Amateur Hour. However, he said the group never achieved success.

Beers said his son, who attended Wissahickon High School

near Ambler, Pa., "didn't care for school or work, but was good with his hands and his guitar". According to the father, Beers had no police record.

Beers said his son "became a rambler" after leaving home, unwilling, he said, to hold a job. The father said the youth had no apparent means of support except through money earned playing his guitar. The father said he had not heard from his son in more than a year, but thought he last lived in Greenwich Village.

The elder Beers said he suspected, but did not know, that his son was apparently using drugs. He said his son, who once was husky, became drawn and ill-looking in recent years. "He wasn't the same boy the last few times."

—from a newspaper report

Mr. Lee Beers, the boy's father, has put Richard's story into poetic form:

THE END OF THE REBEL

I have a story that I must tell
To all the youth who wish to rebel.
Remember the one, too young to die,
If you think it's fun to get high.

My son is dead: I wonder why
He had to be so young to die.
Why rebel, leave home and me?
Was it because I condemned his hair?

Why the drugs, the LSD?
Did he believe I did not care?
Maybe the love in my heart, so true,
Somehow failed to shine through?

He left home just eighteen.
Went on his own; joined the Hippie scene.
Lived the life that the Hippies led.
Now, at twenty-one, the rebel's dead.

The rebel was very much alive
Aboard train number one fifty-five,
Till he and his girl took LSD
For him, both trips ended fatally.

Somehow he managed to take a dive
Off of train number one fifty-five:
Was he pushed; did he jump, or fall?
Only our good Lord knows all.

Maybe the Lord forgave and set him free
From the life he'd lived and its misery.
And for all youth to note, and see,
Just what the end of a rebel might be.

Please heed this warning that the good Lord sent,
Don't go the way this rebel went.
Or do the things that he did wrong.
Stay at home, where you belong.

Believe me, your parents really care,
The love you seek is really there.
Maybe not always a shining glow,
But it's there, believe me, I know.
                                        —Lee Beers

Tony was an upper-middle-class teenager. His parents provided him with a good home. He attended one of the better schools in his city. He always had pocket money. At the age of fourteen he had his own television set and a telephone in his bedroom. At sixteen he was given an automobile. Tony dressed very well, again thanks to mother and dad.

But the more his parents gave him, the less Tony appreciated it and the more he rebelled. Why? Ask Tony and he will simply say, "I don't really know." Perhaps a social worker would say that his family stuffed his pockets but starved his emotions. "There never was really any open conflict when I was younger, but neither was there real togetherness," Tony says.

His rebellion was mostly hidden, or controlled. There were occasional outbursts of anger towards his parents, but the open differences were minimal. Occasionally he would purposely disobey them. Perhaps unconsciously he was getting even with them. Until he was eighteen Tony lived at home and carried on an outwardly normal relationship with his family.

Then Tony went to the university. There he picked up other ideals and philosophies. To the rebellion against his parents was added a dash of social rebellion and a dose of "anti-establishment" resistance. Over the period of a year Tony became a runaway who didn't actually run away; he was a runaway at home. He lived under the same roof as his parents and he slept in the same bed he always had, but that was about the extent of his home life. He ate a few meals at home and spent less and less time with his parents and the rest of his family.

When he was at home Tony spent most of his time alone in his room. His room had become a psychedelic pad with posters, hippie art, rock music, incense, and other paraphernalia of the hippie sub-culture in which he was becoming immersed. Emotionally, socially and spiritually, he was a runaway. He had, in spirit, left home and joined the runaway generation. Like many teenagers of today, Tony joined the "get as far away from home as possible" generation.

The actual making of a runaway in his case came about in a simple and seemingly harmless fashion. He didn't sneak away from the house. He convinced his parents that it would be best for him to live with a few friends in his own apartment. This, he reasoned, would help him "learn to be a man" and to "face life". It sounded so good; it was a smooth job of cutting off the home ties and taking the ultimate step in expressing rebellion against his parents. "The best part about it," he told his friends, "is that mom and dad bought it and I didn't have to hassle with them."

Now Tony was a full-fledged runaway. He attached himself to his new way of life; his feelings, attitudes and philosophies were radicalized. He started to smoke marijuana and occasionally dropped acid (LSD) to "expand his mind". "It was groovy," Tony commented.

He joined his friends' peace movement, at first only in theory, then later he became an activist because "I had nothing else to do." He carried protest signs, "yelled a few obscenities at the pigs", and threw a few bricks. At first, Tony says, it was "more like a game than anything else." Then, "I began to get serious about it. We started to find issues. Soon I was committed to overthrowing 'the system'. The more I was in the movement, the more reasons I found—or was taught—why the system needed to be overthrown."

Tony had found a new target for his rebellion. Next, he joined a "revolutionary camp". There he learned the tricks of the revolutionary trade: how to protest, to resist, to sit-in, stand-in, lie-in; and if none of that worked, how to bring about an open revolution. It grew on him. It became his cause. He believed in it. He was now a revolutionary.

The turning point in Tony's life came when he first realized what had happened to him since he had left home and joined the "movement". It took place while he was taking part in what had been billed as a peaceful anti-war demonstration.

"There wasn't supposed to be any violence," he explained. "But as I listened to our leaders talking about the injustice of war, of capitalism, parenthood, society, and so on, I suddenly realized they were carrying guns in their pockets and were ready to make violence themselves. And here they were, spilling off about peace. I looked at the peace symbol under my neck. I thought about the guns in their pockets. And for the first time it didn't make sense. It didn't add up. So I made up my mind then and there that I was getting out. This was not for me. This wasn't my bag."

Tony then went back to being a non-protesting rebel and runaway. He dressed mod, or what others would call hippie. He wore beads, grew a beard, and "dug the Beatles, Dylan, and Jefferson Airplane and all the other rock stars". More and more he smoked marijuana and "tripped out" on LSD and "speed". Then, at a party, someone introduced him to "smack" (heroin). After about six months, he had a $25-a-day habit.

"You know," he reminisces, "when you go to one of those things you never know who is there. And with drugs floating around, you never know what kind of drugs are being pushed. I guess there were some guys there trying to turn some of us 'speed freaks' on to the hard stuff, because they knew there was more money in that for them. I was so stoned I didn't know what I was doing. I took 'horse' and liked it. It was a different high than I had ever experienced before.

"Another reason why I think I took the hard stuff—because no one gets hooked by intention—is that I was so low emotionally. My lows were getting lower and my highs were not getting me high enough. I guess when I went to that party I was at my all-time low. And 'smack' got me—wow, way, way up there, or maybe it was down there, I really don't know. Anyway, I said to myself, 'This is what you've been looking for.' From then on I knew exactly what I was doing. I went looking for heroin and I loved it."

After three years on hard drugs, Tony turned to Christ and got "unhooked". Today Tony is a Christian. He doesn't carry a peace placard. "Now," he says, "I carry the Prince of Peace in my heart." Two steps brought about a spiritual revolution in him. The first he calls common sense; the second, Jesus Christ.

Tony's story illustrates three different kinds of young people: the rebels, the runaways, and the revolutionaries. Tony was all three. First, he was a rebel. That set the stage for turning him into a runaway. Finally, after he ran away, the stage was set for him to become a revolutionary. On top of that, he became a drug addict. Although labels can be misleading, for the sake of trying to identify the emotional, psychological, philosophical and spiritual make-up of today's youth, we will use the terms rebel, runaway, and revolutionary. They are not young people who come looking for help from Christian counsellors, as the drug addicts do. The latter come because they know they need help. But runaways are not aware of their need. Tony sought help as a drug addict, not as a runaway. Were it not for his drug problem, he might never have sought help.

As outlined in the chapter on the addicted generation, the counsellor must determine to what extent drugs are a problem with the rebels, runaways, and revolutionaries. If there is drug addiction, treatment must begin at this point. In the process, rebellious and revolutionary attitudes can be dealt with. Many rebels, runaways, and revolutionaries, however, are drug users but not addicts.

This does not mean rebels, runaways, and revolutionaries can only be reached if they are addicted. It only means they do not readily seek help. They are not restricted to the streets, hippie havens, college campuses, and the high schools; they are also in the home, at work, and even in the church. Christian youth are affected by the thinking of today's anti-establishment advocates. The number of so-called Christian radicals and Christian hippies is growing. Some are openly radical, others carry their attitudes within them.

There is a need to prevent young people from following today's radical ideologies. This can be done by watching for the signs of rebellion, uncovering the runaways at home, and checking trends of thinking that eventually keep young people completely away from God. Just as there are youth on the verge of becoming addicts, alcoholics or homosexuals, so there are many being influenced by forces outside the home and church to become rebels, runaways and revolutionaries. Following some of the suggestions outlined in chapters 2 and 3 will help to prevent their becoming such.

However, the greatest challenge lies outside the church. Among the confirmed rebels, runaways and revolutionaries, evangelists and Christian counsellors should find a harvest of souls. This can be done through coffee house ministries, through high school clubs and organizations, through campus ministries, by summer beach evangelism work, and through the more conventional out-reaches such as rallies, seminars, and other church-oriented programmes. The counsellor will not meet these young people on a client-to-counsellor basis, but rather on a very loose social contact relationship.

Dealing with an addict is usually on the basis of his need. However, this is not the case with the non-addict rebel, runaway

133

or revolutionary. He senses no need. He feels he *has* what the world needs. The presentation of the Gospel to him means the confrontation of two causes. He may feel Christianity is out-dated, and that his is a new "gospel" to save his generation. He may have a missionary approach in turning others to new ideas. He is addicted to idealism. As one revolutionary said, "We are not just a protest movement, we are literally a separate nation inside America." It is to this nation within a nation that the Christian must go, first as an evangelist and second as a coun-sellor.

THE REBELS

Everyone rebels at some point in his life. Most people know how to work out their rebellion in an orderly and constructive manner. Others, either because they cannot cope with the situ-ation, or because they are faced with obstacles too great to overcome, become bitter and infected with a rebellious nature.

The most common form of rebellion is that which pits the child against his parents. All men are endowed with a basically rebellious nature because of their inheritance from Adam. If parents do not check such rebellion, then it develops until it becomes more and more a part of the child's method of reacting to the world around him.

Childhood rebellion is also fostered by other factors. For example, a child may see his father continually come home drunk. He may see him slap his mother. The child may be beaten. One of the young people at Teen Challenge was tied to a table leg when he was a child, and left in the house alone for hours. Such traumatic childhood experiences add fuel to the flames of rebellion. Unchecked rebellion in childhood and in early teen years sets the stage for a lifetime of rebellion.

Rebellion, however, must have a target. The rebels throw their darts of anger, hostility and rebellion at their parents, at authority in general, and at the church. Parents are the first target. Parents sometimes are to blame for this. They can bring on rebellion if they do not discipline their children; if they are over-permissive; if they do not provide religious training in the home; or if they fail to expose their children to spiritual values that serve as a buffer to rebellion. Unconsciously children resent the fact that parents do not serve as a kind, understanding and loving buffer to their aggression.

Some children are rebellious for selfish, ambitious and "got to have my own way" reasons. Others are rebellious because

134

they are deprived of the good things of life. They feel they have been cheated out of such things as physical beauty, material blessings and a good home environment. One mother told me, "When my son lost his father he became very bitter and rebellious. When his father was living we never had any trouble with him." In another home the teenage daughter was getting low grades in school, staying out late at night, and developing an ever-deepening rebellious attitude towards life. When her alcoholic father was converted to Christ and returned home, immediately her grades went up, she no longer stayed out late at night, and her rebellion completely disappeared.

In the home the parents are the authority figure. If they do not assume their proper authority role with love and understanding, then the child may have a distorted view of other authorities. Parents can either stand in the way of selfish desires, or starve their children of deserving ones. Outside the home there are other adult figures who are doing the same: the teacher, the school principal, the policeman, for example. If the child cannot relate properly to authority in the home, it is not likely he will be able to do so outside the home. The rebellion against authority may result from an adult's standing in the way of letting a child have his own way. Or, the adult may be repressive and not allow the youngster to have the breathing room he so desperately needs and searches for in his relationship with the world at large. The older the child gets, the larger becomes the world he faces, and the more authority he has to relate to. With the help of an understanding and instructive adult, rebellion can be completely removed.

The church is often another target of rebellion, for two reasons. One has to do with the success of the church, the other has to do with its failure. If the church is successfully delivering "the whole counsel of God", some young people are going to look at it as their enemy. They will feel that God is infringing on their right to have a good time. To them, Jesus Christ is a kill-joy. If they become Christians, they think Christ will make them lose all their friends, turn them into "squares", and destroy other ambitions they have. Those who will not accept Christ's claim of ownership over their lives are going to rebel. They may aim their darts of rebellion at something in the church, but they are really rebelling against God. A church that is true to the Gospel is going to encounter such resistance. But if and when this young person decides he wants to accept Christ, this is the only kind of church in which his rebellion can be turned into regeneration and renewal.

135

Rebellion can also result from the failure of the church. Many young people have sought for a meaningful religious experience. They were at one time sincere in their desire to know if God is real and if Christ can be a personal Saviour. But they were told that the Bible is full of myths, that Christ is only a great teacher, and that the Holy Spirit is not a person but an influence. To them, the church was like a social club, a place to go for one hour on Sunday. So they gave it up as a lost cause. They rebelled against it because it was a cold and dead institution. At the very time when they needed some answers to life's problems, they found none.

If rebellion is the result of the rejection of truth, it is something that can be understood and accepted as natural. But when rebellion is the result of spiritual apostasy—the withholding and denial of the truth—then it is a tragic, unforgivable blunder on the part of the withholders and deniers of that truth.

Every generation has had its own ways of expressing rebellion, and getting parents and adults "up tight". Youth in the past often rebelled by dancing the Charleston, wearing flappers, dressing in the mod style of their time, smoking cigarettes, getting drunk, or riding out to the local lovers' lane. At present the most common method of widening the generation gap is to wear long hair, dress in hippie garb, become rock music addicts, and of course the most serious form of rebellion—drug taking. Even giving the peace sign seems to irritate some of the over-thirty group, and young people find it a convenient way of expressing rebellion. Young people who do such deeds may only be expressing a preference in life style and taste, but they may also be expressing rebellion. Other common methods of venting rebellion by teens against parents may be by getting poor grades, wearing sloppy clothes, or dating someone the young person knows mother and dad do not like. One girl we dealt with rebelled by going to church. She knew her mother didn't want her attending a certain church in the first place so she purposely attended every chance she had—to get out of the house and to make her mother angry. A parent asked me how she could get her son out of his room. He gave his parents the silent treatment—hiding out in his room, reading, listening to music, or sleeping. It was his way of rebelling. Some young people will use whatever they can to satisfy their need to rebel. In most cases both parent and child are able to work the situation through satisfactorily; in other cases, this is not so and the generation gap turns into a great gulf fixed.

When a young person reveals his feelings of resentment, bit-

136

terness and rebellion to the counsellor, an effort should be made to see if he is rebelling against known truth or against unknown or misunderstood truth. The concept some young people have of Christianity and the church may be based on half-truths or "hobby horse" truths. They may have come from a church that majored in minor aspects of denominationalism. They may have seen only the negative side of Christianity and not the positive side. They may have seen real hypocrisy in the church. When young people throw out the hypocrisy bit, it may be only a cop-out, but again there can be substance to it. Find out if they are talking about general or specific hypocrisy, and what concept they have of the church and of biblical truth. It will not take long to determine if the rebel is rebelling because of a wrong concept of Christianity, or because of his rejection of real Christianity.

Why do young people rebel against conditions in the home? How do parents contribute to their rebellion? Here are some points to consider:

1. *The "regeneration" gap.* Young people want their parents to have a deep commitment to Christ. They are disappointed and feel let down when they cannot reconcile the behaviour of their parents at home with their profession of faith. One fellow said to me, "I have two dads—a church dad and a house dad." Young people set high ideals for their parents. They can excuse and understand mistakes and human frustrations, but they will not accept outright hypocrisy. When they see the gap between a fruit-bearing, godly Christian and a carnal one, they are likely to rebel, possibly against both parents and God. Communication will not be effective in the home if there is a re-generation gap.

2. *Life in a "pressure cooker" home.* A home that is full of tension, strife, marital conflict, office troubles and church gossip is like a pressure cooker. Young people need the right conditions in the home so they can grow up with a feeling of security. A pressure-packed home will soon produce "boiling over" in the child. One young man told us, "I can't remember one day in our house when there wasn't someone fighting, arguing, or hollering. The only peace and quiet I got was out on the streets with my friends."

3. *Constantly squashing doubts.* Young people naturally express doubts about God. In addition, they have doubts and questions about Christianity, the church and family traditions. If they are not allowed to express their feelings about such things, rebellion may result. It is better to have doubts discussed

137

in the home, when children are younger, than it is to push them off until later. Then their minds will be fed other doubts, and doubt will be piled upon doubt. Questions should be asked and answered in the home where a sound, biblical explanation can eliminate some of the perplexities. It is wrong to tell teenagers, "You shouldn't feel that way; you have no right to question such things." We work with many young people who are sincere doubters. Their doubts are based on sincere, legitimate questions and misunderstandings. If the doubts of young people are handled properly, and if their faith is fed, their doubts and fears will starve to death.

4. *"Forced feeding"*. Honest answers should be given to honest questions, but young people must not be forced to accept the answers. The forcing of parents' Christian ideals and beliefs on their children is likely to result in rebellion in later years. Parents cannot jam religion down their children's throats. They can, however, put on the table such a delicious spiritual spread that their children will want to "taste and see that the Lord is good". I will never forget the first time I challenged my mother and said, "I'm not going to church." She looked at me sternly and said, "All right, son, but you know what is right and what is wrong." A few hours later, while watching a basketball game, such conviction struck me that I literally ran back to church. Arriving as the preacher began his message, I dropped into the pew and sat down. What a feeling of comfort came over me! I knew that's where I should be. It was my decision, and my mother gave *me* the opportunity to make it. I thank God I was never force-fed Christianity.

5. *Demands of the "11th to the 20th" commandments*. In some homes parents add to the Ten Commandments by enforcing home-made rules as gospel truth. These rules, traditions and personal convictions can be set up as if they were the eleventh, twelfth or thirteenth commandments of Scripture. Rules on such things as hair length, clothing styles, extra-curricular activities and so on are often forced on young people as if they were commandments right out of the Bible. Infractions of these rules should not be treated as sins, but as matters of obedience and discipline in the home. My parents taught me to love and fear God. Such teaching did not make it necessary for them to post on the board a list of dos and don'ts. Through my relationship with Christ there were certain things I did not want to do. My parents did not tell me; it was the Lord's revelation. If some family rules are passed off as Bible commandments, and if young people are made to think they will go to hell if

they disobey them, they will develop a negative outlook towards Christianity.

6. *Handling questions properly.* Some young people express doubts, but most of the time they ask simple, ordinary questions. Taking time to answer them is important. Many questions may seem trivial to adults, but they are very important to young people. It is not so much finding answers as it is taking the time and showing the concern. However, if parents can't answer a question, they should say so and not try to fool their teenager with an answer they know is not right or is shallow.

7. *Attitude towards the world youth scene.* Young people are sympathetic with their peers in the nation and around the world. Parents must show understanding and tolerance towards the world youth scene. Comments about youth movements, fads and ideals must be given carefully and judiciously, not critically. Consistently putting down young people as the "bad guys" will create a serious gap between parents and children.

THE RUNAWAYS

Rebellion can lead in several directions. Some rebels may end up establishing a lifetime pattern of lashing out against parents, teachers, authority, society in general, and religion, church and God. Some rebels are anti-social, but within the law; others, outside the law. Some become successful in life because they manage to suppress their rebellion. Most, however, are not smart enough to do that—their rebellious actions constantly get them into trouble. But while some rebels attack, others retreat. They hide, cop out, or get rid of their anger, resentment and bitterness by retreating. They are the runaways.

In 1968 some 150,000 young people in the United States ran away from home and subsequently were arrested. But most of those who run away do not get arrested. These figures would be conservative in terms of estimating the total number of runaways. Some speculate that there were 500,000 runaways during the years 1968–69.

Running away is nothing new. In previous years children and teens ran away, but they ran around the neighbourhood or the town and when night came or they grew hungry, they went back home. My mother always said "good" when I announced I was "leaving and never coming back". She would ask me, "Do you want me to make you egg, ham or cheese sandwiches to take with you?" It was never any fun running away; my mother took all the threat out of it. But nowadays young people are not just running around the town; they're running around the nation and the world, and they're not returning home. About 70 per cent of the young people who come into our Greenwich Village coffee houses are runaways. Innocent teens who come to Greenwich Village on a whim or looking for excitement often get hooked on the way of life. When they run out of money they are forced to accept invitations to stay with addicts, way-out hippies, gangsters, and even psychopaths.

Runaways are not limited to the younger set. One young housewife in her mid-twenties came to Teen Challenge after having left her baby in a doctor's office. She had walked out of the office, made her way across the Canadian border, and ended up late one night in our chapel. When asked why she did it, she said, "I just felt an urge to go away." Further study showed she had begun a runaway pattern at the age of fourteen.

Running away is a form of addiction to some. One young man said, "I've been running away since I was nine years old. I can't stay anywhere more than a month. Something comes over me and I just want to run, run, run. I guess I'll never stop." He walked out of Teen Challenge and I have not seen him since.

Types of Runaways

1. *The full-time hippie runaways*. They live in city or country communes. There are an estimated 500 hippie communes across America. Their speech, dress, drug-taking and political and social ideals are all hippie. Long hair, beards, beads, sandals or bare feet (boots in winter) are all part of their life-style. Some are high school or college drop-outs. They come from a wide range of academic and socio-economic backgrounds. The average hippie runaway is 21, white, middle-class suburbanite, and Protestant. His parents earn between twelve and fifteen thousand dollars a year.

2. *The part-time runaways*. They cannot rightfully be classified as hippies, since they work and function in the "straight" society. But they are thought of as hippies by adults. Not all are long-haired. Most still live at home, but for the most part they run their own lives and "do their own thing". There is often open conflict between parents and part-time runaways because their life patterns and attitudes are in direct opposition to each other.

3. *Holiday runaways*. These are the summer and school vacation beachcombers. Some do drop out permanently, either during a summer vacation or even during a school holiday.

4. *The "wheelaways"*. They are the motorcycle gang members who run away on wheels. They usually have a head-

quarters, but they travel most of the time. They are known for their violence, sex orgies and the terror they sometimes cause in small towns. Not all "wheelaways" are members of organized gangs. Some go in small groups, alone, or in pairs. These are usually not the rough, sex-hungry types.

5. *The "rockaways"*. Since Woodstock (1969) there are groups of young people who go from one rock festival to another. They are the "rockaways". They run away whenever there is a rock music festival. There they find others who share their interests in rock music, drugs and sex. Some of the rock-aways are devout lovers of rock music; others go simply because there is a crowd there. Many go because the music, sex, and drugs fill a spiritual void in their lives.

The book *Purple Violet Squish*[1] lists three types of hippies. Since many runaways become hippies, I include the list here.

Types of Hippies

1. *Hope-to-be hippies*. These are teenagers between fifteen and eighteen. They are attracted primarily by the glamour and mystique of the abandoned free life, without the restrictions of parents and the pressures of having to produce in the "straight" world.

2. *Tribal hippies*. They simply want to try something new and experiment with life. In a kind of tribal togetherness they seek to shake off their terrible guilt feelings and their emptiness, and to satisfy an inner craving for love and understanding.

3. *Synthetic hippies*. Among these are the city hippies, suburban hippies, political hippies, week-end hippies, musical hippies and tourists. They want the world to think they're hippies, but in their hearts they don't have the courage to go all the way. Most of them are under thirty, but some are in their sixties. Among them are business people who get a great kick out of rubbing shoulders with hippies.

The Runaway's "Bags"

To understand the behaviour of runaways the counsellor needs to know something about their interests, or "bags". "Bag" is a term the runaways use to describe their "thing". It is their main interest and concern in life. They consider the Christian who witnesses to them as having a Christian "bag". One fellow said to us, "Don't come out with that religious bag to me." What are the runaways's bags?

1. *The drug bag*. Many actively seek out runaway or hippie

141

havens because they know they can easily find drugs there. Most young people turn to drugs later, after getting involved in the scene and making friends. Some do not fully realize what they are getting into with respect to drugs. But once turned on, they find drugs relieve their anxieties built up because of leaving home. Drug-taking comes from group pressure and from sharing "pads" (living quarters, apartments, or just a room) with others. To be socially acceptable, drug-taking becomes necessary in such an environment.

2. *The sex bag.* Teenage boys are sometimes forced into homosexuality and girls into prostitution. Most, however, get involved in sex vices by choice. Often there are group sex perversions and the sharing of many lovers. "Make love, not war" is one of the hippie slogans. They regard any and all sexual involvement with another partner as being a manifestation of that love. Under the guise of love they give themselves licence to do whatever they want, sexually.

3. *The political bag.* Almost all runaways are politically and socially active. Many decided to drop out because of political and social views. Some are dedicated to peace movements, while others mainly participate in protest rallies or riots.

The Reasons for Running Away

Why do young people run away? Capt. James Lynch, head of the Missing Persons Unit, New York City Police Department, says, "Running away from home has become a fad, a tragic, almost spontaneous answer to problems in either school or the home."

A National Institute of Mental Health study concludes: "Running away may be any number of things, ranging from a cry of despair to a victory yell."

One young girl told me, "My parents threw me out of the house." When I asked her why, she admitted, "They said, 'Live by our rules or get out.' I refused to live by their rules, so I got out."

Some young people run away on impulse, a reaction to a fight with their parents. Most of these return home. Others leave because of a series of conflicts with parents built up over a period of time. A sixteen-year-old girl who showed up at our centre told me of constant conflicts with her mother over church and a boy friend. I learned her trouble was caused by a combination of the mother's paying more attention to her own desires, and the subsequent reaction of the daughter doing whatever she could to excite or anger her mother. When I asked her to call home, she did. The girl said, "Hello, mom, I'm at Teen Challenge in New York City." Her mother quickly shot back, "Well, you just stay there," and hung up. Capt. Lynch asserts, "Our runaway cases involve almost as much adult delinquency as they do juvenile delinquency."

Another contributing factor, often overlooked, is the glamourized publicity given to the runaway havens and the hippie style of living. Such vivid portrayals in the news media often are the trigger that ignites the action. Young people read about the exploits of runaways so much that running away appears to be "in" and fashionable. They begin looking around for a reason to run.

Almost every major newspaper and magazine, when the hippie culture began to emerge, gave it front page coverage. There is no evil of course in such coverage itself—but it was the manner in which it was presented. It all looked like an innocent lark or a cute teenage fad. Thus, teens were lured by the thousands partly by the kind of publicity given such psychedelic havens. Television programmes pictured it also as a refreshing development in our society. As one San Francisco hippie dropout in Haight Ashbury stated, "You can't find love in Haight (hate). They didn't tell us the other side of the story. This is a bad scene." Only when LSD began to blow a few minds did another picture emerge in print, and thus in a positive way did this help warn young people that drugs and the hippie culture were not all so pure and innocent.

Many runaways have provoked their parents to anger and to arguments, to find a reason to justify their leaving home. Others just walk off, hoping to shock their parents and gain attention from family, friends, and church associates. They run away mainly to punish their parents. They usually try to get in touch with someone near home, hoping the parents will somehow find out and try to get them back.

A *Christian Herald* article, May, 1970, about runaways states: "Apart from a few incorrigible delinquents who run away as soon as they are returned to their homes, most runaways are either worried, confused, or indulged children who are convinced that they have little dialogue with their parents, no matter how permissive they may be. Recalling that often busy parents showed little visible concern for their smaller difficulties, runaways contend that they anticipated serious complications over dates, hair styles, bedtimes, marijuana, or social values; or, that there were crises triggered by damage done to expensive furniture or the family automobile; or, most

143

often, by their receiving poorer grades in school than their parents expected of them."

THE REVOLUTIONARIES

It is hard to prove a definite link between rebels, runaways and revolutionaries. There is always movement up or down the scale. Some rebels are not politically motivated or politically rebellious. Some become so because a political issue gives them a new target for their anger. But many radicals and revolutionaries have had no past history of parental or social rebellion, at least not the kind that got them into trouble with the law. Most of those arrested for rioting and bombing had no previous record of arrest for any reason.

What factors in our society produce revolutionaries? Why does the campus boil? Following are some things that have happened during the 1960's that have tended to radicalize our young people:

1. The civil rights and racial issues started by sit-ins in the South and riots in the North.

2. The step-up of the war in Vietnam in 1965, which struck a note of deep concern among many youth. Peace groups sprang up all across the country.

3. The Students for a Democratic Society turned from protest "within" to protest "without", making the universities, the ghettos and the government their targets.

4. Haight Ashbury in San Francisco added hippie culture and style to the newly emerging youth movement. It gave youth a means of expressing its rebellion and rejection of adult life-styles.

5. Eugene McCarthy's success gave the youth movement its first victory when President Johnson withdrew from the 1968 presidential race. Not getting their way in Chicago during the Democratic national convention gave the radical young people their first bitter defeat. Legal protest gave way to violent protest.

6. The continuation of the war, campus strikes and the death of four Kent State University students in Ohio turned many moderates into revolutionaries.

These are some of the reasons young people have turned from being moderates into being protesters, activists, radicals, and eventually revolutionaries. *His* magazine says students are either (*a*) inactivists, (*b*) law-abiding activists, or (*c*) radicals.

Jerry Rubin, one of the leading exponents of radicalism,

says: "We have merged new left politics with a psychedelic life-style. Our life-style—acid, long hair, freaky clothes, pot, rock music, sex—is the revolution. Our very existence mocks America. The old order is dying. The Democratic Party is dying. While it dies we will celebrate the festival of life. We are the politics of the future."

But the revolt is not confined to rebelling against the Vietnam war. One college student said, "When the war ends, something else will be the main target of the protesters and revolutionaries." Large numbers of young activists see the problems of American society—poverty, pollution, the war—as fundamentally the fault, not of the government, but of capitalism itself. The hard-core radicals and revolutionaries believe that reform is not possible through the normal political system. They consider revolutionary violence the only alternative.

Some of the attitudes of youth towards materialism and capitalism are close to what Christians believe. Said one: "So much of the business system depends on messing up people's minds so they'll buy what they're told. They convince women that they will look bad in the natural state so there will be a market for make-up. They've created a whole country full of people who are just too up-tight about themselves to care about each other." They are saying what the Bible says: "A man's life consisteth not in the abundance of the things which he possesseth" (Luke 12:15).

Another student said: "The values we need are love instead of power, brotherhood instead of competition. That sounds corny, except that thousands of people are dying because we don't have them. So now I think of myself as a revolutionary and I'm turned off to capitalism, but it isn't just a question of economics. It's a question of how you teach people to love under a system that depends on teaching them power and competition."

What are the causes of the unrest, protest, violence and revolution in the high schools and on college and university campuses? To find the reasons we must once again look at the home backgrounds and society as a whole. This generation is a product of the past generation. What are some of the emotional, psychological and spiritual factors that are causing our youth to want to revolt and overthrow anything and everything?

1. *Childhood permissiveness.* This generation is a product of mothers and fathers who said, "Our children are not going to go through what we did when we were children." With their

145

prosperity they are able to live up to such a promise. They make the whole world revolve around their children. Their offspring can have anything, do anything. The children run the home. They challenge authority and are allowed to get away with it. Every wish is gratified. Because mother and dad have money, or credit, they never have to wait long to have their wishes fulfilled. These young people come to the university with the same desire for painless, no-waiting gratification. They ran their homes, why can't they run the university?

The result, as suggested by John W. Aldridge in his excellent book, *In the Country of the Young,* is that young people are "paralysed with indecision." He writes:

"But if the pressure of economic necessity is missing, not only is motivation reduced to a minimum, but one is confronted by such a plethora of possibilities for using one's energies that one may become paralysed with indecision and end up deciding nothing at all—or, like mice, in an overly complicated maze, turn psychotic and simply sit down and goggle at the wall."[2]

Eventually youth get tired of "goggling at the wall" and they are then ready to tear down, burn, or bulldoze over the wall—either to get into the university and get some meaning out of it, or to get out of the university and find a solution to their paralysis.

2. *The absence of discipline in childhood and adolescence. A* lack of discipline follows material gratification and permissiveness. As children they got whatever they wanted; they had to pay no price for it, in terms of obedience to house rules and regulations. Aldridge states:

'No restrictions were placed on the child, and parents habitually made it a point, in moments of choice, to let the child cast the deciding vote." The result, he says, is that they became "drunk with the glory of their incontestable omnipotence. They entered the university convinced that whatever is required of them is wrong. Any exercise of authority, any imposition of laws, is a violation of their civil liberties, as well as their divine rights as members of the new world family of adolescents. It is also a violation of the rules of the game that they have been playing all their lives, the particular variety of checkers in which they were always allowed to jump backwards or forwards on the board long before they earned any kings. They are convinced they are right, and where there is not an existing issue to prove it, they will make one. They seem to have a constant need to be right."[3]

3. *The need for identity through opposition.* A child who has

146

never been disciplined, and who rebels but is never resisted, grows up with a feeling of guilt for not having been punished and opposed. The result is an identity vacuum or identity crisis. A child will challenge parents to see how far he can go, secretly hoping to be resisted.

Aldridge states:

The young come to the universities with little or no respect for their parents, hence little or no respect for adults in general, and very little experience with organized authority. At the same time, their life-long exposure to parental over-protectiveness and permissiveness has given them a mass respect for themselves and an absolute faith in their own authority. But the trouble with their own authority is that since it has never been opposed, it has never actually been tested. It has evolved in a vacuum of non-resistance in which wants were satisfied by negotiations rather than through a direct or violent contest of wills.[4]

He goes on to say: "If adults can be made to resist rather than equivocate or compromise, the young will at last have achieved a condition they have never known in their lives before, and that is vital" to them. Aldridge says the school is an extension of the home, the administrators are the equivalent of parents, and rebellion is transferred from one setting to another.

But it is often too late and too much to ask the schools to solve problems that should have been taken care of in adolescence. The conflict the revolutionaries seek and need comes too late in life. This is why only a surrender to a higher authority (a divine one) will remove the deep-seated rebellion of today's youth.

4. *Boredom.* Aldridge puts boredom in its proper perspective. It has become the by-product of confrontation and revolution. He writes:

This is the first student generation to be admitted to the university on the principle that higher education is a right that should be available to all and, at the same time, a necessity for anyone who hopes to achieve some measure of success in middle-class society. The result is that for the first time in history the universities have had to accept large masses of students who may have the proper credentials from the secondary schools, but who possess neither the cultural interest

147

nor the intellectual incentive to benefit from higher education. Such students when confronted with complex ideas tend to sink into a protective lethargy, or to become resentful because demands are being made on them which they are not equipped to meet and have no particular desire to meet. Most of them did not want to come to the universities in the first place, but did so for reasons of practical expediency: parental pressure, fear of the draft, or the promise of a better job after graduation. Hence their natural impulse is to try to compensate for their failure of ability or interest by involving themselves in some extra-curricular activity, which happens to be today political activism.[5]

This generation which has more advantages than any previous generation turns out to be bored. Boredom not only leads to drugs, but it can lead to revolution, just to give young people something to do.

How to Counsel Rebels, Runaways and Revolutionaries

It must be understood that some of the basic guidelines suggested for helping addicts, alcoholics and other people can also be applied to the rebels, runaways and revolutionaries. However, the following suggestions will be useful in relating to the needs of these young people.

1. *Break the "bag" barrier.* The counsellor must get into the young person's "bag", spend some time with him in it, and then try to lead him out of it. This does not mean literally to participate in drug-taking, sex, or political protest. Breaking the bag barrier is getting beyond the drugs, the sex and the political questions to the underlying causes and needs. But before this "getting beyond" can be accomplished, a certain amount of interest must be expressed in the "bag" of the rebel, runaway or revolutionary. They will want to talk about their bag.

Don't try to put a pin in their balloon or bag; don't ridicule, condemn, or scoff. It is the only thing they have in life to call their own. It is precious to them. Try to break them out of their bag and get them into the Christian bag. Some ministers and Christian workers are going around preaching about bags—they are practising bag-breaking—without demonstrating that they have something more meaningful and satisfying. When Jesus spoke to the woman at the well (John 4), He did not condemn her for coming to fill her water pot, but He told her about some better water. The idea is to present an alternative, a better way of life, so the young person will want to break out of his bag.

148

2. *Don't meddle in politics.* The counsellor must be careful lest he meddle too deeply into political questions. Some well-meaning Christians get hung up on political issues and never get to spiritual issues. It is best not to be dogmatic on political questions, while at the same time expressing an interest in political and social affairs. The counsellor might say, for example, "I have strong feelings about the war myself. I agree it's an ugly thing and I wish it would stop. But let's talk about the war that goes on inside a man." It is best to use political and social questions as leads to matters pertaining to the soul. The counsellor who is alert and determined not to meddle will pick out the opportune moment to get to more important issues. The radical, revolutionary student will feel that preservation of human life and the earth itself are the most important issues facing society. Don't downgrade his interest in such; commend him instead. Then try to take him on to the larger spiritual perspectives on such matters.

3. *Don't get hung up on externals.* My wife and I visited a hippie coffee house in Sydney, Australia. As soon as we walked in, one of the young men looked at us, then looked at his friend and formed a square with his fingers and pointed to us. Later he said, "No one is going to listen to you here if you're dressed square."

"Listen," I said, "you are always complaining that adults will not accept you for what you are, and that they are always judging you by the length of your hair, your clothes, and other things. Why do you turn around and do the very same thing to me? Your long hair doesn't bother me; why should my short hair bother you? I'm not going to turn you off because of the way you're dressed. Please do the same for me."

Clothing styles mean a lot to most young people. For some they are only fads, but for many they are an outward expression of an inward attitude, rebellion, or search. One writer has suggested that the clothing of youth has "social and psychological implications" that are "depressing in the extreme". "The World War I uniform," he says, "is cherished as a sacred relic for drama, individuality, and romance of war fought according to principles of a now debased idealism."[6]

The Western outfit with the sideburns is worn because the plainsman "enjoyed the distinction of being in honourable contest with the primitive forces of nature, a kind of contest no longer possible."[7]

Wearing Indian garb is an effort "to remind the establishment of its ancestral guilt. The Indian was the original American

149

frontier Negro, the first victim of our corrupt bureaucratic system. It is to suggest that the young, too, were once happy and free like the Indian, and might have remained so if only they had been left alone by adults to do as they pleased."[3]

Regardless of what the externals symbolize, they are very much a part of youth's personality. To criticize such trimmings is to slur him personally. Clothes and hair styles are part of their identity. This is why it is fruitless for parents to go around trying to get their children to dress "right" and to get their hair cut. Unless the inward emptiness and crisis of the soul is solved, cutting away the trimmings will be of no value. Let no Christian worker and counsellor say, "I can't see your need and your soul for your hair or your dress." "Man looketh on the outward appearance, but the Lord looketh on the heart" (1 Sam 16:7). Beneath the beards, beads, and hair is a person—don't get hung up on the externals.

4. *Magnify the personal experience, or "happening", aspect of Christianity*. Most young people have an institutional view of Christianity. They see it simply as a dead system. They must be made to see the personal experience aspect of the Christian faith. A counsellor should dwell on his own personal experience and relationship to Christ. Talk about answered prayer, the Holy Spirit's ability to lead in decision-making, the overcoming of habits, and other aspects that are relevant to everyday living. Rebels, runaways and revolutionaries need to see that Christ is "the real thing" and that "life goes better with Jesus Christ."

Most of them know what a personal experience with drugs is. They have had the experience of mystical, spiritual feelings. Their use of LSD is evidence of their search for something that will affect their spirits and expand their minds. One LSD user told me that when he was on a trip he "felt a oneness with the universe." Another said, "I took an end run around Jesus Christ and went right to the source—God." Here are a few more descriptions of how LSD users feel on trips:

> I cannot recall whether the revelation came gradually or suddenly; I only remember finding myself in the very midst of those wonderful moments, beholding life for the first time in all of its young intoxication and loveliness, in its unspeakable joy, beauty, and importance. I cannot say exactly what the mysterious change was. I saw no new things. I saw all the usual things in a new miraculous light—in what I believe is their true light. I saw for the first time how beautiful and joyous, beyond any words of mine to describe, is the

150

whole of life. Every human being moving across that porch, every sparrow that flew, every branch tossing in the wind, was caught in and was part of a whole mad ecstasy of loveliness, of joy, of importance, of intoxication of life.

A feeling of great peace and contentment seemed to flow through my entire body. All sounds ceased and I seemed to be flowing in a great, very very still void or hemisphere. It is impossible to describe the overpowering feeling of peace, contentment, and being a part of goodness itself that I felt. I could feel my body dissolving and actually becoming a part of the goodness and peace that was all around me. Words can't describe this. I feel an awe and wonder that such a feeling could have occurred.[9]

These descriptions in some ways could also pass as Christian testimonies of what it means to have experienced crucifixion of the sinful life and the resurrection of the Christ-life. To the child of God who has experienced His power, an LSD trip, or a drug experience, is a counterfeit.

Our mother once remarked: "Make no mistake about it. Most of these kids are seekers and searchers after the supernatural. Why else has the world gone mad over the occult, the mysterious, and the ouija board? They recognize a world beyond and they dare delve into it. The fact that it's evil and leads them on to further destruction is not taken into account by them.

"One of our workers was asked to speak to a group of hippie searchers. She was asked to tell what her evangelistic church believed. After going down the line of salvation, separation and the Second Coming, she told how she got 'high'. She said, 'God created you with a hunger for highs. I admire you for going all out for what you believe in—no matter what your trip might cost you, your mind, or even your life. I would to God that all Christians were as sincere as you are. But God has provided His own way of a Christian high. That is the baptism of the Holy Spirit, wherein one is anointed by God's Spirit and worships Him in spirit and in truth in a heavenly language. This is real communion with the supernatural.' As one person, they all rose in unison and said, 'That's what we're looking for. That's what we want.' They hoped the speaker had a bagful to distribute. But when she told them that they must receive this experience by believing on Christ as Saviour, that was just too high a price to pay."

The counsellor should magnify his own "trip" to the cross of Calvary and show that what people are seeking in narcotics and

151

in revolution is found through Christ. When a former hippie and LSD-user was asked if he thought he would ever go back to using the drug, he said, "No, because now I have found the ultimate thing. I have no need for the old ways."

5. *Reveal Christ as a "revolutionary" in the proper sense.* Militants and revolutionaries like to point out, "Jesus Christ wore long hair and He also was a revolutionary." They are right on both counts, but they are wrong in their understanding of what kind of revolution Jesus promoted. The counsellor must make clear the type of revolution Christ advocated. He worked within the system. "Think not that I am come to destroy the law, or the prophets: I am not come to destroy, but to fulfil" (Matt. 5:17). His was a revolution of ideals, of principles, and of truth. True, He did reverse the whole concept of religious and social progress, but He did not riot, or sit-in, throw bricks, or burn down synagogues, or lead marches through Jerusalem. When He was asked about taxes, He said they were to be paid. In spite of the fact that the Roman government was corrupt, Christ did not spend His time trying to lead a campaign to abolish it. He came to conquer the human heart, not Rome. His methods were not revolutionary (though they were supernatural), but His message was.

When a long-haired youth said to me, "What's wrong with long hair—didn't Jesus wear long hair?" I replied, "Yes, and Hitler wore a moustache. Does this mean that I should fear or hate everyone who wears a moustache?" The fact that Jesus wore long hair was a sign of conformity. Long hair was the custom of the day. The Pharisees, Sadducees, politicians and tax collectors—the squares—all wore long hair. To be a revolutionary in Christ's day you had to shave off your hair. When the revolutionaries identify themselves with Jesus, pin them down to the true meaning of His revolutionary message.

6. *Expose them to an evangelistic atmosphere and a Holy Spirit presence.* A hippie walked into one of our rallies and said, "Wow, the vibrations in this place are terrific!" He was caught by the presence of the Holy Spirit. He sensed God was there. Most young people are sensitive to other people. They can pick up adult feelings of hatred, anger and fear. They also know how to pick out the "vibrations" of their hippie life which they call peace and love. Therefore, it is not difficult for them to sense the "vibrations" of the Holy Spirit.

For soul-winning to take place with this type of person, they must be brought into an evangelistic atmosphere, but not too soon. Many churches have made a mistake by promoting a big rally without laying any groundwork of seed-sowing. The response is usually a disappointment—young people walk out, mock, or just sit indifferently. Big rallies should not be a substitute for real Christian witnessing. No evangelistic rally can be successful until preliminary preparations have been made.

Often those who run the Christian coffee house ministeries and do on-the-street witnessing make the mistake of not following through by not introducing the young people to a Christian "vibration" rally. Often at a service where Christians come together to worship the Lord, the young person can sense the personal presence of Christ and the Holy Spirit. One young lady told us how she felt as she sat in a rally where I preached. She said, "My mind told me this was garbage, but my emotions and my spirit told me something else. When the altar call was given, I accepted Christ. Now my mind and my emotions are in one accord with Christ."

The now famous Woodstock festival, and other similar rock festivals, have certain similarities to an evangelistic, revival crusade. Woodstock was a place for them to sing and hear their message, to feel the presence of others with similar feelings—a place to sense the unholy spirit of the music, as well as to trip out with the aid of drugs. What the Woodstock generation sought is a substitute for a personal experience of Christ. What young people are finding in the church through Christ is what the Woodstockers were seeking at their revival festival.

7. *Use attractive, thought-provoking literature.* Most of the runaways, especially the radicals, represent youth of high intelligence. While many of them may not have control of their emotions, they are nevertheless deep thinkers. Give them literature dealing with the particular subject that is their bag. Literature written by sound biblical scholars has a tremendous appeal for students we have worked with. After the counsellor has gained his attention and confidence, the young person will usually accept a Bible and promise to read it. Most of them claim to know the Bible, but in reality they only know *about* the Bible and have never studied it. They will say they are going to read it as literature. But whatever their reason (some accept the Bible to read and try to refute it), if they read it, it is bound to have a powerful and profound impact on them.

Dealing with rebels, runaways and revolutionaries—like dealing with addicts—entails a long counselling process.

8. *Aim for the heart, not the head.* Many counsellors make the mistake of trying to reach a student only on an intellectual level. It is not possible to win an argument with a young person

153

and then expect to lead him to Christ. The counsellor who aims for the head—to defend God, the Bible, Jesus Christ—may win a debate but lose a soul. Remember, "the natural man receiveth not the things of the Spirit of God: ... because they are spiritually discerned" (1 Cor. 2: 14). This does not mean the counsellor should ignore the mind and the head. Isaiah did say, "Come now, and let us reason together" (1: 18). To reach the bright, smart young person, the counsellor must know how—to a certain degree—to communicate on his level. This does not mean the Christian worker needs a college degree to reach the bright young person. It does mean he must be knowledgeable and able to hold his own in discussions and conversations.

But reasoning can go only so far. The danger is to go too far and try to prove a point without letting the Holy Spirit "prove" it. There are some young people who reason out the truth before making a commitment to Christ. They make an intelligent decision to accept that "without faith it is impossible to please him (God); for he that cometh to God must believe that he is ..." (Heb. 11: 6). If they agree to the premise, then they must be willing to lay reason and man's knowledge aside and take the step of faith and accept Christ. Faith is the bridge between human reason and spiritual reality.

9. *Love, love, love.* Loving the drug addict may come easier to the Christian worker than loving the rebel, runaway or revolutionary. The addict most often responds to love. He may hate, but his hatred can be understood and accepted because of his condition. The addict, alcoholic or delinquent has a low melting point. They respond quickly to the "bug with love" process. Many younger, part-time runaways will, too, but not the hard-core rebels, radicals and revolutionaries. They view the Christian as part of the "system" and look upon the counsellors as part of religious, capitalist manipulation. The counsellor must prove he is not "plastic". He must prove he is "for real".

The addict will display his anger with deeds, the radical with words. His words, like knives, will cut deeply into the Christian counsellor. He will challenge the counsellor's sincerity, intelligence, motives, morals, faith—almost anything. Many workers leave our coffee houses feeling like they want to "shake the dust" off their feet. To say the least, it takes love, love and more love to reach and win the rebels, runaways and revolutionaries for Christ. They must be tapped with the drill of love.

NOTES

[1] London, Oliphants, 1969.
[2] John W. Aldridge, *In the Country of the Young* (New York, Harper & Row, 1970).
[3] ibid.
[4] ibid.
[5] ibid.
[6] ibid.
[7] ibid.
[8] ibid.
[9] David Solomon, *LSD: The Consciousness-Expanding Drug* (New York, Berkley Publishing Corp., 1966).

9

THE SEXUAL GENERATION

A girl drug addict strolls the streets waiting to "turn a trick" (sell her body) to the highest, even the lowest, bidder.

A girl, an employee of a "madam", waits in an apartment house for her next customer.

A twenty-five-year-old woman, dressed in a fur coat, diamonds, and other expensive clothing, drives her Cadillac to Long Island to meet Mr. Businessman—husband of someone else—in a motel.

A fifteen-year-old girl and a seventeen-year-old boy, alone in her house, let their passions run too far; they engage in sexual intercourse; she gets pregnant.

A young lawyer dates his office secretary, ending the evening in bed with her.

Eight married couples eat, drink, joke together. They finish the night by tossing their car keys into a bowl; the women pick out a set of keys and go to bed with the man who owns them.

What do these actions have in common? Fornication? Adultery? Prostitution? Promiscuity? Yes, but they also reveal: (1) sexual hunger, (2) a distortion of the difference between sex and love, (3) a search for spiritual fulfilment, and (4) the effects of the "new morality".

We live in a society that condemns the street-walking prostitute but condones wife-swapping and "playboy" exploits. But the two are one and the same. Each of the above persons, to one degree or another, and in his or her own way, is expressing the same need.

The sexual generation poses three different, but in some ways similar, problems: (1) premarital sex, (2) pregnancy, and (3) prostitution. There are young people who engage in premarital sexual intercourse (the "premaritals"), those who become pregnant, and those who get hooked (prostitutes). The premaritals may remain sex-users, or they may get married and never violate their marital vows. But they may become sex abusers, and prostitutes themselves—either by the less-accepted manner (on

156

the streets), or by the more-accepted manner (dating, sharing apartments, motels, or living in common-law relationships). We will look at these three problem areas and the people involved and discuss how these problems develop. Then we will suggest some helpful guidelines for the counsellor who deals with such problems.

The Premarital Generation

Many young people who pride themselves on not being drug users or addicts have fallen into their own kind of addiction—premarital sex. They have taken the church's silence and lack of courage in facing the problem as either a licence to practise premarital sex, or as a sign that no one cares or would understand if they wanted to talk about it. Some church-going young people feel the same way. Their thinking is changing drastically on the matter of premarital sex indulgence. If they are not reached, they may face a lifetime of misery from a mistake, or even get hooked into a sex trap and never get out.

The subject of sex must be handled properly from the pulpit, the dining room table, the classroom and the living room. Sex must not simply be condemned, it must be understood. A young person's ignorance can only lead to experimentation—and trouble. Ann Landers said it well when she stated: "Only a fool would tell a teenager to stop thinking about sex. They are thinking about sex and will continue to think about it. What they need is sound information so they will know *how* to think about it."

Moral pronouncements against sexual sin are simply not in vogue with many of today's clergy, religious leaders, and youth counsellors. Too many, I fear, are not courageous enough to urge students and other youth to live by the biblical standards. Also behind this silence is the fear of being unpopular among the so-called secular-minded youth who take nothing on faith but must have scientific proof and what they term a rational approach to sexual mores.

We are reaping the effects of muting the biblical code on premarital sex. In one college 92 per cent of those questioned approved of sex relations if the couples felt they were in love, even though they did not intend to become husband and wife. In *The Sexual Wilderness* Vance Packard writes about the results of his survey among young people aged twenty-one to twenty-three. "To the question asked, whether regardless of age or stage, full intimacy would be considered 'appropriate' if both

157

persons desired it and had a 'sense of trust, loyalty, protectiveness, and love':

U.S. Male Students . . . 70 per cent
U.S. Female Students . . . 60 per cent"[1]

Playboy's own national student survey showed only 18 per cent of the males, and 49 per cent of the females, who reported they had not had premarital sexual relations. Stated another way, 82 per cent of the males reported to have practised premarital sex, and 51 per cent of the females said they indulge. In an identical survey of 1,030 secular college students the result showed 66 per cent holding that sex relations before marriage were not wrong and 29 per cent said such relations were wrong. I think the comment of one girl in a university in New York City, as quoted by Vance Packard, sums up the attitude of the premaritals, "A girl doesn't have to be madly in love with every boy she sleeps with." She thinks that sometimes intimacy with a boy to whom she is only "casually attracted" could be "very important to her development."[2]

What is behind the premarital sex problem? To find answers we must look at the problems and needs of young people themselves. Our search for answers must take us to the Scriptures, to the lessons of history, to the testimony of psychiatrists, pychologists and professional counsellors. The following are some of the factors to be considered.

1. *The reaction against Puritanism*. One of the favourite arguments used to justify immorality is the so-called suppression of sex by our forefathers—our Puritan heritage. In an effort to get away from the "under the rug" approach to sex, the pendulum has swung to the opposite extreme. True, many young people do have hang-ups about sex because of the hush-hush attitude of days gone by. Children did grow up with the idea that sex was dirty, a part of the curse, or something to be endured but not enjoyed—a means of producing children and nothing else. Those who came from such restricted or repressive sexual backgrounds often suffered unhealthy guilt when their biological urges started to develop.

On the other hand, proponents of the "new morality" have gone too far in breaking away from "old-fashioned" morality. They are now using the old restrictions as a licence to do whatever they want. Young people need a wholesome, healthy, balanced approach to sex. But we are not going to right any past wrongs by making sex a game, a toy, a cure-all, or a liberation from past sexual misinformation.

158

The moral revolution has come about not only because of a reaction to Puritan ideals, but also because there is a rebellion against any and all morality. When we speak of morality, we think immediately of matters of sex, but morality has to do with all matters of behaviour and conduct. In throwing off standards of righteousness and holiness, our society has created a spiritual vacuum. Values which seemed absolute have been desacralized; decisions once clear-cut have been relativized; and simple ethical certainty, of the sort available to the average man, has gone. To a few, such bottomless freedom may be exhilarating, but to the ordinary man the impact is devastating.

When men lose their sense of established standards, they tend to fall victim to an urge for pleasure or a lust for power. And when the loss of standards occurs during a period of peril, men seem to prefer pleasure to power.

The old morality was in need of renovation, but it had its better side, and we have discarded the total fabric too indiscriminately.

Because of the spiritual vacuum, it has been easy for playboyism to come forward as the new authority—the new cult or religion.

But what has happened is that he (the playboy) is emancipated from past prejudices only to be victimized by contemporary ones.[8]

The moral revolutionists in seeking to rid themselves and us of one set of problems have fixed another rope in which they are hanging themselves slowly but surely. The new morality is the old immorality turned inside out—or painted with another coat of paint. They may have done society a favour in pointing out some of the falsehoods of past inconsistencies; however this does not qualify them to move in with their own set of rules. A new kind of wrong does not right past wrongs. "There is no liberation in escaping from one bondage only to be signed up as a devout believer and practising member of the pleasure establishment."

Hugh Hefner, editorializing in one of his special magazine publications entitled *The Sexual Revolution* takes great pains to justify premarital and extra-marital sex by blaming God, the Bible, and Christianity. He states: "But what sort of God would have man deny his God-given sexual nature?" However, he fails to quote any biblical source in which God states such denial.

He further writes, "As much as religion has done for the development and growth of society, sex has done more." Again, he fails to state just how or in what way sex has helped our society.

His conclusion to the sexual problem, and his solution to his belief that religiously-inspired sexual suppression is harmful to society is summed up in these words: "To some these views represent a decline in moral standards—a turning away from the divinely revealed Word of God, as expressed in the Bible, the Ten Commandments and Judeo-Christian heritage that a majority of Christians share; to others they represent a facing up to 'facts of life', an enlightened search for a new morality more in keeping with modern man's greater understanding of both himself and the world in which he lives—a quest for a new code of conduct consistent with our conduct itself based upon reason rather than superstition.

"But whatever viewpoint one espouses, there is common agreement that a sexual revolution is taking place and that the old religious restrictions have little or no influence on the sexual behaviour of a sizeable segment of our society. For these citizens, at least, a new, more acceptable moral code must be found."[4]

We must not surrender to some of our intellectuals, writers, thinkers, philosophers, Hefnerites and clergymen who succumbed to the notion that if people cannot live up to the biblical standards, there must be something wrong with the standards.

Norman Vincent Peale in his book, *Sin, Sex and Self-Control*, writes about freedom from all authority and all restraints. "This trend began some fifty years ago as a revolt against Victorian prudery, and no one denies today that Victorian attitudes towards sex were rigid, repressive, and unrealistic. But the curious thing was that the revolt was led, more often than not, by individuals whose attitudes towards sex were hardly normal to begin with. ... Gradually, and perhaps inevitably, the revolt against repressiveness in sex became a revolt against conventional morals. It was Hemingway, idol of a whole generation, who could write that 'What is moral is what you feel good after, and what is immoral is what you feel bad after.' What nonsense. Under this weird code of ethics Hitler could have told himself that slaughtering the Jews was a moral act because it made him feel happy. Millions of people gladly accepted his dictum as some kind of gospel."[5]

2. *A love-sex conflict and misunderstanding.* The reasoning

160

of some young people is: "If we love each other, why can't we have sexual relations? We are going to get married anyway, so why not?" Others take a more liberal approach and state: "How can we know we will be compatible if we do not know each other sexually before we are married?" A young man will say to his girl friend, "If you love me, you'll show it by going all the way with me." The young lady on the other hand reasons: "I'll lose him if I don't give him what he wants."

The tragic notion has been inflicted on today's youth that sex is love, and that if you love someone you should express it through sex. They think that to indulge in pre-marital intercourse is to prove love. The wildest concept of all is that by sharing the privileges of intimacy before marriage the couple will find out if they are meant for each other. Research reveals, however, that premarital sex is no guarantee against marriage break-up. Divorce records show that there is a greater rate of divorce where there was premarital sex. If sex were love, then perhaps the trial marriage, or "shop around" approach would work. Love may result in sexual intimacy, but sexual intimacy does not always, or necessarily, end or begin with love. Most often sexual intimacy is lust, under the guise of love. *Love requires neither sex nor marriage for satisfaction.* People who are in love want to marry, but love does not necessarily need sex to prove itself.

Premarital sex creates more problems and more marriage failures because the people who were enjoying sex thought they were also growing to love each other. Later they discovered that sex blocked the development and maturing of true love. Young people who come together in body only do not allow themselves to come together in mind, spirit and personality. They do not see each other for what they really are. This is comparable to drug usage. While the addict is shooting dope, his emotional and mental growth are stunted and stopped. So it is with those who get high on sex. To build a marriage on such a relationship is to build on quicksand. Eventually one or both partners wakes up; they see each other and themselves as they really are and the sex or marriage balloon bursts. Both suffer a shattering experience. Neither one may be able, from that point on, to determine what is love and what is sex.

"Love" that is sex alone is a barrier that keeps real love from being expressed in so many other important ways that are absolutely vital for any lasting relationship or marriage. Being one in flesh before being one in spirit ruins any relationship.

Too early sexual involvement can blind the pair to the other important aspects of their relationship that they should be building as a foundation for their marriage. All too often they fall into bed together rather than talk out the many things that need to be shared and discussed. Once sexual intercourse starts, their interpersonal communication slackens in many a case. Thus in their coming together the couple may lose the very thing they sought to ensure—intimacy and companionship.

The danger of premarital sexual relations between lovers is a weakening of their feelings for one another on the one hand, and the possibility of too great involvement on the other hand.[6]

Those that meet together, flesh to flesh, will not meet together heart to heart, spirit to spirit, and eye to eye. It is the non-physical communication that reinforces the sex act. The former is essential for the fullest enjoyment of the latter. No marriage can last on sex alone. Premarital sex is a marriage blocker, not a marriage mender or maker.

The evidence of antiquity and the findings of modern psychology concur in the conclusion that sexual intercourse is not one act among many; it is an act without comparison, a possibility for achieving and expressing human fulfilment unique unto itself. Thus the abuse of sexuality is a serious assault upon man's very nature. Sexual intercourse involves more than the body; it involves the whole person, or, more accurately, two persons. Whether they give themselves wholly to each other is one thing, but that they are wholly involved is beyond doubt. No act of sexual union may ever be regarded as recreational or as one person's private business, for someone else is always profoundly implicated and the participants will never again be the same towards one another as they were before coming together. Once done, the experience will never be undone, and its effect, though imperceptible, is indelible. If they are husband and wife, the embrace should be the source and symbol of the common life they are building together. But if they are not husband and wife, the sexual act is of such significance that its unitive power is frustrated. Intercourse without obligation depersonalizes the parties involved, uniting them in an act of mutual exploitation. It is not because it is temporary, but because, in a sense, casual sex always involves permanent consequences, that it is intrinsically wrong.[7]

162

If sex were love, and if premarital sex guaranteed a successful marriage, then the best thing a couple could do is to learn all they can about the techniques of love-making and sexual intercourse. Clinics could be set up to teach such methods, and the result would be that everyone would live happily ever after. But young people are finding out that although they may be "making out" more, they are coming out with less in the end, in terms of loving and caring for each other. If sex guaranteed a good marriage, then the best man or woman in bed would make the best kind of partner. But in many cases what one is in the sex act, and what one is apart from that, are often two different things. The how-to sex manuals cannot tell a couple how to survive outside the bedroom.

It is true that some marriages are hindered because of incompatibility in sexual matters. But this only adds further proof that sex is not love, and love does not guarantee successful sex. They are not always one and the same. Incompatibility in sex can be caused by tensions in the non-physical or non-sexual relationships of the couple, or it can be caused by a misunderstanding about sex itself. Most marriages do not break up because of too little sex, but rather because of sex without love, and sex sharing without love sharing.

Many young women have been tragically disappointed by trying to use sex to sell their boy friends on marriage. A girl explained: "I figured if I let him have me, I would have him. But the more we were intimate in sex, the less we were intimate as persons." Many young men, when dating a girl, will go all-out for sex, purely for physical gratification. But these same fellows want *their* brides to be virgins. If such a fellow tests his girl friend to see if she will give in (really wanting her to keep her chastity), and the girl does give in, the fellow immediately will lose his respect for her and the relationship may go downhill from that point on.

3. *Sex as a pleasure and as a game.* Some persons are confused about sex and love, others are not confused—they know just what they are doing; they go after sex for the sheer pleasure of it. For them sex is a matter-of-fact thing, casual and recreational—a game. A young high school student said, "Most of my friends do not consider sex to be a problem. It's just something we like to do and to have fun with." He was honest, yet self-deceived.

Others who want sex for sex alone sometimes cover up their desire by saying they are in love. Few people are honest enough to admit that they are breaking the seventh commandment for

163

the simple and understandable reason that they enjoy sexual intercourse. They justify themselves by stating that they are in love with one another. For these people sex is a pastime to be indulged in, in the same way a person drinks, smokes, eats, goes to movies, and so on. The Russians once lived by this philosophy; they called it the "drink of water" approach to sex. Whenever you were hungry sexually—like being thirsty for a glass of water—you reached out and took someone to satisfy your sexual appetite. But they have since abandoned this attitude, because:

"Within a few years hordes of wild, homeless children became a real menace to the Soviet Union itself. Millions of lives, especially of young girls, were wrecked; divorce sky-rocketed, as did abortions. The hatred and conflicts between polygamous and polyandrous mates rapidly mounted—so did psychoneuroses. Work in the national factories slackened. The total result was so appalling that the government was forced to reverse its policy."[8] The Russians found that the "no holds barred" approach to sex did not work. The unconscious sex drive plays havoc if it is not brought under conscious control; if sex drives are given free rein, civilized life is impossible.

American society, to an ever greater degree, is headed in the direction of casual sex. Novels, the lyrics of popular songs, movies, television, magazines and advertising all seem to be saying sex is fun, fun, fun: "If it feels good, do it. Because it's fun and no one should be denied it," the message seems to be. The conclusion of the sex advertising bombardment is that you have not lived until you have proven, and enjoyed yourself, sexually. "Teenagers are stimulated by advertisers to buy more and to want more. Advertisers suggest that the way to be popular is to rev up the sex appeal. Sex screams from the billboards. Everybody is lying down with someone."[9]

God intended the sex act to be pleasurable. The Puritans and Victorians implied it was evil. Some pious people refuse to admit to themselves and others that they derive pleasure from it. But sex for pleasure only—any time, any place, with anyone—is a gross distortion of what God intends the sex act to be. To treat something so pleasurable and beautiful, and divinely instituted, as a glass of wine, a game, or as you would a drug, is to cheapen it and rank it with the animal habits. Sex for the sake of sex alone debases both the one who plays the game and the one who is the object. The playboy implies: "I am a machine. I have been created purely as a physical being whose primary function is to enjoy himself and to satisfy his craving for food, water and sex." The person who plays the sexual game deceives himself into thinking he is proving his manhood, when in reality he is saying he is not a whole person made up of mind, spirit and body; he is saying, instead, that he is just body and flesh. "The paradox of the playboy philosophy is that, while seeming to glorify sex, it really depreciates it. . . . When one makes sex a plaything, he forfeits the real thing. Playboys grow old wondering why they are playing more but enjoying it less."[10]

We have found that with many drug addicts one of the factors (at least on the surface) which led them into drug usage was that they engaged in sex pleasure at such an early age that by the time they were in their late teens the thrill and kick of it had worn off, so they opened themselves to new searches for kicks. A fellow said, "I smoked at twelve, was drinking at thirteen, drinking more at fourteen, engaged in sex at will at fifteen, was in gigs (orgies) at sixteen. By the time I was seventeen I was ready to die. I had tried about everything the world and the devil had to offer; drugs became the next step."[11]

The result of sex as a game, or sheer pleasure, "that it becomes progressively less exciting, less thrilling, more barren and more sterile. That's why so many of these people turn eventually to alcohol, or drugs, or twisted versions of sex, anything that seems to offer new kicks."[12]

4. *Sex as an escape.* Fornication often is the result of trying to escape a problem. Long before drugs came along as the new way to escape life's realities, sex was number one on the escaper's hit parade. Before the drug crash pad there was the car pad, the teenage motel on wheels where young people could park, pet, and play with the fires of sex. "More than any other single factor in the past thirty years, the automobile has exerted the strongest influence on teenage behaviour. . . . It is a status symbol and a passport to freedom. Six gallons of gasoline can propel a couple of teenagers into another world. A car can be a portable bedroom—'even with those crummy bucket seats,' as one teen stated."[13]

When mother and dad are away, the teens will play. If the home is a "pressure cooker", if mother and father fail in their responsibilities, if there is a moral and spiritual vacuum in the lives of young people, sex can become the most natural and the easiest form of escape.

Various studies have shown that school drop-outs are more likely to take sexual liberties and subsequently "get into trouble". Those who have high ideals, who are goal-conscious,

165

have less need to turn to sex to prove themselves, to find love, and to have a sense of accomplishment. Those who drop out of school, or are failures at school, or in life, have a sense of worthlessness. They look to sex for the satisfaction they could and should be getting out of other fulfilments in life. Sex is one of the most convenient forms of escape, in that it requires no education, no talent, and no character to make an attempt at it.

A young woman related, "I couldn't wait to get out of my house and away from my parents. I decided that getting pregnant would be one easy way to get out." Those who use sex as a getaway, and to fulfil emotional or spiritual needs, are often the most lonely, disillusioned, distressed and disappointed with sex itself. "With each indulgence the level of physical and emotional expectation gradually rises so that an increasingly greater thrill is required to satisfy the urge. Eventually the thrill begins to diminish, but the hunger for stimulation is ever present, now stronger than before. Without finding full satisfaction, the hunger need settles into the monotony of filling and emptying."[14]

As with taking drugs, in sex the pleasure and thrill can also build up tolerance. With each indulgence the need or expectation becomes greater, and thus the potential for disappointment is likewise greater. It is not that the sex act itself is perhaps less pleasurable; it is that the emotional need is greater. The effect, however, is that the sex act seems not to satisfy.

Sexual dissatisfaction leads in various directions, just as drug tolerance leads to more powerful doses, or to more of the same drug. Some seek heightened pleasure by playing the field; married couples by infidelity, divorce, wife-swapping; or more sexual power through smoking marijuana. More and more, so-called "respectables" are trying to turn on more and better sex with pot. A *Playboy* magazine national campus survey of students' attitudes on today's major issues (*Playboy* magazine, September 1970) revealed the following differences of sexual practices among non-marijuana smokers and marijuana smokers. The survey found that among the non-pot smokers 20 per cent of the males and 62 per cent of the females had never practised premarital sex. However, among the pot smokers, only 6 per cent of the males and 14 per cent of the females had never been involved in premarital sexual activities. The increased sexual activity among pot smokers is significant.

One fellow told us, "I kept having sexual experiences to prove to myself I was a man. But the more I got involved the less pleasure I was getting. So I started needing alcohol or marijuana to loosen me up. The only trouble was, I found if I didn't mix sex with booze or pot, I couldn't get turned on."

Because under the influence of marijuana the smoker is less inhibited, feelings regarding sex become free and open. Marijuana not only expands the mind—it loosens the morals. Some doctors are now prescribing "pot" for sexually incompatible couples. Such a prescription is felt to aid middle-aged or older couples who are "bored" sexually, or when one or the other partner cannot experience total sexual expression due to emotional conflicts. Some single girls and men are now carrying marijuana around to give to dates as a method of accomplishing seduction—just as alcohol and sex is mixed for the same purpose.

The danger of using "pot" as a cure-all for sexual release is that it can become a permanent tool in a couple's sex life. One fellow said, "I got to the place where I feared any sexual contact, even social contact, if I didn't have 'pot'." But the most tragic outcome of those who look for sexual power in marijuana is that they may not be able to control unleashed lusts. Married couples who smoke together can end up in bed with their closest friend's wife or husband. It is now popular for married couples who are already practising swapping partners (swingers) to use pot to assist them in their weird search for sexual fulfilment. However, even where such practices never took place, married couples who previously never for a moment entertained the thought of sharing sex with a friend, sadly end up doing so when stoned with pot.

Marijuana, in our estimation, supposedly helps those couples who have never known spiritual and emotional togetherness. The sex part of their marriage was no different from that of prostitute and client-partner—the only thing they really shared in life together was sex. Such physical relationships soon wear out. Any couple living together body with body, sex symbol with sex symbol, is going to end up sexually bored. For these couples "pot" provides a momentary new sex kick. Most, however, do not know the devil they may unleash in themselves. The eye is never satisfied with seeing—and the sex explorer may not be satisfied until he has experienced all, conquered neighbour's wife, or whoever.

Middle-class people now use "pot" to expand their shrinking sex lives. The users say that marijuana makes them less inhibited, help them find fuller self-expression, helps them to relate easier, and blocks out external distortions. The use of

167

marijuana to heighten sex satisfaction reinforces our argument that premarital and extramarital sex exploits lead only to sexual *dis*satisfaction, not to sexual satisfaction.

5. *Sex as a temptation*. We should not overlook the fact that sex is a natural part of the human make-up. Sexual desire and expression of affection are natural. Because of this and the external forces in society, sex is a temptation even to the dedicated Christian. Sex, like other forces in life, can be good or bad, right or wrong, natural or unnatural. The same act that brings pleasure can bring misery. "Other desires in life may be rather easily deterred or sublimated, but not so with sex. God has given men and women strong attraction towards one another. It is this intense force which, if not directed to honour God, surges like a mighty river, leaving untold problems in its wake."[15]

The beauty of sex has been marred by sin. Because of this we find ourselves in the inescapable position in which the apostle Paul found himself when he said, "The good which I want to do, I fail to do; but what I do is the wrong which is against my will" (Rom. 7: 10, NEB). Sex is a temptation because the flesh wants to go in one direction and the Holy Spirit in another. The flesh is in conflict with the Spirit. Controlled sex can be a blessing; uncontrolled, it can be a fire that destroys. The enemy continually tries to use it against the Christian. He wants to take a thing of beauty and turn it into just a "thing" and to drag it into the gutter and outside the bounds of righteousness and holiness.

Another factor in sex temptation is the people who do the tempting. The tempter (Satan) has a bunch of little tempters helping him with his temptation business. They portray sex as America's favourite pastime. Advertisers seem to have an organized effort to extend and intensify desire. They have succeeded in brainwashing the American male into believing that the truly successful man is the truly sensual man. Even the federal government goes along with the sex stimulation process. A job corps centre bought $10,000 worth of books with such titles as *Orgy at Madam Dracula's* and *Sex Turned On* as part of a reading programme. An official of the centre, now closed, described the books as "soul material".

Counselling About Premarital Sex

Counselling must begin with those in their early teens and with pre-teens, when puberty begins in the female and sexual awareness begins in the male. While sex education courses are being recommended and conducted on the grade school level, this may only further complicate sex questions if personal counselling—either formally or informally—is not instituted as youngsters reach physical maturity. There is a difference between classroom sex education and personal and individual counselling with young people. The latter is a step beyond the textbook approach. It is the come-down-to-the-young-person's-level-and-talk-about-sex approach, for which there is no substitute.

Most of those we have dealt with who have been heavily involved in numerous sexual practices are actually ignorant about sex. One fellow said, "I learned everything I knew about sex on the street corner. Now I know the two-bit street corner sex counsellor knew nothing. If only someone had sat me down and talked to me before I got married, I wouldn't have gone through so many difficulties."

One researcher dealing with prostitutes found that most of them were not fully and rightly informed about sex. Ministers and Christian workers should not assume that a young person who has been converted from a life of promiscuity is properly informed about sex. Most of the young people in Teen Challenge who have experimented sexually from an early age are confused, perverted, or unsure about proper sex information.

The best way to begin is with an honest, open discussion. Neither "beating around the bush" nor oversimplification, nor straight-laced prohibition are adequate approaches to sex counselling for today's young people. Ann Landers, who ought to know when it comes to youth's sex problems, says, "what they need is sound information so they will know how to think about it." Most of us would rather deal with any other problem than sex. But the counsellor can be effective in counteracting some of the unhealthy, mysterious, gutter sources of information about sex. Rather than get his knowledge only from books, sex education courses, magazines, peers, or other adults who volunteer information, the young person needs to get it from a trustworthy resource person. Especially in need of counselling are the teens who haven't yet tried sex but who are on the verge of doing so. They are thinking about it and attention must particularly be given to those who are going steady.

In urgent need of the counsellor's help are those who already decided to become members of the "premarital sexual relations club". Finding out who they are is the hardest task. Only a few counsellors have the ability and the rapport with young people to obtain such information, either by careful probing or through the willing submission of information by the young person himself.

I believe that sex attitudes are formed early in life and that it's important to reach young people at that critical point where they are ready to break away from traditional external authority and are groping for self-discovered standards of their own.

Youngsters talk about sex a lot, but apparently they are ignorant about the general functions of the body. They do not discuss their concern about sex with adults very much, and when they do they are often given inadequate answers. We must also deal with the attitude of the high school girls who, in their bull sessions, instead of discussing how to turn a boy down, often talk instead about the danger of pregnancy and how they would break the news to their parents.

We need ministers and Christian counsellors who will take the time for straight, frank talk about sex and about the role of religion in sex. Some parents I have talked with feel they cannot instruct their children in sexual behaviour because they don't feel capable of explaining it. They hem and haw and make excuses and act as though children have no right to ask about sex. One mother I know told her daughter, "Don't even mention sex to us again. You should respect your mother more than that. Don't embarrass me that way again." This breakdown of communication puts an unfair burden of responsibility on the child.[16]

Following are suggestions about how to counsel young people with sex problems:

1. *Provide a comfortable setting.* The counsellor must ask himself, "Am I the kind of person others would feel comfortable talking with about something so personal and intimate as their sexual hang-ups?" The Christian counsellor who hasn't solved his own sexual hang-ups will not be able to make others feel comfortable when discussing their problems. Young people complain that they just do not know anyone in whom they have enough confidence to approach.

The counsellor should not express shock, disappointment or disgust when the person comes with a confession of sin, or to talk about a problem. A young lady, twenty-eight years of age, came to us—she was pregnant. Her family were faithful members in a suburban evangelical church. Their daughter was actively faithful as well. When she found out she was going to have a baby from an unconverted man she had been dating, she came for help. "I made a mistake, and there was no one to turn to. I cannot tell my parents, they are along in years and would just not be able to understand. This would just shock them too much."

After discussing her case fully we accepted her at Teen Challenge as an office worker. This had been one of the first cases over the years of a Christian girl getting into trouble who has come to us for help and advice. My first reaction was to condemn and to sermonize, but it immediately became apparent that the situation called for compassion not for condemnation. She had already suffered waves of tremendous guilt, nothing more needed to be said to add to it. What she needed was someone to talk to and who would, as she said, "understand".

From our first talk together we did not moralize, condemn, or seek to punish her. Our task was to accept her just as she was and to provide words of comfort for her guilt, not to reinforce it.

Often adults and Christians develop the attitude that sex sin is different from all other sins—and that man is God's instrument to punish one who has fallen. Apparently, David, the psalmist, found a comfortable setting when he went to the Lord after his sex sin, for he wrote in Psalm 32: 5: "I acknowledge my sin unto thee, and my iniquity have I not hid. I said, I will confess my transgressions unto the Lord; and thou forgavest the iniquity of my sin." He wrote as well in the opening verse of the same chapter, "Blessed is he whose transgression is forgiven, whose sin is covered." We might add to this our own translation, "Blesed is he who understands and forgives the one who has transgressed, who doesn't try to uncover the sin God has already covered."

Avoid such reactions as, "Oh, how could you do a thing like that!" or, "Don't you know that's wrong?" or, "God will punish you for this." That will only cause the person to go deeper into a shell of guilt or fear. The first reaction should be one of understanding and compassion, so the individual will open up and pour out the whole story.

A sex problem is often hidden behind other problems. In such cases the sex problem must be uncovered. "A person's problem may not be a sex problem as much as a life problem. . . . He will set up several sessions to look at his school life, his family life, his spiritual life and his social life."[17] By working at some of the surface problems and showing a genuine interest in the counsellee's overall life situation, a relationship can be built upon which the sex problem will either come out naturally, or the counsellor will be able to dig it out.

171

2. *Take a positive approach.* The counsellor should not try to scare young people into chastity or out of promiscuity by painting a picture of sex that is only sinful, ugly or dirty. The young person will have already found out that sex can produce guilt and even be disappointing. Sex should be presented as something you step *up* into, at the right time and in the right way, not something you stumble or fall into.

Young people should be taught that sex surrounded by the sanctity of marriage is something that is wholly good. For example, share the fact that "the physical pleasures a man and woman find in each other amplify and confirm their sense of commitment and joy in each other. Outside of this relationship, sex is a distortion of the divine plan of God. Sex was designed as a means (not an end in itself) of assisting in the development of that most intimate of all human relationships between husband and wife."[18]

"Married lovers come together free of guilt and shame. They have fewer qualms of conscience than those who are haunted by the ghostly reminders of previous affairs. Jealousies born of comparisons with former partners are avoided by a husband and wife who wait for marriage before being active sexually. It is a rare husband who is completely happy in the knowledge that his wife has slept with some other man before she married. Even the most sophisticated lover is proud to marry a virgin whom he alone possesses. The predominant reaction of wives discovering their husbands' premarital experience with previous girls is unfavourable. Sex reserved for marriage starts out with a clean slate upon which the marriage partners write their own love story in their own way from the beginning."[19]

If the sexual generation can be made to see the beauty of sex as God intended it to be, the counsellor and parents do not have to dream up scare tactics. Young people must not fear sex, but rather respect it and wait to "step up" into it.

"Down through the ages, some of the most thunderous don'ts levelled at mankind have to do with sex. This is not surprising, because sex is just about the most powerful and explosive force that is built into us.

"Don't rely too heavily on 'don't'. While there are negative reasons for not doing something, there are often positive reasons for doing the reverse. Seek for them, find your motivation in them, and you will come much closer to your goal."[20]

3. *Exalt the authority of the Scriptures.* In the final analysis, whether young people keep themselves pure sexually will be

determined by their acceptance of Jesus Christ as Saviour from sin and Lord of their lives—including one's sex life. They must accept the Word of God as their final authority and the only authority in matters dealing with sex. He did not invent sex just to tempt people, but to add to their earthly and spiritual enjoyment. When God confined the sex act to the boundary lines of marriage, He gave man the ability to live within these regulations and He warned that violations of His commands in this regard would bring sorrow and misery. He knew what He was doing.

The choice is inescapable, and I am convinced that in this confusing and complicated area of sex conduct self-discipline is the key. Not grim, authoritative, threatening rules from without, but patient, watchful, steady, intelligent responsibility from within."[21]

Young people need to be challenged to make the right choice for themselves, as they come to know and accept God's authority. It cannot be a case of the counsellor's saying, "You must not do it because I said so," but rather a case of the young person's deciding, "I am going to abstain from premarital sex because I feel this is best for me and it is what God wants me to do."

"Make him see that there is one authority that he won't resent—and that authority is himself. If he gives the orders, if he demands the discipline, if he sets the standards high, then he won't resent the controls."[22]

4. *"Tell it like it is" about the backlash of promiscuity.* In addition to asserting the authority of Christ and the Scriptures in matters of sexual relations before marriage, the counsellor must "tell it like it is" and give stern warning of the possible after-effects. "Sex outside marriage is a bad bargain when you measure what you stand to gain against what you stand to lose. It's just not worth it," says Ann Landers.[23] It may be helpful if another young person who has gone through some of the sorrows of an affair, or an unwed mother, can be brought into the discussion.

One of the most serious after-effects, especially for a young person who has had high moral teachings instilled in him, is the feeling of guilt. One college student has theorized that one of the reasons for the unrest among today's campus youth is that they are trying to overcome their feelings of unconscious guilt from their immorality. This is one of the bad bargains that must be weighed against the momentary thrill that sexual intercourse provides. Here is part of a letter we received from a girl:

"For the past three months I have prayed and prayed. I have asked the Lord to forgive me and to take my sin away. I prayed that he would help me. I even went to church in the afternoon alone sometimes and sat there and cried, but sometimes I only felt half forgiven. I knew God was there watching me, but I was afraid He wanted to kick me out of His kingdom forever."

Another after-effect of premarital sex is the feeling of having been exploited. A girl told me, "At first I really thought it was true love; he said sweet nothings to me, but then I discovered he was just using me; I was just a body."

In the letter quoted above, the girl wrote: "The boys are all out to 'get the girls'. They are cool if they do, and the girls have to fight it. The trouble is, the boys plan and scheme every possible way to break a girl down. Some use the rape method, some are more subtle. Some will lie, and make you think they can be trusted, and all along they are just waiting for a weak spot. Some talk their way through. I have been out with all of them and until Billy came long I held up. But girls are weak, too. It is hard sometimes to say no. A person can stand only so much. Boys want to marry 'nice girls' and yet they are all-out to break every 'nice girl' down. It doesn't seem fair."

5. *Forgive the fallen*. The young lady whose letter is quoted above is typical of many who write with similar problems. Whether such letters come because it is easier for the guilt-ridden person to write to someone they do not have to encounter personally, or whether they come because they do not have anyone in the church or the community to turn to for help—we do not know. We fear it is the latter reason that prompts many such letters.

Many are forceful in preaching against petting, promiscuity, and fornication—but few know how to handle the sinners. And so some sin the more.

Whether it is a problem of petting, promiscuity, or premarital or extra-marital sex, the guilt may be the same. Many young ladies have felt like one teenage girl who spoke to me about her petting. "I feel like a slut," she said. It was as though she had committed the full sexual act as far as the guilt that followed. For such guilty persons the counsellor is the bridge from condemnation, shame, guilt and depression, to forgiveness, cleansing and freedom. If the counsellor is the parent of the fallen, or pastor, Sunday school teacher, youth leader, or close friend, the guilty will also feel they have personally offended the counsellor. This presents another problem in counsellor-counsellee relationships.

The counsellor must watch for the fallen client, especially the Christian who has failed, who has a need to do penance. Guilty persons—psychologically, emotionally and spiritually—feel a need to do something for their wrong doings. They want to punish themselves in payment and penalty for their sin. One young convert at Teen Challenge returned from a weekend at home and became sick. "God is punishing me," he told me. He then confessed he had committed fornication. Perhaps he became psychologically ill to punish himself. Rather than accept the chastisement of spirit and soul the guilty want physical or emotional chastisement to pay the penalty for their sin.

The guilty may also feel a need to be punished by the counsellor. They may be saying to themselves, "He (the counsellor) is disgusted with me," "He doesn't want anything to do with me any more," "I won't be accepted any longer." This feeling of self-rejection is projected to the counsellor to satisfy the client's need for punishment. Avoid being caught by such a punishment complex and of being manipulated by the fallen person into a position as a whipping lash against them.

Those who have fallen into sexual sin need patience and pity, not punishment. The counsellor's role is to be an agent to bring healing, not to haunt the client. The most serious crisis the church faces today is the need for leaders who know how to forgive the sensuous and the sexual generation. When the fallen can see forgiveness coming through a human instrument, then perhaps they can find assurance in Christ that "as far as the east is from the west" so far has He removed their sexual sin from God's remembrance. The counsellor's attitude should be, "Neither do I condemn thee."

6. *Other tips.* The counsellor should not forget other problem areas in addition to the sex problem. One factor in sex problems is the person's inability to accept himself as he is. Many of the young men who come to Teen Challenge as drug addicts have hang-ups about their physical make-up; they are too short, too fat, too skinny, too ugly, or whatever. They have an identity crisis. This often affects their sense of manhood and sexuality. This dissatisfaction with self leads them to emulate others, or to seek acceptance with their bodies. A person who sees himself in the "image of God" and as the "temple of the Holy Spirit" will not put a cheap price tag on himself and will think twice about giving his or her body to anyone, without regard for God's will.

Other helpful suggestions have to do with keeping the right company, having a large circle of wholesome friends, and avoiding the dangers of going steady. Those who do go steady can avoid temptation if they double and triple date. Going steady in isolation puts the couple in a position of sexual temptation; it also stunts the development of a well-rounded outlook on life. Young people who develop a wide circle and variety of friends are better prepared for life later on, have a greater opportunity to find the right partner, and most of all, will find themselves less frequently in compromising, tempting situations in regard to sexual matters.

Young people must also be instructed to avoid petting and borderline promiscuity. Warnings of the dangers of "arousements" should be made firm and clear. Too many play the "see how far we can go" game and do everything but commit the final climactic sex act. Jesus said those who practised mental or "thought" adultery are guilty of the actual deed. No one ever wins in such a game of promiscuity. Those who spend too much time alone, who keep the wrong company, who expose themselves to risque movies, and who go to sensuous parties or gatherings, or who read novels, magazines, or literature that is sexually stimulating—are moving out of the sexual safety zone and into the "passion pit". Norman Vincent Peale's advice to young people should be offered by all Christian counsellors. He advises, "Make a commitment. This is the key, I think, to sanity in sex. You have to use your intelligence to discern the values of self-restraint."

Unwed Mothers

Let us look at the why, what and how of the problem of counselling those involved in the unfortunate tragedy of pregnancy and out-of-wedlock childbirth. Why does it happen? What courses of action can be taken by the mother-to-be, the young man involved, and the families and friends? What should be done before and after the child arrives? Should the baby be kept? What should be said, what not said? What should be done, and not done?

Why do girls get into trouble? Pregnancy may be the result of rebellion. It may be a way to get even with parents for wrongs inflicted, or a way to get attention.

Pregnancy often occurs just because a couple fell into temptation and made a sorry mistake. Young people are open to temptation, they play with fire, and have no one but themselves to blame for the outcome. In spite of the pill, this still happens. There are those who had never previously indulged in sex relations, but who suddenly found themselves in a compromising situation. In the heat of passion they let the barriers down and pregnancy resulted. Pregnancy often happens in cases like this because no spiritual or moral precautions were taken. The couple did not plan or intend to have sexual intercourse.

Young people who determine, through the help and strength of the Lord, not to engage in premarital sex have the best and only protection. Those who say, "I couldn't help it", or "It just happened", or, "I made a sad mistake" could have avoided trouble if they had made spiritual and practical disciplinary preparations. The fires of passion must be fought with fire— the fire of God's power. This letter shows what can happen when a young person is indifferent about the fires of sexual passion:

"I am known as a well-respected girl by my friends and family. I held a secretarial job after graduating from high school, and I attended junior college for two quarters. A good friend got me a date with a boy whom I knew about but had never actually met. ... I dated him about one month and he told me he cared for me. He had a good personality and tried to be a little too cool sometimes about wine, women and song—and he was part of the crowd. We went to the show one night and afterwards he told me we were going to his home. Well, I didn't like that. It didn't look right and I was afraid—of me and him. We argued but he got his way. ... I went inside but I wouldn't go near the bedrooms. I stayed in the den. Then things began to happen. It kept getting worse and worse until sin took over completely."

She could have avoided trouble, but her moral restraint was very weak; she put up only a shallow fight. There were no spiritual forces behind her to help in the fight.

In cases when, in spite of sincerity and Christian commitment, the young person fails, the road back is long and difficult. But the trip must be made. The fact that restoration is possible is seen in the life of David in the Old Testament and in the example of Mary Magdalene who many feel was the woman Jesus forgave for adultery and while her accusers sought to kill her wrote "love letters in the sand".

The difficulty in the case of the Christian girl who becomes pregnant—and cannot leave home—is that the evidence of her sin is paraded before herself and others for about six months. And if she keeps the child, for years later. The key is a counsellor who will serve as a close friend to the girl during pregnancy and following the birth of the child.

We have seen too many in our street ministry who were

177

condemned and cast out of the church by unforgiving and *unforgetting* church members who never let the unwed girl, or the young man involved "live it down"—or should we say live it back up to a place of regular fellowship in the body of Christ. Even family members and relatives have been victims in such cases of Christian condemnation.

We must advise young people as forcefully as we possibly can to avoid sexual sin—but when it happens nothing is gained by a "Why did you do that", or "You shouldn't have done that", or "Get yourself out of this mess" attitude. We must honestly, practically, calmly, hopefully, positively face such situations. There is no way in ignoring the persons involved that the problem will go away or turn a wrong back to a right. The counsellor's duty is to turn evil into good.

When a girl does get into trouble, what can she do? She has several choices: marriage, keep the baby without getting married, or terminate the pregnancy. These are not very good choices. Each one has its own built-in set of problems. If the unwed mother decides not to keep the child, one of three things is likely to happen: She can put the child up for adoption, get an abortion, or abandon the child.

Some girls try to terminate the pregnancy themselves. Some go to a state that has legalized abortion, if they can find a doctor who will peform the operation and if they have enough money. Some wealthy girls go to England or Mexico. There are underground "abortion rings" which pregnant girls can patronize, at the great risk of life or arrest. But terminating one's pregnancy is a drastic solution. A girl may have no ill effects physically, but she may suffer serious psychological after-effects: guilt, shame, nervousness, worry, depression, fear of exposure, etc.

If the girl, and especially her parents, will face the situation forthrightly, without becoming hysterical, and consider all sides of the problem, they may decide that putting the child up for adoption is the best course—for her, the family, and the baby. In this manner everyone can be assured that the child will grow up with a family ready, willing, and able to give him a good home. There are of course unavoidable psychological after-effects of this step, but it is the most practical and just action for the child.

1. *The pressure marriage*. A girl wrote to us, "Please pray that the fellow who made me pregnant will marry me." This "shotgun" approach is perhaps the worst solution. The girl, boy, or parents, who decide on this course of action are think-

178

ing only of themselves, of saving face for their family. The young people are rushed into a responsibility that neither wants or is prepared for. Many pressure marriages end up in divorce. The couple feels trapped. As soon as the child comes along, the father may leave.

2. *The diplomatic marriage*. The couple, again perhaps under the influence and pressure of parents, agrees that perhaps the best thing to do under the circumstances is to get married. Even though marriage had not been planned or intended, they feel this is the best way out. Such a marriage is built on a weak foundation; it is likely to crumble. Just as an older married couple might stay together only "for the sake of the children", a young couple might marry for the same reason, but that is not a strong enough bond to make the marriage last "till death do us part".

3. *The "let my mother raise the baby" solution*. Some young men who have come into our Teen Challenge programme as addicts have come from homes where they were raised by their grandmothers, who played the role of stand-in mothers. Sometimes this works, but often it causes serious problems. If there are other children in the family, they may resent the baby.

4. *The "do it yourself" solution*. The unwed mother may decide to keep the child and raise him herself. She may live with her family, go on welfare, or get a job and hire someone to take care of the baby while she works. This rarely provides an adequate answer for either mother or child.

Our experience at Teen Challenge convinces us that adoption is the best direction to take. The counsellor should never be a party to abortion, nor should he recommend a forced marriage. He should strive to help the girl face the problem head-on; bring all persons involved into the counselling; consult professional agencies; and help those involved return to normality as soon as possible.

Counselling the Prostitute

"Where's the red light district?" a friend asked me while I was showing him New York City. His question was based on the assumption that there was a place where young women paraded their wares. He came from a country where such districts exist and where many such lights shine brightly. However, in most U.S. cities the "red light" district has given way to the "white light" district. That is, prostitution is no longer confined to certain areas, nor is it conducted in certain rooming houses or apartments in one special section of the city. Most prostitution

179

is carried on under the white lights of any city street. It is carried on under the white lights of motels and bachelor apartments. The absence of a red light district does not mean there is less prostitution; in fact, the opposite seems to be the case. Prostitution has become more integrated into the whole of society—so integrated that it is often difficult to distinguish prostitution as a trade or business.

It might be well to point out here that the definition of a prostitute is "common and venal lewdness among a class of women" who are "devoted to base or unworthy purposes". The popular and more familiar image of the prostitute is the street-walking harlot, or the high class prostitute, both of whom make a profession of it. I would like to expand this to include the unofficial hidden prostitute whose actions may not be lewd on a day-to-day hiring basis but nevertheless is "base" even if it is not as frequent.

Prostitution has existed since antiquity. The story of Rahab (Josh. 2: 1) is one of the first records of prostitution in Bible days—and interestingly enough, the first record of the conversion of a prostitute. Overall, the term "harlot" is mentioned forty-four times in the Bible and the word "whore" fifty-three times.

Many prostitutes claim to have chosen their profession purely for economical reasons. While this is true especially for the addict prostitute, it may not necessarily be the primary motivation behind the non-addict prostitute becoming involved in such a life.

Prostitution is a very easy way—from a labour standpoint—to make a lot of money, but there are always emotional and spiritual factors that set the stage for a young girl to entertain the thought of such money-making. But when the prostitute does have an opportunity to live well and securely without prostituting herself, she will usually turn it down. One high-class prostitute told me proudly, "I had all kinds of men ask me to marry them. Some were very rich."

"Why didn't you accept their offer?" I asked her.

"I just didn't want to," was her answer. The truth was that she was "hooked" on her way of life and probably would have still been in it if she were only getting half or less the amount of money for selling her wares. Therefore, it seems that more is involved than an immediate economic problem.

There is no special method of counselling prostitutes. The same guidelines mentioned in previous chapters should be followed in counselling the prostitute. The prostitute is no worse than the homosexual, the rebel, or the addict. The woman of "ill repute" needs the same compassion, understanding and faith for deliverance as anyone else does.

Where the Tricks Are No Treats

Rose had been standing on Winchester Boulevard for almost two hours and business was dead. Sal came by several times to see if she had "turned" one. His concern was only to sell a bag of heroin. Rose was a prostitute who needed a fix, but she also needed to sell herself to get enough money for her pain killer. Usually the cars would be lined up four or five deep along the street with customers ready, willing, and able to pay for their desired pleasure. But tonight was slow. Patrol cars were heavy in the area.

Rose knew if she waited long enough something would turn up. She was used to the waiting game. The worst was when she was sick and business was poor. Then she would have to settle for some weirdo—and maybe have to perform some perverted form of the sex act to earn her money. She began to wonder if maybe this was going to be one of those nights.

About ten-thirty Freddie, one of the neighbourhood winos, came by. "Come on, Rosie," Freddie propositioned her.

"Get out of here, Freddie. Go find Marie, she likes your kind," Rose responded.

"Please, Rose. I like you," Freddie continued.

Rose knew she couldn't get rid of him so she walked on down the street. She spotted Elaine across the street, she had just turned her trick and was on her way to an apartment two blocks away to finish the deal. Rose wished it were her—and the anxiety mounted. Back in front of the Sunshine Cleaners she stood back at her post, eyeing each passer-by. Her eyes met the eyes of each man as he passed wondering if the next would be a client. It had been about four hours since her last shot of heroin and the effects had almost completely worn off. She still felt a little warm—and "straight", as addicts term the act of getting high—but by eleven or eleven-thirty she would really need an injection.

She spotted Sal. "Sal, Sal," she yelled running after him. "How about some credit please? I'm sick, I'm real sick," she begged and lied about being sick, thinking about the hour deadline she had to meet.

"Your credit's no good, Rose. You already owe me for six bags. I want cash," Sal said as he walked on.

Once again she walked back to the doorway of the cleaners.

181

She thought about Henry, her partner, who was in jail. If only he were around she would be taken care of. Rose and Henry were co-owners of her body. She sold her body and Henry hustled around for the dope. He also pulled robbery jobs so he always had extra money and bags of dope. Usually when there were no tricks to turn she didn't have to worry. But Henry was doing nine months on a drug possession charge so things were tough for Rose.

A man in his early fifties finally approached Rose at about eleven-forty-five. "I've got ten dollars, honey. What have you got?" he asked.

"What I've got is worth more than a measly ten bucks," Rose snapped back at him faking her disinterest to see if she could get enough for two fixes. .

"Look, it's late," the little fat man said. He was no newcomer to this kind of badgering. "Do you want ten dollars or don't you?"

"Don't," Rose said firmly trying to call his bluff. The little man started to walk away and she was just about to call him back when he turned around and said, "I'll make it twelve dollars and no more."

Slowly she walked towards him and gestured with her eyes and head that she would accept the offer and together they walked to the basement of an apartment dwelling. In five minutes her duties would be over—the twelve dollars would be in her hand—and then she would be off to find Sal and fifteen minutes after that a needle would be in her arm. In her moments of bliss she would forget the fact that tricks are no treat—but tricks do finance her "highs" and that is the only treat in life she has ever known.

Types of Prostitutes

1. *"White slavery" prostitution*. Sally, a young girl in our Teen Challenge home for girls, got into a form of white slavery prostitution through her involvement with a motorcycle gang. To pass her initiation she had to prove that she could ride a bike and jump sixty feet in the air and land upright. What she did not know was that she also had to prove herself to the leader of the gang by committing sexual acts with him. She soon learned that the primary purpose of the gang was not to ride motor-cycles, but to indulge in all kinds of sexual perversion. By becoming a member of the gang she became a sex slave to all of the male and female members of the gang.

The old form of white slavery, in which girls are recruited

182

and captured to sell their bodies, is no longer widespread, but the above does describe another form of a partial and voluntary type of white slavery. Male drug addicts often manage to turn their wives or girl friends to prostitution to help them make money to support their habit. This too is a form of white slavery.

2. *The street-walker prostitute.* She is the teenage girl or young adult who has run away from home, or who has gone to the big city hoping to be a career girl. It is difficult to get the job she wants and she finds life hard in the city. But there is always a young man, or a middle-aged man, who will help her out. He may rent a room or invite her to live with him. Of course, in return, she feels obligated to satisfy his sexual needs. If she is not careful, and if she finds herself financially and emotionally desperate, she may start a habit. She may meet another girl, who tells her how she can make some real money, and thus she is introduced to full-time prostitution.

3. *The drug addict prostitute.* With her, prostitution is a secondary problem. Her first problem is drugs; prostitution has come about as a result of the addiction. The easiest way for the female drug addict to get money to support her habit is by selling her body. Few female drug addicts were first prostitutes and then drug addicts. Almost all of them do their business by walking the streets. Often the drug addict prostitute not only supports her own habit but also that of a male drug addict partner. She makes the money and he does the "scoring" (purchasing the dope from the pusher). Some of these relationships are like small businesses. Each works for the other to obtain dope. In some cases they marry, in most cases not.

4. *The office prostitute.* If you were to ask the single men in an office if there are any prostitutes among the secretaries, they would probably say no. But a closer look reveals a form of unofficial, sophisticated prostitution. If you were to ask the same men which of the secretaries are promiscuous, they might tell you. This means you would have located what I call the office prostitute. This is the young woman who dates the young bachelor. They go to a movie, to dinner, then to his apartment for dancing, alcohol—and sex. No money is passed into her hands, but she is paid off for her services. The young man may have spent fifty dollars on her during the evening. At Christmas or other occasions she may be showered with gifts. All the attention he pays to her, all the generosities extended to her, are intended for one purpose—sex. The young woman is always available. A prostitute? Certainly she would never consider her-

self such. Neither would her male partner. She dresses nicely, comes from a good family, is socially concerned—and no one would compare her with the prostitute who walks the streets. But there are many similarities.

The above situation represents the most widespread kind of habit of selling one's body. It is not prostitution as most people think of prostitution. But it does exist in almost any office in any of our cities. Another name for the office or "white light" prostitute is a "party girl". Again she does not ask for a set fee—this is a matter simply understood with her date. The party girl will also refuse occasionally to keep her status, in her own eyes, of being a non-prostitute. This form of "white light" prostitution makes it unnecessary for there to be a "red light" district. The men who need to buy their sex don't have to drive downtown to some dark street. All they have to do is walk across the office floor. They don't have to go through the degrading process of handing over twenty-five, fifty or a hundred dollars in hard cash for "services rendered". All they have to do is show a girl a good time and dish out the money in other forms, and they have accomplished the same thing.

5. *The "credit card" prostitute.* She is sometimes referred to as a "call girl". From a social or economic standpoint she is the high-class prostitute. She makes most of her arrangements with customers over the telephone. She has contacts through business associations. She usually does business with the executives. In some cases they are able to pay the prostitute with their credit cards. There are even call girl prostitutes who have printed business cards referring to their work under the heading of public relations. The call girls are the money-makers. Some call girls have been known to make up to fifty thousand or seventy-five thousand dollars a year. But such girls have big overhead expenses: expensive clothes, a good apartment, and money for such occupational hazards as abortions, court fees, doctor's bills, and even answering devices. If she drives a car, she must maintain her image—and Lincolns and Cadillacs are her style.

How and Why Does a Girl Become a Prostitute?

Why the female drug addict turns to prostitution to support her habit is understandable. One habit becomes necessary to support the other. But why a teenage girl, or a young working woman, becomes a prostitute is hard to understand. Even harder to comprehend is the housewife who "moonlights", that is, prostitutes to make extra cash for the home. In some cases the husband may know of and even condone her practice.

184

When this is the case, then of course both of them are sick spiritually and emotionally.

The teenager who gets involved in prostitution often starts on the road through promiscuous sexual activity. This is a way of rebelling against parents who don't pay any attention to her, or who are over-strict. She is promiscuous to fill the emptiness within her. Such rebellion through sex is never intended to lead to prostitution. Usually that happens unexpectedly. Slowly the habit creeps up on her and she finds herself hooked.

Eventually, every prostitute is in it because she wants to be. Many find it glamorous, exciting, and strangely gratifying. Dr. David Reuben, M.D., in his book, *Everything You Always Wanted to Know About Sex*, quotes a prostitute:

"I know some people think it's terrible to be in the racket, but they don't understand what it's really like. Always knowing that men are running after you, knowing that they leave their own wives just to make it with you, controlling them just with your sex—there's nothing else that can make a girl feel so powerful."

Dr. Reuben goes on to say, "All prostitutes have at least one thing in common—they hate men. Why is that? The full answer is a complicated one related to the deep underlying emotional problems that drove them into the game. Basically, prostitution is an ironic form of revenge against all men."[24]

More light is thrown on the prostitutes' emotional and psychological make-up by Dr. Harold Greenwald in his book entitled *The Elegant Prostitute*. He found among a group of twenty call girl prostitutes, some who took therapy from him, and others whom he interviewed, that not one of them had come from a family where there was a well-adjusted marital relationship between the parents. He stated:

Not one of these girls reported growing up in a happy home where her parents got along well together.

The attitude of the parents towards the children seemed to be one of complete rejection. . . . The open rejection caused them to feel unwanted and unloved and unworthy of being wanted or loved.

They discovered at an early age that they could get some measure of affection, of interest, by giving sexual gratification. . . . In giving this sexual gratification they were rewarded by overcoming, no matter how temporarily, their feelings of loneliness and unworthiness, and at the same time expressed hostility towards the parents.[25]

1. *Don't probe into her prostitution habits.* In one of our Teen Challenge centres a prostitute went to the director about an evangelist who was holding services at the centre. She requested, "Please keep that evangelist away from me." The director wanted to know why. She said, "When he counsels me he has an unhealthy curiosity about my past. He has a sensual spirit; I can spot his kind." The prostitute can pick out those who are interested only in her body and in her habits.

As in dealing with the alcoholic, the addict, the homosexual, and other habit-bound persons, the counsellor must find out if she is thirsting for "living water". This is the kind of probe that Christ made with the woman of Samaria, a type of prostitute. The question in dealing with a prostitute is, does she want to be clean?

2. *Give the prostitute a father image.* Because most prostitutes either hate men or have a bitter attitude towards them, they need someone—after conversion—to relate to them who is strong yet tender and understanding. They do not necessarily need a male counsellor, but they do need either to live with or be associated with a family or group in which the love of Christ is manifested through a father, a husband, or other men. They may find it difficult to relate to men. Dr. Greenwald says "Because they had such a poor sense of self, it is very difficult for them to achieve any kind of satisfactory relationships with other people. The individuals with whom they tended to establish relations were apt to be equally unstable. In addition, since these girls feared and mistrusted other people, they were shy and awkward in any relationship except a commercial one."[26] They will be reluctant at first to become socially involved or even to date. But in time it is possible for them to fall in love, to marry, and to have a happy and normal marital and sexual relationship.

3. *Help the converted prostitute through her times of discouragement.* Like anyone else who has had a severe emotional problem, prostitutes are subject to great periods of loneliness. This may come in the form of guilt and a feeling that she is not a person of worth. The memory of her life as a prostitute may come back to haunt her and sink her into the depths of depression. The counsellor must understand that this is to be expected, and help her to come out of it. Such discouragements seem to be necessary to prepare her for a Christian walk. In fact, discouragements can serve as a strengthening process.

The prostitute must learn to forgive. She must forgive those whom she may have blamed for leading her into such a life. Be it parents, a bad marriage, or whatever, she must come to the point of saying, "I forgive you." She may not have to say this in the presence of the person or persons involved. In fact, to mention it to these people may do more harm than good. But she does need to forgive them in the presence of God and the counsellor. She also needs to forgive herself. Can she forgive herself for not fulfilling her role as a daughter, a mother, or a wife? Can she forgive herself for not fulfilling her role as a woman? The counsellor should confront her with such questions, especially during her times of depression. Such forgiveness is essential to her recovery from her life of prostitution and for her growth as a Christian.

4. *Counsel her about dress and mannerisms.* Sometimes the ex-prostitute can make it hard for herself, in terms of recovery, by dressing or using her body in such a way that she attracts attention to herself. Because she has gained attention in the past by selling her body, she may unconsciously continue to seek attention by revealing her body or by sensual body movements. In seeking this attention she may fall into a trap. Through Christian teaching and by her relationship to Jesus Christ she will develop inward beauty. She will learn to be accepted on the basis of her inner qualities, not on the basis of what men see on the outside. When she learns this, she will realize that she does not need the other means of getting attention.

NOTES

[1] Vance Packard, *The Sexual Wilderness* (London, Longmans, 1968).
[2] ibid.
[3] William S. Banowsky, *It's a Playboy World.* Copyright © 1969 by Fleming H. Revell Company, Old Tappan, N.J.
[4] *The Sexual Revolution* (HMH Publishing House, Chicago, 1970).
[5] Norman Vincent Peale, *Sin, Sex and Self-Control* (London, World's Work).
[6] Evelyn Millis Duvall, *Why Wait Till Marriage* (London, Hodder and Stoughton, 1965).
[7] William Banowsky, op. cit.
[8] Norman Vincent Peale, op. cit.
[9] Ann Landers, *Ann Landers Talks to Teen-Agers About Sex* (New York, Fawcett World Library, 1963).

[10] William Banowsky, op. cit.

[11] Norman Vincent Peale, op. cit.

[12] ibid.

[13] Ann Landers, op. cit.

[14] William Banowsky, op. cit.

[15] Clyde M. Narramore, *Psychology of Counselling* (Grand Rapids, Zondervan, 1960).

[16] David Wilkerson, *I've Given Up On Parents* (New York, Hawthorne, 1967).

[17] Clyde Narramore, op. cit.

[18] Larry Richards, *How Far Can I Go* (Chicago, Moody Press, 1969).

[19] Evelyn Millis Duvall, op. cit.

[20] Norman Vincent Peale, op. cit.

[21] ibid.

[22] ibid.

[23] Ann Landers, op. cit.

[24] David Reuben, M.D., *Everything You Always Wanted to Know About Sex* (David McKay, New York, 1969).

[25] Harold Greenwald, *The Elegant Prostitute* (New York, Ballantine Books, 1958, 1970).

[26] ibid.

10

THE TRAPPED GENERATION

"Hey, George, are you coming with us Saturday? We're goin' ta downtown Brooklyn," a fourteen-year-old from the Coney Island section of Brooklyn asked. As they talked about their upcoming venture, it came as a surprise—and a shock—to me that this would be their first trip to downtown Brooklyn, a trip of about ten miles.

Where Trouble Is a Fifteen-Year-Old Boy

"Usually it was the little things that triggered big things. I mean, another rival gang member would make fun of one of our gang members' debs or dolls (gang girl friend) and we would build it up as a big thing and use it as an excuse to fight." Sundown, the vice president of the Roman Lords, was speaking. We were standing on Chester Street, one block away from Stone Avenue, the dividing line between the Roman Lords gang and the Egyptian Kings. The two represented two of Brooklyn's most notorious gangs. Across Stone Avenue a huge mound of dirt created an artificial turf battleground where the Roman Lords and Egyptian Kings rumbled (gang fighting).

"Sometimes one of their dudes shoots a zip gun from off that hill down on our street," Sundown complained. "This can start an all-out war. I don't like it when they do that."

"You never do the same?" I asked. Smiling, Sundown said, "Well, yeah man. I guess we do."

"What else starts a rumble?" I asked.

"Well, we go around I guess you could say—we look for trouble. If things are dull we make up a situation and build it up as a reason for getting at them. For instance, one of our members will come to us all excited saying the Egyptian Kings are going to grab one of our fellows and stick a knife in him. Or he'll say, 'They're out to get blood.' But it will just be somebody making up a story—just to get something going. Then we'll start getting prepared to rumble. Their president will hear about it and get his gang ready to fight back. Only he'll be thinking we're starting it—and we're thinking he's starting it. But it really doesn't matter who starts it; the important thing is who finishes it—alive."

"What weapons do you use?" I asked.

'Zips (a home-made pistol), blades, pipes, home-made brass knuckles, clubs, and sometimes a sawn off shotgun." Sundown ran down the list.

*   *   *

The above interview took place seven years ago. It could not happen today. The sun has gone down on Sundown. He no longer carries a knife. Now it's a needle. He, like thousands of other gang members—such as the ones we came to New York City to reach in 1959—are no longer in existence. Why? A white horse came riding into the teen gang turf and rode off with its members. In other words, "horse", better known as heroin and the addiction that resulted broke up New York City's teenage gangs which was the reason the Teen Challenge ministry began in the first place. While other cities do have some gang activity, for the most part drugs is the thing in the inner city. Rumbles have given way to robbing for a fix.

But there is still fighting, shooting, and other problems that once characterized the typical gang rivalries. Only now it is not organized. The gang presidents, vice presidents, war lords, sergeant-of-arms, and the whole gang organization is gone. Today the style is small groups and cliques of fellows—or every man out to defend himself.

When I went to New York City to take part in the ministry of Teen Challenge, I was told there were young people in the ghettos who had never been out of the slums until they were teenagers. I couldn't believe it, but now I was hearing it for myself. These teenagers are victims of the inner city, which is a nice way of saying ghetto or slum. They are, along with so many others, part of the trapped generation.

It is estimated that in the next ten years, because of population shifts, 75 per cent of all Americans will be living in urban or suburban communities. Millions will be "walled in" and trapped by a ghetto, without the common blessings of green grass and fresh air. In addition, there will be overcrowded streets, limited school and recreational facilities, and worse, deplorable housing, plus such problems as drug addiction, crime, poverty, unemployment and juvenile delinquency.

This generation of trapped children, teenagers, and young

adults stands as a challenge to the church, as well as to all America.

One of our Teen Challenge workers describes the ghetto as "the electric atmosphere of Coney Island mixed with the suspicion of the jungle". But no description does justice to the ghetto, nor does any description adequately portray the injustice of it all. The ghetto produces some of the most terrible blights in American society. The ghetto spawns notorious gangs, militants and revolutionaries. Worst of all, the ghetto gives birth to drug addicts, alcoholics, prostitutes, and petty as well as professional criminals. That's no surprise when you consider that in New York City alone 800,000 people live in buildings that the state legislature declared unfit for human habitation—in 1901! Bad housing is one of the chief causes of the discontent, embitterment, and low morale among low income families. The average rent a ghetto dweller pays is about $60.00 a month. However, *The New York Times* reported, on January 28, 1969, the case of a woman who was paying $106.00 a month for an apartment—the walls had been torn down and only three-foot high barriers separated her four "rooms". "The bathtub has been stopped up for weeks," she complained, "and the refrigerator doesn't work."

Simple problems become so complex. Living in the ghetto we found that in order to get anything done, you can't be too nice. We here at Teen Challenge had to threaten to hold back the rent money many times before we got action. It took almost three months to get an apartment cleared.

In the bleak existence of ghetto life babies become the sole purpose for living. They are the only dependable source of happiness. A ghetto mother must have a cuddly, understanding infant to accept her devotion. As babies grow up, however, they bring problems, so the mother must have another baby. In the book, *Born Old*, the condition of slum children is described this way: "Neglected, filthy and miserable, they are shut and locked in lonely tenement rooms; they are cast out to roam the city streets, early learning the ways of crime and violence—these are the little people. Born without warmth or love, subject to the lusts that govern those who give them birth—the muggers, prostitutes, alcoholics, addicts, and pushers—these little ones face a world they hate from their beginning. Robbed of their childhood, of love and care and attention, they exist just as their procreators exist—and the vicious circle grows wider."[1]

I have been writing about people who are hooked, who are

addicted to drugs, alcohol and sex, or to hatred and rebellion. This chapter is about those who are hooked or "addicted" to a geographical location. Almost like a drug, the ghetto way of life is drilled into their minds from childhood. Again, like heroin addicts, they find it difficult to kick this "drug" for which they are not responsible.

In his book, *Riots in the Street*, Richard Wolff states: "Often the Negro is trapped in a vicious cycle from which he cannot extricate himself. Little in his environment is likely to give a Negro child a sense of aspiration and direction. There is no male model to imitate, and slight reason to assume that education offers a way out of the slums. A lack of education and aspiration makes it virtually impossible to find a job with dignity and status, even where discrimination sets in, and the conviction that it is pointless to try, resulting in a diminishing capacity to take advantage of opportunities as they do arise. In the technical language of the sociologist, such a person develops a self-defeating mode of living, which keeps him trapped in the slum condition."[2]

What can the Christian worker do to help reach the trapped generation?

A black minister and several other men from his committee sat in my office. They represented a newly-formed group in one of New York City's ghettos that had been organized to try to help drug addicts in their community. They had come to discuss the possibility of Teen Challenge's conducting on-the-street rallies for addicts in their area. The purpose was to introduce the work of Teen Challenge, and to tell addicts and their families how they could enter our rehabilitation programme. As I offered suggestions about the kind of help we could give, I sensed that they were suspicious of my motives; they frankly discouraged the project. I could not figure out why. They wanted to help addicts. They had asked me how we could help them. After a while it dawned on me why they were refusing to go along. They did not want Teen Challenge, and, more particularly, white people coming into their neighbourhood to carry on a project *for* them. They really wanted us to come in and work *with* them.

In the past white churches have gone to the black communities with the attitude of doing something for "these unfortunate people". But black communities will not accept this attitude any longer—and it is to their credit that they won't. The various minority groups in the ghettos are no longer willing to sit by and let others do things for them—even against

192

them—whether they be acts of charity or whatever. They want community control. The blacks I was talking with were trying to tell me, "Don't come without first co-ordinating your efforts through us and with us."

In previous years it did not occur to us to approach individuals in a black or ghetto community for the purpose of mutual co-operation. But now any work undertaken by the church, a Christian organization, or even by an individual Christian counsellor must be done on the basis of community control and co-operation. The result of our not having done this in the past is that the blacks feel that they have been exploited by whites and by the churches. Now, when white Christians want to go into black communities, often they are told to stay out, or they find it hard to be accepted and taken seriously.

"The role of the white Christian will not be heroic, glamorous, or directive," Richard Wolff explains in *Riots in the Streets*. "The day of the missionary is not over—the day of mission control is. The same holds true in the Negro (ghetto) community. White Christians can have an effective ministry if they go to serve humbly and with love, as Jesus did."[3]

The counsellor must never give the appearance that he is better than those he is working with, or that he is doing them a favour by coming "down" into their environment. If the Christian worker gets the reputation for being a "white knight in shining Christian armour", he will soon be shot down—verbally. He must never show the attitude, "I'm doing you a favour by being here." Such an attitude means the counsellor is not accepting the ghetto residents on equal terms with himself, not accepting them as persons of worth, as being on the same level with those of his own race, colour, or economic status. He must avoid distinguishing ghetto dwellers as "them" and white, middle-class Christian workers as "us".

How then can Christians have an effective ministry in the ghetto?

1. *Gain community confidence*. The first step in going into the ghetto, either to establish a community-based ministry, or to go periodically to present a gospel witness, is to gain community confidence. Motives will be scrutinized carefully. Residents will watch to see if the Christian worker is a fly-by-night "do gooder" who is coming in to help himself, or if he is coming in sincerely and genuinely to help the community. Christians cannot go into the ghetto simply to ease their consciences from racial guilt by getting on some "do-gooder" bandwagon. The ghetto community will no longer stand for this.

An example of this took place when a group of suburbanites went into a ghetto street in New York City's Spanish Harlem to clean up the garbage, to paint and fix up the neighbourhood with a one-day project. When the afternoon was over, they returned to their nice neighbourhoods, feeling that they had made their commitment to the unfortunate people of the ghetto. Most of the people there, however, felt this was a "whitewash". While the suburbanites thought they could change the neighbourhood with soap, water and paint and help alleviate the problems of the ghetto, the people of the ghetto community felt that they were doing this to ease their own consciences. They would have preferred some kind of long-term commitment to get rid of some of the root causes of ghetto problems.

The white person will be watched to see if he has come to "whitewash", to work out some middle-class white hang-up, to exploit, or if he has come to get involved in the total needs of the community. The counsellor will have to prove himself. This may take weeks, months, or years. The people will ask, "Do you really want to help us? Do you really want to understand us? Have you come with your preconceived theories? Do you really care?" Only time and the counsellor's nitty-gritty involvement will prove the genuineness of his commitment.

Teen Challenge CURE Corps workers in one of the worst areas in New York City, Fox Street in the Bronx, have gained over many months this necessary community confidence. The fact that the programme has continued in the ghetto for more than two years in itself says something to the community about our commitment and motivation. The federal government's domestic Peace Corps organization, VISTA, had tried to start a programme on the very same street, but their workers were run off the block just before we arrived. Many white-sponsored, church-sponsored programmes come and go. Because they do not get quick results, and because the people are not willing to make a long-term commitment, these programmes fold. This breaks down the confidence of ghetto residents in church-sponsored programmes. Our CURE Corps workers lived for a time on the block where they were working. They experienced the same frustrations and tensions the other people there do. Now some of the men on the block tell our girls, "You let us know if anyone mistreats you." Some blacks have protected them and stood up for them against other blacks. They can walk the streets at all hours of the day and night; they are accepted as a

194

part of the community. Their motivation has been tested and proved, so they are able to relate to the members of the district. One black woman on the block commented, "You must really mean business about God. You live here with us and you really don't have to."

2. *Be open to change.* To become a worker in the ghetto, one must be open to change. Nice programmes, which sound successful on paper, and which may have worked in other areas, often do not work in the ghetto. Those who stick stubbornly to their preconceived ideas and programmes often fail. One must remain flexible, ready to adopt new ideas and to make changes as a result of better understanding of the culture, the thinking, the attitudes, and the life-style of ghetto people.

One example of being open to change has to do with time consciousness. Those who are used to the simple middle-class habit of starting things on time soon learn that in the ghetto almost all functions start at least thirty minutes late. We have a little joke around Teen Challenge about American time and Puerto Rican time. The latter represents a difference of thirty minutes.

In the ghetto the counsellor deals with people who operate essentially by feelings rather than by organization. They get up when they feel like it, eat when they feel like it, sleep when they feel like it. Their lack of organization is evident and real. One of our workers explained, "We had to adjust by not getting uptight because of some of their customs. In counselling, we find that much is done on an 'accidental' basis. We just happen to see them, or run into them on the street. We have tried many times to set up appointments, and many times our clients did not show. It takes time to orient them to schedules and to the seriousness of keeping their word."

A counsellor must be ready to learn, to change his concepts, and to allow the people of the ghetto to teach him. It takes time to get white thoughts and suburban ideals washed out of the counsellor's mind. A good example of this is what happened when we took a visiting pastor and his church's young people to one of the ghetto neighbourhoods where we have a ministry. We were setting up sound equipment for an open air street rally. The pastor saw a little black boy, patted him on the head, and said, "How are you, little Sambo?" Immediately the little fellow looked up and said, "What did you call me? I'm no Sambo." Unfortunately, that exchange was broadcast to the neighbourhood over our sound system. Soon people gathered and the crowd began to get hostile. "You'd better pack up and

195

leave," one man suggested. However, one of our workers explained that the term the pastor had used was not a term of race prejudice, but rather one of affection. After further apologies, our team was able to stay and conduct the meeting. But that slip of a white tongue was almost enough to trigger some angry reactions against our whole group, which included whites, blacks, and other ghetto Christians.

Those who continue to think white in the ghetto will sooner or later find themselves out of a job and a ministry. Even one's theories about the causes of drug addiction, poverty, prejudice, and other problems in the ghetto must be kept to oneself. All those who enter a ministry in the ghetto must first learn the culture from the people before they can teach others.

3. *Have a vision but don't be a visionary.* A worker told me, "At first I was so stirred up with my vision I really thought I was going to save all of New York City." This young man had come from a midwestern college and was full of enthusiasm and zeal. Then he learned some of the hard realities of urban life, and the problems of reaching the ghetto. But unlike many visionaries, he had come to try to understand the tremendous obstacles that must be overcome and the limitations that these hard realities place upon one's vision. In the process he did not lose sight of his goal. He still had vision. But he did lose some of his lofty, visionary ideals.

Many who undertake the challenge of the ghetto have great visions that go up in a puff of smoke when they face the cold, hard facts of inner city life and the people with their problems. This is especially true when they are faced with rebellion and rejection of the Gospel on one hand, and the struggles of new converts on the other. One must learn to understand such problems, and be prepared to accept them, but still have faith, hope and vision.

The soil upon which the gospel seed is planted in the ghetto is extremely rocky. The seed-sower must have patience and longsuffering. One of my teachers in college said, "Every pastor who goes into a city to build a church needs to have a ten-year vision. You may not remain there for ten years, but you should undertake your ministry as if you were going to stay that long." The same may be said for the counsellor's ministry in the ghetto. He must make a long-term commitment to it. Progress cannot be measured by the same standards you would use in middle-class America, or in a regular church programme. There are results, of course, but until one learns to measure them by different standards, he may have a sense of failure.

Our CURE Corps workers dealt with one young man for about a year and a half before he went to Teen Challenge. He did everything he could to "drive us mad", as one worker said, "from pop guns to stealing our car radio antenna". Even after his conversion progress came quite slowly. An indication of his rate of progress was his comment, "Hey, I only cursed three times today." A counsellor must learn not to judge or condemn in such a situation, but to wait for the Holy Spirit to do His work.

4. *Understand the environmental hazards.* The next thing the counsellor must do is understand the environmental hazards of the ghetto and the pressures those who live in the ghetto must contend with: problems of housing, unemployment, poverty, family and home conditions, prejudice, etc. These obstacles often make it difficult for new converts in the ghetto to grow in their Christian faith. It is not easy to serve the Lord in these conditions. And yet many of them often are model Christians, lights in dark places. They live in situations that the average American and the average Christian never sees. The ghetto dweller is nourished in the sights, sounds, and smells of the inner city. These conditions drain him spiritually.

Mary Earls, one of our CURE Corps workers, made this comment about life on a ghetto block: "My main impression from living in the ghetto is picking up the air of oppression—the atmosphere—which is so full of sin and evil that one can almost reach out and touch it. It is a combination of noise, frustration, street fights at all hours, the dogs barking, and the juke box playing until 5 a.m. All of this wears out your spiritual nerves."

I used to wonder why storefront churches in the ghetto held so many services during the week. I thought it was too much for them and that the saints were worn out. But I soon learned how important these services are in the life of the Christian in the ghetto. These meetings are his only escape from a rat-infested apartment, crying children, from drug addicts who parade up and down his apartment stairs, and from the tensions on the block. It is no wonder they go to church four, five, or six nights a week. It is no wonder they enjoy their own type of Christian soul music with its rhythm and beat. Their services are a wholesome escape, as well as spiritual and emotional therapy.

The Rev. Mr. Calvin B. Marshall, who pastors a Negro church in Brooklyn, feels that Christianity has a proper place in the ghetto and in the black revolution. In an article in *Time* magazine (April 6, 1970), he gives some insights into the value

197

of the church and of the Christian message in the black community. He states, "If we were nothing here (in the white society), at least we were children of God. At some far-out point in time, all these things would be rectified and we would get our golden slippers. Our religion *had* to mean more to us. We had to emote, but we had to lose ourselves in it. We had to sing and shout, and after it was all over we had to have a big meal and have something going on Sunday afternoon. Because when Monday came, it was back out into the fields, or back to the janitor's job, or back in Miss Ann's kitchen scrubbing the floor." Another black minister, Atlantic Samuel W. Williams, in the same article said, "But because those churches are still the only institutions in the black community completely controlled by black people, they will continue to have an influence, however much the younger blacks may feel that the churches no longer speak to the black world's needs."

Those who identify themselves as Christians in the ghetto must make such a complete, drastic break from sin that their conversion sends vibrations through the whole neighbourhood. Everyone seems to know when a ghetto sinner gets saved. Because the life of sin is what it is in such an environment, a conversion means a drastic change of life. And because of the environment, ghetto churches have had to demand a complete separation from the old life. Most ghetto dwellers know that to identify themselves with the "hallelujah" church or the evangelical Bible-believing mission on the block means that such pleasures as drinking, dancing, going to gigs (wild parties), and gambling must cease. When he does become a Christian, he may pay the price of lost friendships, persecution, even the loss of relatives, and he loses his position as being part of the "in" people of the block. And when one's life revolves entirely around one city block, or within one tenement house dwelling, this can be a very severe price one pays to serve Christ in the ghetto. The approach to ghetto churches is often legalistic and turns many young people away, but essentially they are trying to protect their converts, especially the new and the young ones. Most of the unconverted know the separation that the born-again Christian experience demands, and therefore they are reluctant to accept Christ. The counsellor must understand this factor in dealing with those in the ghetto. This often explains why those who accept Christ in the ghetto do not mature as quickly as new converts do elsewhere. The ghetto resident must pay a high price for being identified with a storefront church, or any church for that matter.

5. *Respect the possible dangers of ministry in the ghetto, but do not be fearful.* A young man bragged, "I'm not afraid. I go walking into those troubled areas any time I want to. I know the Lord is with me." On the other hand, I have heard some say, "You'll never catch me going into Harlem." Some are bound by fears and others are reckless and proud. They don't respect the possible dangers. Neither extreme is good. However, danger barriers can be broken down. The Christian worker can overcome his fears and operate comfortably. It makes a difference in a Christian's witness if he feels at ease. If ghetto people sense that you fear or distrust them, they will distrust you in return.

The only way to start in the ghetto is to go first with a member of the community. If the area is controlled by a gang, or by some militant group, make yourself known to the leaders and gain their confidence. As I write this we are trying to hold open air street rallies in an area in Manhattan known as Spanish Harlem. This particular neighbourhood is controlled by the Young Lords (the Spanish counterpart of the Black Panthers). As we always do when going into a Spanish neighbourhood, we make sure we have the Spanish-speaking converts to head up the teams. One of our girls, Cookie, approached the leaders of the Young Lords and explained the work of Teen Challenge. She tried to show the Young Lords that we were concerned about the needs of the neighbourhood, as they were. Because of the positive approach, they respected our work and said it would be all right for us to come into their neighbourhood.

Once a contact has been made in the ghetto, or key individuals have become the worker's friends, they become the key to meeting others. After a number of visits, the worker often finds he can move freely throughout the neighbourhood. Occasionally when we drive in some areas, drug addicts will walk away, thinking we are the police. Then someone will recognize us and give the word that we are all right. The addicts will stop walking away and allow us to talk with them. One addict said "I thought all this God stuff was phony until I deliberately watched one of the workers for months, and he did not get angry or lose his cool. I decided God was for real."

When there is trouble in a community—a gang war, riot, or other disruption—the worker should be careful about going to or staying in the area at that time. Under riot or gang conditions, a person who under normal circumstances would be your friend can turn hostile. Unless a worker is absolutely sure of his position and influence, he should not try to be a mediator, or act like a hero. Some counsellors command enough respect in a community to help prevent riots, gang wars, or street brawls, but one must definitely be sure he has such confidence before stepping in as a referee. In some past riots even black leaders were not able to stop the violence once it started. The Christian must remember that he is in the ghetto first of all to minister to the spiritual needs of an individual, and not to take on the role of a police officer, or a social worker.

Those who are afraid of the ghetto must get over it if they are going to be effective in ministering to minority groups. Too many Christians do not accept the challenge because they over-react to possible dangers. I have tried to get suburban Christians to come into the inner city for an evangelistic effort. Only a handful have enough assurance of their commitment to Christ to overcome their fears. They watch too many newscasts, read too many stories in the newspapers. We cannot allow the fear of militants to hold us back from ministry in the ghettos. We have proved in various neighbourhoods in New York City, on hundreds of occasions, that "God hath not given us the spirit of fear; but of power, and of love, and of a sound mind" (2 Tim. 1:7). There are dangers and there are risks, but those who are committed to doing the Lord's work must accept them, while entrusting themselves into God's protective hand. To do less is to doubt the Lord who is "my shepherd, who leadeth me beside troubled tenement houses; yea, though I walk through the streets filled with robbers, muggers, militants and criminals, thou art with me, thy nightstick comforteth me; thou preparest a pulpit for me in the midst of would-be enemies. Surely trouble will not follow me, and I shall dwell in the ghetto safely" (author's paraphrase).

6. *Get involved but not entangled*. Another important factor in working in the ghetto is that the counsellor should get involved but not entangled. The temptation is to get too involved, that is, to get into political and social matters while losing sight of one's call and Christian commitment. Those who minister in the ghetto must be prepared to get totally involved, but not at the sacrifice of not preaching the Gospel of Jesus Christ. The counsellor should be well-informed about all social and community agencies available to help people. We have been able to get through to people spiritually because we helped them with a practical problem such as housing. Our CURE Corps teachers run a pre-school programme and they are able to talk to mothers about the problems of their children, then about their own personal problems. We first gained their trust as teachers

200

of small children, and in time they saw our true concern and accepted our workers as people, not just teachers.

Many an evangelical has begun to meddle in the political, social and economic affairs of the community. These problems cannot be ignored, but they must not be allowed to divert us from the preaching of Christ and the ministry to the heart. There is the possibility of using the political and social structure of the community so as to gain a better hearing, which should be done. However, the Christian worker must remember that his power base is the Word of God and the Holy Spirit. He must try to erect a pulpit, not a soap box. He is to build faith, not seek new legislation. If a Christian counsellor can work to improve social and economic conditions, he should do so, but not if it means he is no longer respected for his Christian commitment.

7. *The counsellor must deal with his own prejudice.* In almost every conference I attend on ghetto ministries, the discussion turns to the matter of race prejudice. It's sad to listen to various pastors, Christian workers and laymen defend the fact that they are not prejudiced. They usually do this by telling about the coloured lady or coloured man who was or is their friend. The "I'm not prejudiced because I have a coloured friend" line is phony. Many blacks are beginning to see through it. They wonder why the white Christian feels he has to prove he is not prejudiced.

William Pannell states: "Frequently we suffer while some brother tells us how glad he is to be with us. 'Us' being 'you dear folks'. From there we are likely to hear about the 'dear old coloured lady' some place in his history, and how he loves us all 'in the Lord' . . . You see if you have to *tell* me you love me, I tend to suspect you immediately. I suppose this is why Jesus Christ never walked up to a man and said, 'Hey, I love you.' By going into all that rather syrupy introduction, you call attention to some difference among us. Because you didn't use the same words when speaking in your group. Be yourself. We can judge whether you like us or not. 'Blessed is the man who feels no need to tell us he loves us. He shall be invited again.' "[4]

The white Christian worker who goes into the ghetto must deal with his prejudice, and the best way to do so is to admit that he has it. I would not be honest with you if I said I was not prejudiced. We all are. It is part of human nature to prefer one's own culture, religion, nationality, and race.

Richard Wolff in *Riots in the Street* says, "The Christian is aware of the fact that prejudice is inherent in human nature.

201

Not race prejudice specifically, or any other particular prejudice, but prejudice as such. This is part and parcel of the innate disposition of man. ... Ultimately it is sin against God. ... The basic change has to take place in us and can only occur through a new relationship with God, where acceptance and forgiveness are experienced anew so that in turn it can be extended to others."[5]

Being prejudiced means you look differently upon a person of another race. It also means, to one degree or another, that you treat that person as being less of a human being than you consider yourself and your own kind to be. Such unconfessed, unsurrendered prejudice will show itself sooner or later in the counsellor's ministry. When prejudice is dealt with, the counsellor will come to the place where his reaction to people will be like that expressed by one of our workers who said, when asked if a certain convert were white, black, or Spanish, "I never noticed."

NOTES

[1] David Wilkerson and P. Murphy, *Born Old* (London, Lakeland Paperbacks, 1968).
[2] Richard Wolff, *Riots in the Streets* (Wheaton, Tyndale, 1970). Used by permission.
[3] ibid.
[4] William Pannell, *My Friend, the Enemy* (Waco, Texas, Word, 1969).
[5] ibid.

11

THE INTEGRATION PROBLEM

During one of my crusades in Sydney, Australia, a group of ministers and laymen, who were the sponsoring committee, met together in preparation for the rallies. They were discussing the matter of follow-up and what to do about those who would respond to the invitation. One man spoke up and said, "We can't send them to any of the churches. There isn't one good enough. I wouldn't recommend anyone to go to any of the churches in this city. We will have to start special meetings just for them."

After lengthy discussion the same layman rethought his position and stated, "Perhaps it would be a mistake to try to start our own church or another organization. This committee is only temporary, but the churches—no matter how we feel about them and what they lack—at least they will still be here tomorrow. Let's work through the churches and do our follow-up through them." Everyone agreed this would be the best procedure.

Never has the church been under so much attack—not only from without (that is to be expected and understood)—but also from those within its ranks. Many people feel that the church, any church, is a dead institution. Many recent converts from the college campus and out of the hippie life-style have carried over their rebellions into the Christian life. It is not easy for them to get free from the hang-up they have regarding the church. They often feel it is part of the "system" that needs to be changed, overthrown, and revolutionized. No one would deny that there are some legitimate reasons for them to feel that way. There is, however, a radical element that wants to throw the baby out with the bath water. In an effort to change the system, or bureaucracy of the church, and to break away from programmes too structured to meet the real needs of the people and the outsiders, they have developed an attitude which says regarding the church, "We don't need you. I am the church. The church is where a person is."

Even among some older, well-established Christians and those raised within the church there is a breaking away into small groups which become in some cases substitutes for the regular structured church programme. These prayer groups, banquet-type meetings, and underground cells have been part of a great spiritual awakening among Christians, especially those from the old-line denominations where the Gospel has been too structured, institutionalized and formalized. Many people in these small groups are finding new faith, or the new birth for the first time. They also are entering into the charismatic experience of speaking in other tongues as they are baptized in the Holy Spirit, as in the days of the book of Acts. This, I believe, is one of the greatest spiritual events in this century.

But in going out of the church to the small groups, these people have subtly reacted against the established, organized, regular church. Some of those who for so long were dead in their churches have been so glad to be liberated from them that they fear going back, lest they become over-critical of them. Some openly refuse to accept the established church in any form. If and when they do attend, they go with a built-in set of criticisms. No matter how good the function of the church is, or the efforts of the pastor and the members, they are not prepared to accept it.

In one country I visited an organization that used coffee houses as a means of reaching the untapped generation. New converts were required to sign a pledge that they would not join any church. They would meet together for Bible study in their coffee house, have prayer meetings, and try to carry on the same functions of a church. The organization itself became a reactionary church, its members parading around saying, "We've got something better than the rest of you have." They snub their noses, as it were, at those who are the church "squares". In discussing plans for an evangelistic crusade, their director stated, "We don't want any of the churches sponsoring this crusade. There isn't one good enough for us to send any of our converts to."

We have learned through the years of our ministry in Teen Challenge that no evangelism or counselling ministry can be totally and lastingly effective if it does not associate itself with the church. I am convinced that many good evangelistic efforts fail in the end because of an anti-church attitude. They feel that the church is not doing its job, so they have to organize their own little group and get the job done themselves. They end up evangelizing but not nurturing anyone in the Kingdom of God.

204

It's like bringing a baby into the world and then telling the doctor, "I don't need you any longer." Or it's like saying, "Let's get out of the hospital before it kills the baby." This is not to say that some churches have not spiritually "killed" new babes in Christ. They have. Others perhaps have not spiritually killed them, but they have stunted their growth, or raised them to walk as cripples, or kept them on the bottle, or done other spiritual damage.

Yet I say to those Christian organizations outside the main church body—and to those counselling and evangelizing independently of any church group—work in the system or your efforts may be in vain. Good, bad, or indifferent, the church is a divine institution. I do not mean to say that God is pleased with any and every church body or organization, but He is pleased with the concept of "assembling yourselves together". According to Hebrews 10:25, we are not to forsake the fellowship of the church.

Integrating the untapped generation into the mainstream of the church poses many problems. Some of them are seemingly insurmountable. But it can be done, and it is being done. Former drug addicts are finding their places in the church—even former alcoholics, prostitutes, criminals, and other sinners saved by grace. They are being accepted on the basis of the fact that "old things are passed away, and all things are become new" (2 Cor. 5:17). Their pasts are not being held against them. Only congregations and churches that understand the untapped generation, and are willing to face the problems of integration, are able to have this kind of testimony.

The key to integration is first of all the counsellor. If he develops the right attitude—a positive one rather than a negative one—the gap between the streets and the church can be overcome. The counsellor must take the hand of the pastor and the hand of the new convert and bring them together. Then the pastor can take the right hand of fellowship he has extended to the new convert, and take his congregation, and bring them together. It is often a cold and reluctant hand that the congregation extends—but congregations can be won. The counsellor must prepare the church for the convert and the convert for the church.

Many churches have ministered to only one type or class of people. A person from a different background, culture and lifestyle is made to feel strange. Or the new convert may feel strange by reason of his own fears of coming into a new environment. These barriers must be overcome. The church must

205

widen its ministry to receive any and all. There must be the integration into the church of sinners saved by grace, who have come out of different segments of the world and who come from different levels of sin. The church must not be guilty of spiritual discrimination. Can he who was saved from the sin of pride say to him who was saved from the sin of homosexuality, "I want no part of you"? Or can he who was saved from the sin of indifference say to him who was saved from the sin of sexual promiscuity, "I want no part of you"? Can the church members say, "Find your own kind of sinners saved by grace and fellowship with them"? A church is unbalanced if it does not have a cross-section of converts. It needs saved businessmen, saved housewives, saved working men, and saved drug addicts, alcoholics, sexual perverts, and others.

There was a time during our Teen Challenge ministry in New York City that we would not work with any church. Our theory was, "The only Christians who can adequately care for a new convert are those who helped bring him to birth." But we found that we could not evangelize and take care of their spiritual growth at the same time. We learned that God gave "some evangelists, and some pastors and teachers" (Eph. 4:11). Our calling was to sow the seed, and, up to a certain point, have Bible studies, prayer meetings, house visitation, and other methods of follow-up, but eventually our goal was to integrate converts into the church. We do realize our responsibility to help new converts get established, but since we are not functioning as a regular church body, we feel it is our duty to bring them into contact with churches. Our calling was to sow seed; others were called to help the growth of that seed and to develop the harvest into polished fruit. I am now convinced that lasting fruit can only result when the evangelist, the soul-winner, and the Christian counsellor co-operate with the local church. They can do this either by officially co-ordinating their work with and through the church, or at least by affiliating with a church. If the Christian counsellor takes the approach that "the church is no good", or "I am the only one doing the job", then those he helps bring to birth in Christ will have no respect for the church and will become a law unto themselves. These converts tend to become spiritual "freaks"—independent, spiritually aloof, proud, and lacking spiritual growth and maturity. Often they get side-tracked by some doctrinal quirk. Those converts who get started on the wrong foot often walk spiritually crooked the rest of their lives.

When we first began our rehabilitation programme for

addicts, alcoholics, delinquents and others, we held services right in our centre on Sundays. When on occasion we did take them to a regular church to worship, they felt very strange and out of place. Sometimes they were critical. "Why isn't this place like Teen Challenge?" they asked. Or they said, 'This church is dead. What's wrong with these people?" When they left Teen Challenge to go out on their own, they had a hard time fitting into a church. At Teen Challenge they were accustomed to worshipping the Lord informally. The new converts sang, prayed, and testified; the meetings were spirited and enthusiastic. They found it hard to adjust to more structured services. Because other Christians expressed their love and devotion to Christ in a more reserved manner, they thought their churches were dead.

Our Teen Challenge congregation was made up of people from similar backgrounds. It was not a normal church situation. We had to bridge the gap between the world of Teen Challenge and the outside world of the regular, established church. When we started to take our converts to various different kinds of churches, they soon learned the different forms of worship. They learned not to judge a church, its people, or its services by how loudly or softly they sang, by how they prayed and preached. They learned to judge a church by the quality of its worship. After participating in various forms of worship they were able to decide what kind of church they wanted for themselves after they left Teen Challenge. They met different pastors and church members, so they did not feel as strange as they might otherwise have felt, had they started going to church without any previous contact. During some of these services they made their decision to accept Christ, or other spiritual commitments. Because the church felt it had had a part in the birth of that soul, it took a responsibility towards helping the person in his Christian development.

The resistance of some pastors and congregations to members of the untapped generation is most often due to lack of contact. The less contact church folk have with the untapped generation, the more they fear them, or are prejudiced towards them. Most of what they know about young people comes from what they read in the newspaper, or hear from friends and neighbours. Once this barrier has been broken down, these preconceptions are alleviated. The pastor and people will see the grace of God in the lives of former habit-bound persons and accept them as they are. I have seen some churches and clergymen, once they begin to mingle with and relate to these young people, go out of their way to make up for past indifference. Whole churches have been revolutionized by the flow of "new blood" into their congregations. When they get their eyes away from a small circle of the same type of people attending their services week after week, and begin to get involved in the problems and needs of the untapped generation, a whole new ministry opens to them.

However, the sheltered, isolated church often becomes a stereotype church and its people are not prepared to accept those from a different side of town, a different side of the tracks, or from a different social or economic background. The silent majority shouts, "Why don't these people better themselves? Why don't they work and provide for their families like the rest of us?" The problem often is that these people are not welcome in some churches where they could hear a gospel message and receive a conversion experience that would motivate them to be the kind of citizens they should be. When they do seek to better themselves socially (and going to a nicer uptown church is a part of climbing the social-economic ladder, whether we like to admit or not), often they find that they are not welcome.

Middle-class Protestant evangelicalism in America is often hard to break into. When outsiders try to break into the fellowship, they are frozen out, not trusted, or respected. So the new convert is forced back into his old culture, his old neighbourhood, his old friends, and back to his old haunts. Even when he attends a church in the ghetto, or on the side of the tracks he came from, often he finds it is just as hard to break into the fellowship there.

I am not speaking of racial consideration alone; I am speaking about integrating the "vilest sinners" into the church, those from unpolished, uneducated backgrounds who might have severe growing pains in the church and upset the normal routine of its operation. This is not a racial problem alone. There are black congregations that find it hard to accept the untapped black generation. There are ghetto churches made up of poorer classes of people who discriminate against wealthy people. Integration and prejudice work both ways.

Why Churches Fear the Untapped Generation

Why does a church fear opening its doors to the untapped generation? First, there is a fear that former addicts, homosexuals and others like them might backslide and adversely influence other youth in the church. Of course, there is always this possibility and the chances of its happening are greater than for the "average" Christian. But this fear should not hold back the church from opening its heart and its doors to those who are "different" or who have been "different". If the church has strong leadership and a good sound programme to hold its youth, and if the majority of the youth are mature in their faith, they will not be overcome by backsliders. However, we must face reality. Our Christian youth who come from a more sheltered background must not grow up in a spiritual hothouse.

Church youth who are never exposed to other types of young people, and to those from different or less stable backgrounds, are not adequately prepared for the world when they grow up. Christian young people, well-grounded in the faith, have made tremendous strides in their spiritual growth once they were exposed to the spiritual needs of the untapped generation.

When Teen Challenge converts give their testimonies in suburban and rural churches, often the young people are over-inquisitive about their backgrounds. Some have an unhealthy curiosity. Does the fault lie with our converts? Or does this happen because these youth have been over-protected, over-sheltered, and kept from any contact with the outside world to such an extent that they have suppressed desires that come out later?

A pastor complained to me, "One of your fellows took one of our young people away from the church." That happened because the so-called Christian youth was a ready target for such influence. The backsliding was already there, another backslider simply came along and happened to bring it out.

This leads to another great concern of churches and pastors. It is the question, "If former addicts, homosexuals and others start coming to our church, will they start marrying some of our young women?" This is a serious problem. The fear is understandable.

It is not good for a girl from a sheltered background to marry a man who comes from an extremely different culture and background. The solution seems to lie in the manner in which the parents, the pastor and the church leaders handle each particular case. For example, breaking up a couple who have been dating, primarily on racial grounds, can cause an adverse reaction and make them all the more determined to marry—in rebellion. When adults advise young people against marriage, they must have sound reasons. It is better to approach it from a cultural and social standpoint. Young people from two extremely different backgrounds, no matter what their race or colour, have a high potential for trouble in their marriage. The pastor should caution young people who are developing such a relationship. If they persist, and if after prayer and consultation with all parties involved the pastor and family still feel the relationship should be broken up, such measures should be taken very carefully. There have been exceptional cases in which people from extremely different backgrounds have married and have been very happy. On the other hand, there are cases of difficult and shaky marriages because the two people had too much to overcome. Young people reason that "love can conquer all". They feel that the combination of their human love for each other, plus their Christian love, will make for an untroubled marriage. They must realize that when a person comes to Christ, all his problems are not automatically solved.

The church that has a good number of young people who socialize with others of similar backgrounds will not have such a serious problem in this regard. However, in churches where there are not many Christian youth, especially fellows, and where the young people are too sheltered, there is likely to be trouble. My father was a pastor and once he looked at two rows of young girls sitting in church and said to the adults, "There are not enough young men in this church, folks, let's pray them in and let's bring them in." They did—and it worked.

Another fear churches have in working with the untapped generation is that if a few of them come into the church, "we'll have a church full of them". They feel this will hinder them with others in the community whom they are trying to reach. Converted addicts and others like them are often quite enthusiastic in wanting to help others like themselves. Converted hippies and runaways will want to bring their friends to church. However, if a large group comes together, they could disrupt the meeting. It is best to bring street people into the church singly or in pairs. If a person is addicted to drugs, he may need the kind of help that only a Teen Challenge-type programme can provide. The pastor and those working with youth will have to make such a judgment. Because of the great number of young people now on drugs, and because of the limited number of people the rehabilitation centres can care for, the church must make every effort to reach the addicts and the drug abusers. If the regular church ministry cannot meet the spiritual needs of this person, then referral should be considered.

If a church is not willing, or is unprepared to try to work with those whom former addicts, rebels and others typical of the untapped generation will bring with them, counsellors should help them to find another church that is in a better position to accept the responsibilities of such a ministry. No church should fear that it will lose new people because it becomes involved in reaching the untapped generation. Churches should not be built on the type of person who would not come because he feels the church is catering to the wrong kind of people. In most cases the outsider will have more respect for a church that is making its presence felt among the unfortunates of this world.

How to Integrate the Untapped Generation Into the Church

1. *Develop a right attitude towards the church.* There are two types of Christian workers and counsellors: those who are a part of the church and work through a particular church or a group of churches; those who work with an organization that is independent of any one church, but is supported by churches some distance away. Counsellors working closely with a church will have no problem bringing about integration, unless the church has an "outside" ministry to the untapped generation so it will not have to work with them *in* the church. This is a subtle way of trying to avoid certain types of sinners.

Those who work independently often act this way. "No church will co-operate with me," the director of an evangelistic work told me. "Have you given them any reason to want to co-operate with you?" I asked. Those who feel that the church is not doing anything, or that "I am the only one with a burden", naturally find it hard to find churches that will co-operate. Those who indict the church for its lack of vision, and browbeat the people and beg for funds, are understandably turned off by the church. Those who are out to "get the church" and just take from it—rather than give to it—are going to be bitter towards it. Such an attitude works against the counsellor. He will tend to gather his converts around himself. Such converts usually do not last, or they are weak and become embittered themselves.

The independent counsellor must remember that he is dependent on the church for his support and for prayer backing. He must take the initiative in establishing a good relationship with a number of churches, or at least with one church with whom he is trying to work. Counsellors should not become church "draft dodgers", that is, they should not go from one church to another, attend one special service after another. It is easy to go to the big meetings, to hear the best preachers, to go to the most publicized rallies, all the while keeping yourself from being drafted into a specific responsibility in the church.

211

If the counsellor is a full-time worker in a Christian organization, he perhaps will not be able to limit himself to one church, or to a specific work in that church. However, even if the counsellor is in full-time Christian work, it is not a good idea for him to float from church to church, dodging the draft of regular weekly service, paying tithes, and other obligations. This certainly is not a good example to those he is trying to introduce to Jesus Christ.

In dealing with new converts the counsellor need not defend the church. He can try to understand the accusations of those who feel the church has failed them or even done them an injustice. Some will be bitter because they turned to the church in time of spiritual need and were not satisfied. Find out if they rebelled against the church because it did not minister to them, or if they rebelled against the truth that was declared. The counsellor should not add fuel to the bitterness, prejudice, or doubts that some people have towards the church. Often a new convert will try to get the counsellor into a debate about the church. The most common argument is about hypocrites. This is a trap every Christian worker should avoid.

Argument may be avoided simply by admitting that the church does have hypocrites. This agreement will usually disarm the person. We suggest that Christian workers might use this approach, "Yes, the church does have hypocrites, but what better place is there for them to be? If you are going to drop out of any group that has hypocrites, then you will have to drop out of life. There are hypocrites in politics, in democracy, and in communism, and in business and industry, and in almost any organization you can think of. Furthermore, the Bible does not cover up the fact that among God's people there were hypocrites. God deals with the problem openly and honestly—just read the history of Israel or Paul's letters to the early Christian churches. Hypocrites are very much in evidence and the problem is dealt with properly."

The client will no doubt cite specific incidents of a hypocritical parent, relative, neighbour, or friend. The counsellor should agree that perhaps what this so-called Christian did was wrong but that vengeance belongs to God. The counsellor should point out that he wants to show the client that there are Christians who really do care and back up what they believe.

It takes time, but the new convert must grow before he can see the true value of the church.

2. *Find the right church for each convert.* Some churches are better suited to meet the spiritual needs of one convert; another

church is better for another convert. The counsellor may need to take the convert to various types of churches until the convert learns which one is best suited for him. There are personal tastes in the kind of spiritual diet we feed our souls. Personality, education, and culture often determine the type of church in which the convert will feel most comfortable. Some prefer a large church, others a small one. Some prefer a more formal type of worship, others, the more informal and evangelistic type of service. The decision is often based on the kind of fellowship extended to the convert. His spiritual needs are important, but so are his emotional and social needs in the early days of his conversion. He needs to be surrounded by a strong fellowship of believers who are patient, loving and understanding. He also needs an active church. Converted addicts at first find it hard to know what to do with their spare time. They need a church which has a busy, yet meaningful variety of Christian activities.

3. *Work with the pastor and other officials of the church.* Gain the favour of the pastor, deacons, other church workers, and the congregation in general. If the pastor knows, trusts and respects the counsellor's ministry, there will be no problem for the counsellor to bring converts into the fellowship of that church. Pastors and their people are lukewarm towards counsellors who carry a chip on their shoulders, who seek to lord it over the pastor, and who give the impression that they are making a greater sacrifice than anyone else.

Tell the pastor about the type of people with whom you are working. Invite him to visit the areas where you are working. Have him meet some of the people involved in your programme. Many apprehensions about certain young people are based on the fact that Christians are not in a position to know how to relate to them. The counsellor can overcome these fears. When the counsellor gets active in a church, he should co-ordinate his activities with the pastor. After a new convert begins to attend church, and after he becomes a member, the counsellor should not interfere with his duties in the church. He should not continue to counsel unless asked to do so by the pastor, or in co-operation with him.

4. *Do not integrate too soon—or too late.* Many members of the untapped generation are not able to find the help they need in the average church. They need special ministry in a special environment. A person hooked on drugs or alcohol can't walk into a church one day, accept Christ as his personal Saviour, and walk back into society the next day. Those on the fringe

areas of addiction may be able to get the help they need in the church, but hard core cases need special attention.

It is a mistake to bring large groups of troubled, disturbed, distressed, rebellious youth into services that are primarily geared for other types of young people. This often causes trouble. The only time it should be done is when the service is promoted entirely for such kinds of youth. Young people who come into services in large groups act to please, or compete with, their own crowd. However, when they are alone, or in small groups, they are more themselves; the Spirit of the Lord has a greater opportunity to speak to them. The counsellor should work with such youth on the streets, or through other means, before bringing them into the church.

During a service at which I was to speak in Great Britain, a young Christian worker brought a group of mods and rockers into the service to see a film. They watched part of it, but when it got to the point where there was a Christian message, they began to carry on, started smoking, and one by one walked out. Finally the whole group was gone. After the service the young man who had brought them said to me, "Your film wasn't any good. My friends didn't like it."

The reaction of the mods and rockers was typical, but the counsellor did not understand some of the basic principles in working with youth. He was hoping that in one service he could accomplish something with his friends that he had not been able to do in preparatory work. He was embarrassed and sought to blame his failure on the film or the church. The counsellor must gain the respect of delinquent youth first before they can be controlled when they go to a regular church service.

However, there is a point when it is good to bring the un-tapped generation into a service. The counsellor cannot produce the atmosphere of evangelism and the moving of the Holy Spirit in any other way. Such services and rallies turn the church into a "delivery room". We lose many potential converts by not bringing the lost into the church where the Spirit can travail upon the seed that has been planted in them. The counsellor needs a church. He needs this evangelistic atmosphere, but he must not bring youth into it too soon or too late. Timing is important. Often the Christian worker is not aware of this principle. The Holy Spirit will direct the counsellor as to the right time and place. The success of youth crusades is due to the fact that Christian workers and counsellors have laid the proper groundwork of witnessing, prayer, preparatory counselling, or pre-counselling with the unsaved. Through proper timing the unsaved are brought to a crusade and the work of conversion takes place.

Guidelines for Churches

1. *Develop an open door policy*. Every church must take a long, hard look at itself to see if it is guilty of practising what I call "catership". Is it a closed corporation? Does it shut out those who would change the composition of its congregation? Does it shut out certain types of people? This happens if the church gears its outreach to selected segments of the community. If there is not a large number of the untapped generation within the sphere of the church's outreach, it should not neglect those in the immediate community to look elsewhere. But if the church is in a position to reach the untapped generation, it must not by-pass them for a different or better clientele.

Does the church allow former members of the untapped generation to take part in its various functions? Are they welcome at services but not in various groups within the church, at social functions, and at other special events? If these questions cannot be answered in the affirmative, the church does not have an open door.

Whatever types of people the church caters to eventually determines the composition of that church. A church that seeks only certain types of unconverted people soon takes on the characteristics of that class of people. If a church shows that it wants and welcomes the untapped generation, then integration is possible. It is not easy. It can upset, and it has upset, the normal and often smooth (too smooth in some cases) operation of the church. Not all members will go along with this broadened vision. Some pastors who have decided to broaden their outreach to all segments of the community have been frozen out of their churches, or they have lost key members. (I use the word "key" to describe the key financial supporters.) It takes great courage to face up to the integration problem. Those who decide to do so are likely to face opposition from those who are against such a ministry. The backlash of intolerance, prejudice and "closed corporationism" can make it difficult to accomplish a ministry of integration.

A church going through the throes of reaching the untapped generation must, with compassion and understanding, be taught, preached at, and prayed over to prepare for such a task. (Once again, I interject that I am not necessarily writing about racial integration; that may or may not be a factor in the integration of the untapped generation into the church. I am

215

speaking of integrating those with a different religious, social and cultural life-style into the church. Some white churches would be more opposed to having long-haired youths coming in their doors than they would be to having blacks coming in.)

The pastor should not challenge the attitudes of his congregation without making the necessary preparation. The counsellor, regardless of how negative the reaction of the church may be, should always maintain a positive attitude and do as much as he possibly can to bring about integration. The counsellor should not purposely work against the church or buck the "closed corporation" congregation. If there is no welcome, go to another church. A new convert can get caught in the crossfire of such a problem and become a victim of it. He should not have to go through such an experience so early in his Christian life. There are many other churches that do practise the open door policy. The counsellor must find them and work out the integration problem through them.

A church in a small rural town where there are no slums or ghettos wanted us to send them some of our problem people. They wanted to import the needy. Evidently they felt guilty for not having helped the ghetto types, or like some they may have felt it fashionable to reach them. This is not necessary—we suggested to this group that they assess their most immediate needy problem and start at that point. Every community, to one degree or another, has members of the untapped generation. A vision must be developed to see them. The church does not need to import them. However, when a congregation begins to minister to such, the grapevine will buzz. The word will spread that Pastor Smith's church, or whatever the name, has put out the welcome mat to the "now" generation. The congregation must be prepared to handle the growing pains of such new converts. A church accustomed to doing "business as usual" stands a chance of getting upset when new people with new problems start coming in. Those young people from unstable, socially-maladjusted backgrounds may do a little bit of stumbling on the road to maturity.

During one of our staff meetings at Teen Challenge we were discussing some of the problems our new converts were going through. Some of the staff were reacting under the strain and pressure of these problems. A few felt that such problems were an indication of a lack of spiritual power, perhaps the personal failure—or even sin—of some of the workers. One of them said that if we were really "on fire for God" such problems would not exist. Then one of the other staff members spoke up and said, "We must remember, we are dealing with problem people. These are not the usual, run-of-the-mill problems. These cases have baffled doctors, social workers, psychiatrists, and ministers. In our situation we must expect these kinds of problems." Then my mother remarked, "Yes, and where there are no oxen, the crib is clean."

When a church decides to nurture the babes in Christ who come out of the juvenile jungles, the addiction centres, the ghettos, and the youth sub-culture, it must expect dirty diapers, spilt milk, and crying and whining. That is a part of growing up. The church that wants to enjoy only the peace and calmness of "the same old people and the same old services" should stay away from the untapped, unwanted generation. At Teen Challenge we have a busy, dirty crib. But spiritual births are constantly taking place. And spiritual manhood and maturity do come.

2. *Don't baby the new babes in Christ.* The church need not spoil the newly-converted. It is possible to display a misguided attention and spoil new converts. One pastor, to bolster and encourage a converted drug addict, kept pushing him to the front. He magnified his testimony and set him on a pedestal. The young man couldn't take all the attention, became proud, and then stumbled and fell. The pastor thought he was doing the right thing for the young man, but in his sincerity, however, brought about his undoing.

There are other dangers in glorifying a convert's past. A preacher's son tried drugs so he "could have a bigger testimony". An evangelist, who had been in the drug scene in the past, began to overplay it and overstated his drug involvement. He felt pressured by others to talk about it, and his story grew more dramatic all the time. Finally, he fell under the pressure of guilt for having embellished the story. He fell back into his past and did what he had said he had done, but had never actually experienced. Counsellors must avoid over-exposure and exploitation of a convert's past.

Neither should converts be displayed to brag about one's success. Although the transformation of addicts, rebels and others is living proof of the grace and power of God, if it appears to a new convert that his conversion is being used to prove the validity of someone's ministry, he is going to feel manipulated. This does not mean churches and organizations should never use converts' testimonies. They can and should be used in the proper way. When chosen and screened by the pastor and counsellor, their testimonies can be very effective.

Babying new converts keeps them from sprouting their own spiritual wings. Some churches are afraid to "let go" of converts. Behind this is a fear of losing them. It is also an admission that perhaps their faith is not strong enough. New converts must have breathing room.

I know of a young man who was converted at a particular church and became an instant spiritual "star" and trophy. He spoke at ministers' meetings, conferences, rallies and other special gatherings. He became an expression of the pastor's and the church's soul-winning ego. When he inquired about Bible college, he was told he didn't need it. What he really wanted was to get out from under the church's control. He wanted to prove himself elsewhere. But friends told him, "You'll never make it on your own." They refused to support his efforts to try out his own wings. They didn't want to lose their star. As a result, the young man became bitter. He had a disagreement with the pastor, left the church, and eventually backslid. Then they told him, "Didn't we say you weren't ready to go out on your own?" Given an opportunity to face testing and to "pilot his own ship", he would no doubt have grown quickly and would have returned to the church later to become a spiritual leader. He fell because he had no foundation. It happened because the church loved him too much.

3. *Trust new converts.* The opposite extreme of babying new converts is to keep them under suspicion. Certain types of new converts do need extra attention for a period of time. The pastor, counsellors and members of the congregation must keep an eye on them during the early stages of their Christian development, but this must be done carefully and tactfully so as not to give them the impression that they are not trusted. Such converts will be very sensitive to this kind of treatment. Some of them have been under suspicion all their lives. Many have never been given an opportunity to accomplish anything they can be proud of. At the first sign of failure they were fired from their jobs or thrown out of their homes. Through Christ, for the first time they feel like "somebody". They need the chance to live on an equal basis with other Christians. They need to be trusted with responsibilities. When they struggle, give them the benefit of the doubt. Those who work with them must have what we call a "third eye", the eye that watches over them without their knowing it.

In some cases there has been difficulty because wives—or parents and relatives—of new converts don't trust them. In such a situation the young man feels he is on constant trial, and that

218

if he makes one wrong move he will be pounced upon. A young man I am counselling is having difficulty with his marriage because his wife has every one of his moves under suspicion. He told me, "Brother Don, I have no breathing room."

The same kind of attitude can come from the church. I know of another young man who had difficulty with his pastor and with his wife because they would not let him go anywhere except with his wife or someone in the church. They told him it was for his own good, but he knew it was because they didn't trust him. "It's hard," he said to me. "What more do I have to do to prove myself, if they don't treat me like a man? Don't they believe I'm a new creature in Christ Jesus? I know my past is behind me, but they don't seem to think so." Finally, he gave up his membership in the church and told them, "I'm not going to be a dog on a leash any more." He moved into a circle of fellowship where he felt trusted and respected.

New converts should not be kept from certain tasks in the church just because of their pasts. Of course, there are certain responsibilities the pastor and the church will not give to any new convert, regardless of his past. When a person comes from a troubled past and is denied the opportunity to participate in some Christian service, he tends to feel it is because of his past. This is where the counsellor must make the situation entirely clear.

4. *Learn how to handle backsliders.* Often the immediate re-action, when a convert falls, is to cut him off completely from fellowship. This may have to be done, if it appears he has no sorrow or repentance and no desire to be restored to Christ and the fellowship of the church. But what about those who are interested in recovering? Should the counsellor look for them? Should they be left alone until they are ready to return on their own? Should the burden and responsibility be placed entirely on the backslider, or should the counsellor resume some of it?

When an addict, or others in that category, falls back into his old life, it is a shattering experience. Not only is he out of fellowship with the church and with God, but his whole life has fallen apart. If a person who has never been an addict, rebel, or runaway backslides, he can still usually function as a normal member of society. He can work, care for his family, and have social contacts. However, when an addict or alcoholic back-slides, it is quite different. He has failed not only as a Christian, but as a parent, husband, or son. He loses his job, friends, and everything. Therefore, his discouragement is greater and it is harder for him to recover. He will feel that he has failed the

219

church, the pastor, his counsellor, and others who have worked with him. That's why he may run away.

Therefore, the counsellor will have to go after the backslider. Tell him he is welcome back to the fellowship of the church, and that he can be restored in faith. It may take a number of visits on the streets or to his home, and much counselling and prayer, before there is victory over his sin and failure. If the backslider still does not respond, he should be left alone and dealt with through the prayers of the church. If the counsellor knows where he is, he should visit him periodically just to show that he has not been forgotten, and that the church is still praying for him and is interested in his restoration.

The backslider's family will need special prayer, counselling and attention during this period of testing. In their frustration they must not do anything that would create a gap between themselves and the backslider. The family's immediate reaction is often to do something drastic. However, a patient and understanding spouse, parent, relative, pastor, or Christian worker can help to bring the backslider back to the Lord.

While walking along a New York City street, I spotted a former client approaching me approximately three quarters of a block away. We had come to know him quite well and had seen the grace of God revealed in some measure within his life. However, he reverted to drugs. There had been no contact with him for nearly a year. As soon as our eyes met, he quickly walked across the street to avoid me. Apparently, he was too ashamed to face me. Running after him I hollered, "Walt, Walt." But he kept on going. Finally catching up with him, I said, "Walt, it's good to see you. How are you doing?"

"Well, all right, I guess," he hesitatingly answered. As we chatted he finally admitted what I already knew—that he was back on drugs.

"Why don't you come back, Walt?" I asked. He seemed disinterested, but I knew this indifference came from his shame. Then with a strong sense that my words were being anointed by the Holy Spirit, I proceeded to tell him, "Walt, it was no accident that we met here tonight. This just didn't happen. God sent me out here right on this very street to meet you and to tell you that God is not finished with your life." He listened carefully.

"Do you know something, Brother Don," he said. "You're right. I do believe God sent you to find me. I'm usually never in this neighbourhood, but I couldn't get drugs where I usually hang out so I came over here."

As a result of that meeting he did come back to Teen Challenge. It was not easy to face those who had once known him during his days of victory and deliverance. Walt was to leave and return once again before he finally matured and became rooted, grounded, and settled in the faith.

In another case it took a little hand-scribbled note to a drop-out client to get him back. He was living with a prostitute and would not come out to talk with me. I sent in to him the message of concern with another drug addict. The note read—"Dear Bob, if God is speaking to you, call me. You know where you belong. I hope to hear from you."

In a few days he did call and break the silence barrier. The little note helped him get up enough courage to come back. It is often such simple contacts that can trigger an interest that lies buried under fear, guilt, shame, and sin. Perhaps, the prodigal son decided to "arise and go" home because the father had sent out messengers with the word that a welcome mat was out on the doorstep.

The backslider's immediate need is not sermonizing, but comfort and food for his faith. Later, judgment can be made as to why he failed. However, he should not be cuddled and babied. In one case, a Christian family helped a backslider when he gave them a sad story of financial difficulties. He blamed his backsliding on his money problems. The family gave him money, which he used to support his drug habit. He was doing what in the drug world is called "working an angle". Instead of helping to restore him, this family aided in keeping him in sin.

The most important thing for the counsellor is not to give up on backsliders from the untapped generation, especially the addicts. Often new converts become too proud of their new lives and they get spiritually lax. I have seen many who have fallen because of this, but in the end they were stronger because they learned through their experience that they must put on the whole armour of God and keep it on at all times. In the case of the addict, he never forgets what a shot of dope feels like, and this and temptation may present itself even many years after his conversion. Sometimes it is only through a relapse that an addict learns how important it is to walk in the Spirit. Converts from the untapped generation must live the Spirit-filled life to maintain their victory in Christ.

CONCLUSION

This has not been a happy, "inspirational" book to write. The people about whom it is written are not the leaders but often the dregs of society; still they are human beings and, most of all, they are people whom Jesus Christ loves. What we have tried to say is that Christ's love for these people must be shown through other human beings, Christian counsellors, workers and pastors who can say with the apostle Paul, "For the love of Christ constraineth us" (2 Cor. 5:14). No other motive will suffice.

This book is about serious human needs. All men have needs of one kind or another, but somehow the needs of the untapped generation seem to be worse than most. We have not tried to elevate or exalt the miseries of sin. We must keep ourselves from a morbid delving into iniquity. But Jesus told us to "look on the fields; for they are white already to harvest" (John 4:35).

We have tried to write confidently, however, that the enormous human needs can be met through the Gospel of Jesus Christ and by the power of the Holy Spirit. The cost is great, to be sure, in perseverance, faith, courage and hard work. In the end, we at Teen Challenge give ourselves to this ministry because we believe not only that the needs are great, but because we believe our job is a fulfilment of Christ's commission to all of His followers: "Go ye into all the world, and preach the gospel to every creature" (Mark 16:15).

We are going day by day into the world of the untapped generation. This book is an appeal for you, the reader, to follow us into that world. We have tried to tell you, without embellishment, what it is like, about the real people who live under the scourge of sin and addiction, and how Christians can be involved in reaching these people for Christ.

The things we have learned in our witness, our counselling and our rehabilitation work at Teen Challenge we are glad to share with the churches and with all Christians, as the task is too great for any one church or organization. For whatever successes we have seen, we are truly grateful to the Lord. Our prayer is that as you come to the end of this book, you will sense something of our burden, something of our very strong feelings about reaching the untapped generation for Christ.

For the Love of Mike

A Molly Murphy Mystery

Rhys Bowen

Constable • London

CONSTABLE

First published in the USA in 2003 by Minotaur Books,
an imprint of St Martin's Press, New York

This edition published in the UK in 2014 by Constable

A CIP catalogue record for this book
is available from the British Library.

ISBN 978-1-47210-309-3 (paperback)
ISBN 978-1-47210-310-9 (ebook)

Typeset in Great Britain by TW Typesetting, Plymouth, Devon
Printed and bound by CPI Group (UK) Ltd, Croydon, CR0 4YY

Constable
is an imprint of
Constable & Robinson Ltd
100 Victoria Embankment
London EC4Y 0DY

An Hachette UK Company
www.hachette.co.uk

www.constablerobinson.com

*This book is dedicated to the memory of
my great-aunt Sarah, who shared Molly's spirit
and also survived working in a sweatshop, going on
to become a teacher and woman of letters.*

ACKNOWLEDGMENTS

With thanks to New Yorkers S. J. Rozan and Annette and
Marty Meyers for believing in my books, to Rochelle Krich
for attempting to set me straight on all things Jewish, and as
always, special thanks to John, Clare, and Jane for their great
suggestions and for making me work hard.

One

J. P. Riley and Associates,
M. Murphy Notes:
Monday, Oct. 14, 1901
   Followed JBT from his office at 38 Wall Street.
   Observed him entering 135 E. Twelfth Street at
   approximately 7:40 P.M.

Actually I had been guessing at the time. I heard the clock on Grace Church, a couple of blocks away at Tenth and Broadway, chiming the half hour and it hadn't yet chimed the three quarters, but in my profession guessing wasn't really good enough. I'd just have to get myself a watch. I sensed my mother turning in her grave at the thought of such presumptive ideas. No one in Ballykillin had ever owned a watch, apart from the family at the big house, and they didn't count, being English. It was a pity I hadn't managed to get my hands on Paddy Riley's pocket watch before the police took his body away. Now it was probably on some sergeant's watch chain, where it was going to stay put, and as for myself, I wasn't making enough money to indulge in luxuries. If you want a real confession, I wasn't making any money at all.

After a rather eventful summer during which I found

1

myself without an employer, I had decided to run J. P. Riley and Associates (I being the associate) without him and had taken over a couple of the divorce cases that were still on his books. The first of them was resolved by the parties in question, who reconciled during a romantic summer encounter at Newport, Rhode Island. I learned this from the wife, who sent me ten dollars, 'for my time and trouble'. Since I'd been tramping all over the city, locating the different actresses and brothels that the wandering Mr Pfitzer had been visiting, the ten dollars hardly covered my time and trouble, but there wasn't much I could do about it. These society people knew each other and I'd not be likely to find any more clients if I aggravated the few I had. But the cheek of it still rankled. I wondered if she'd send her doctor ten dollars for his time and trouble if the patient recovered after his ministrations!

But I was learning to hold my tongue when necessary nowadays and sent the good lady a receipt for her donation. The other investigation was still ongoing, which was why I was spending a long, dreary evening on the sidewalk of East Twelfth, between University Place and Broadway, observing the brownstone opposite. I hadn't yet discovered who lived there, but I knew it was a woman, as I had heard the man I was following, Mr John Baker Tomlinson III, ask the maid if her mistress was at home. Her mistress, mark you, and no mention of a master. Maybe this time I had struck gold. No man of quality would visit an unchaperoned woman after dark without jeopardizing her reputation.

By 11 P.M. my suspect still hadn't emerged and I began to wonder if he was intending to stay the night. Not a happy thought for him, having to face an angry wife tomorrow morning, nor for me. It had begun to rain around nine and I had forgotten to bring an umbrella. I could feel my bonnet becoming soggier by the minute. My cloak was beginning to smell like wet sheep.

I stamped my feet and walked up and down a little, before I remembered that I was supposed to be invisible. My departed employer, Paddy Riley, could remain motionless, blended into the shadows for hours. I would never learn his patience; in fact I was beginning to question whether I was cut out for this line of work after all. I liked the excitement all right and it beat working in a sweatshop for eighteen hours a day or gutting fish at the Fulton Street market, which seemed the only other options for an Irish girl fresh off the boat. There had been a companion's position, but we won't go into my reasons for leaving that. It was still too painful to think about. Even after three months the ache wouldn't go away. Let's just say that proving I could do quite well without Daniel Sullivan was the main force that drove me to stand on a wet, windy sidewalk when most respectable folk were already in their beds.

There was a light on in the upstairs bedroom – a soft glow which hinted at a gas bracket turned down low, and not the harsher brightness of a new-fangled electric bulb, which seemed to be the rage in this city – but the blinds were drawn. Was it too much to hope for that the wicked couple would come to the window and be silhouetted in passionate embrace? In fact, so far I had not managed to catch Mr Tomlinson doing anything that might be grounds for divorce. I had loitered outside his Wall Street office. I had followed him to lunches at his club (all male) and dinners at restaurants (with respectable companions), but not a single hint so far to confirm his wife's suspicions that the illustrious Mr Tomlinson was carrying on an illicit amorous liaison.

And if I now could provide proof that Mr T had been straying, what then? I'd earn myself a big fat check and Mr

Tomlinson would be out on his ear – which was a shame as I rather liked him. In observing him from afar I had seen him to be polite, courteous, and with a good sense of humor. Again I asked myself whether the private investigator's life was really for me. What I wanted was something other than divorce cases, although Paddy had maintained they were his bread and butter. And bread and butter were surely needed at the moment.

The rain was now driving from the East River, forcing me to move into the comparative shelter of a flight of steps leading up to a front door. My back pressed against the brickwork of the house, I tried to look on the bright side of things. At least I wasn't starving. I had a splendid place to live and the chance to carve out a real profession for myself if I could only stand the elements!

I glanced up as the light in the upstairs room was extinguished. The curtains remained drawn. I watched and waited. Nothing moved, no door opened, no wandering husband slunk out of Number 135. I wasn't sure what to do next. Would I really have to hang around until morning? Not a pleasing prospect, given that the weather was getting worse by the minute. Fortunately Mr Tomlinson had chosen his dalliance in my own corner of the city. My own room was but a ten-minute walk away down Fifth Avenue. I could slip home to change my clothes, have a bath and a good sleep and be back in position before dawn broke, this time equipped with an umbrella. Of course, Mr Tomlinson could emerge from the house at any time during the night and I'd miss my opportunity. If I left my post, he'd undoubtedly slip out while I slept and I'd have to conduct a nightly vigil all over again. Besides, Paddy would never have left his post and I was trying to live up to his example.

I resolved to stick it out a little longer. If anyone could

endure wind and rain, then it was surely I – having been raised on the wild west coast of Ireland where the rain usually fell horizontally and was whipped so hard by the driving wind that it stung like a swarm of bees. And nothing more than a shawl to wrap around me in those days either! Nothing like this long warm cape I had inherited from Paddy. I pulled it more closely around me and stuck my hands into the pockets to keep them warm.

Down at the other end of the block, on Broadway, the city was still awake. I heard a hansom cab clip clop past, the clang of a trolley car bell, raucous laughter, shouts, running feet. The city was never peaceful for long, but at least it was alive, which was more than I could say for County Mayo.

I stiffened as I heard a police whistle blowing, but the gale picked up and sounds were muffled again. Then I saw two figures coming along Twelfth Street toward me. I froze and stepped back behind the flight of steps, hoping they would pass by without noticing me. It was at times like this that I realized being a woman alone was a distinct disadvantage. Although I was still in a highly respectable neighborhood, only one block from the patricians of Fifth Avenue, things went downhill pretty quickly in the other direction and Broadway was not a street on which I'd feel comfortable walking alone at night. The footsteps came closer – a heavy measured tread of boots. I held my breath and pressed myself against the railing. They were almost past me when one of them turned. Before I knew what was happening, big hands reached out and grabbed me.

'Well, lookee what we've got here, Brendan!' a deep Irish voice boomed. 'One of them did get away after all. And she's a little wild cat all right!' This last comment uttered as I tried to wriggle free from his grasp and swung a kick in the direction of his shins.

'Let go of me this instant!' I sounded less rattled than I

5

really felt. 'I'll call the police. I heard a police whistle just down the block. They'll be here in a second.'

'Call the police – that's a good one, eh, Brendan?' The big man who had hold of my wrists chuckled. His taller, skinnier companion laughed too – a higher hee hee hee followed by a snort through his nose which I found very annoying.

'You don't think the New York City police can deal with the likes of you?' I was still attempting to remain calm and haughty. 'Now unhand me immediately.'

'A proper little firebrand, and Irish too,' the big man said, as he attempted to bring my hands behind my back and I attempted to stamp on his toes. 'We are the police, as you very well know.'

Relief flooded through me as I recognized the familiar uniforms under their rain capes. 'Then you're making a terrible mistake, officers. I am no criminal. I'm a respectable citizen.'

This caused them more mirth. 'A respectable citizen – and my father's the pope in Rome! You did a bunk through the back window when my partner and I raided Tom Sharkey's saloon a few minutes ago. So where did your fancy boy get to? Left you to face the music alone, did he?'

It was just beginning to dawn on me that they thought I was a woman of a very different occupation. 'Jesus, Mary, and Joseph. I'm thinking the pair of you are in need of glasses,' I said angrily. 'Look at me. Do I look like a woman of the streets?'

'She is kind of dowdy looking and she's not even wearing any rouge on her cheeks,' Brendan commented. 'Maybe we have made a mistake.'

I decided to ignore this unflattering assessment of my charms. 'Of course you've made a mistake. But I'll accept your apology, given that the light is so poor,' I said.

'So maybe she wasn't the young girl who escaped from the bawdy house,' the larger officer conceded, 'but she's still up to no good. What would a respectable woman be doing out alone at this time of night?'

'If you really must know, I'm a private investigator, out on a case,' I said. 'I'm observing a house opposite.'

If they had been mirthful before, then this time their jollity positively overflowed. They nudged each other in the side and staggered around guffawing while I gave my impression of Queen Victoria not being amused.

'If you don't believe me, I have my card in my purse,' I said. 'I am a partner at J. P. Riley and Associates. You must have met Paddy Riley.'

'Paddy Riley?' The large constable gave me an incredulous glance. 'Paddy Riley? You're not expecting me to believe that he'd ever work with a woman, are you? He hated women. Couldn't stand the sight of them. And anyway, Paddy Riley's dead and buried, in case you didn't know.'

'Of course I know. I'm carrying on the business without him, or I would be if you two great clodhoppers would just leave me in peace.'

He still had hold of my arm and I tried to wrench myself free.

'Oh no, you're coming with us, my dear. Whatever you were doing, I'll wager you were up to no good.'

'Observing the house opposite, she says,' the skinny one called Brendan commented, looking smug. 'Do you think she could be working with the Dusters, scouting out places to rob?'

'Holy Mother of God! Of course I'm not scouting out places to rob. If you'll just let go of me, I can produce any number of respected citizens who will vouch for me. In fact if you take me to your police station, I'm afraid you're going to look very foolish because I happen to be a good friend of—' I bit my tongue and left the rest of the sentence hanging. I was dying to see their faces when I told them that their own Captain Daniel Sullivan could vouch for me, but I wasn't going to use his name every time I was in a jam. He'd be only too delighted to remind me yet again that I was playing with fire and no good would come from trying to be part of a man's world.

'A good friend of whom, my dear?' the large officer asked. 'The mayor, was it? Or the governor? Or maybe our new President Teddy himself?' He grinned at the other policeman again and dug him in the ribs.

'You'll see,' I said, determined not to lose my dignity. Then I added, as they began to manhandle me away, 'And please put me down. I am not a sack of potatoes. I have two good feet and can walk on my own.'

'Just as long as you don't try to do a bunk on us,' the large officer said.

'Do the Dusters ever use women?' Brendan asked as we started to walk away. 'I know the old Gophers had some terrible fierce women working with them, but I don't know that much about the Dusters.'

'They're getting very tricky these days. No knowing what they'll try next,' the other officer said.

The rain had eased off and the street lamps were reflected in puddles.

'Who are these Dusters?' I asked.

'The Hudson Dusters? You've never heard of them?' Brendan sounded surprised. 'This is their territory, west of Broadway all the way to the Hudson.'

'Are they some kind of gang then?'

'One of the biggest – along with the Eastmans and the Five Pointers, of course.'

'That's enough, Brendan. She knows very well who the

Dusters are. I'll wager one of their squealers will identify her for us in the morning.'

I heard the sound of a front door slamming behind us down the street and looked around to see a tall figure in a long great-coat and top hat hurrying in the direction of Fifth Avenue. It looked like Mr Tomlinson but I had now missed seeing him come out of the house. Since one of my captors liked to gab, I couldn't resist asking, 'So that house I was watching, the one with the two bay trees in pots beside the front door – you don't happen to know who owns it?'

Brendan took the bait right away. 'That's Mrs Tomlinson's house, wouldn't you say, Brian?'

'Your mouth's going to be the death of you, boy,' the older policeman snapped. 'You should know better than that. Next you'll be lending her your nightstick to break in with.'

'I wasn't doing no harm . . .'

I hardly heard this exchange. My brain was still trying to digest what Brendan had said. 'Mrs Tomlinson?' I said, looking appealingly at him. 'You don't mean the wife of John Baker Tomlinson, do you? I've been to her residence. It's on Fifty-second Street on the East Side.'

'No, this is an older woman – a widow. Maybe it's your man's mother.'

Terrific, I thought as we sloshed our way down Sixth Avenue toward the Jefferson Market police station. I had spent an entire evening risking pneumonia, getting myself arrested, and all to watch Mr John Baker Tomlinson III visit his mother! As a detective it appeared I still had a long way to go.

Two

The Jefferson Market police station was in the triangular-shaped complex that also held a fire station, a jail, and the market itself. It was a mere stone's throw from my house on Patchin Place and I looked longingly as we crossed Tenth Street.

'Look, Officers, I live just across the street,' I said. 'If you'd just take me home, my friends will vouch for me.'

'You're not going anywhere till morning,' the brusque constable said, giving my arm a warning squeeze. 'We've been instructed to bring in any individuals behaving suspiciously and a young woman, out alone late at night, counts as suspicious in my book.'

'But I've explained what I was doing.'

'You can explain it to my sergeant.' I was shoved into the police station. 'When he gets here in the morning,' he added.

'You mean I have to stay here all night?' For the first time I began to feel alarmed. I had been in jail once before and I had no wish to repeat the experience. 'You can't keep an innocent person in jail with no cause.'

'You watch your mouth or I'll have you for resisting arrest,' the constable said. 'Go on. Down to the lockup with you.'

Oh, but I was so tempted to call upon the name of Captain Sullivan. Watching their faces when they realized their mistake would have been worth any lecture that Daniel might give me. But as my mother always told me, I was born with too much pride. I pressed my lips together and said nothing.

I was manhandled down a dank, echoing hallway that smelled of urine and stale beer. I passed a cell full of dark shapes. The shapes stirred themselves as we passed and ribald comments from crude male voices were hurled after me.

'Shut your mouths in there.' The constable rattled his nightstick along the bars. We paused in front of the next cell. It too was fronted with bars instead of a wall and full of more shadowy figures. My heart leaped in fear that I might be locked up with men like those we had just passed. Before I had time to voice these fears, a key was produced, a door within the bars swung open, and I was shoved inside. I half stumbled and was grateful to see myself staring at a delicate foot and a skirt.

'Over here, dearie,' a rasping voice said from the darkness. 'Move yer bum over, Flossie. The poor thing looks like she's about to faint.'

I wasn't really the type who fainted, but this was not the moment to protest my apparent frailty. I gave a grateful smile and sat on the few inches of bare wooden cot that had been offered to me. As my eyes accustomed themselves to the gloom, I saw that my cellmates were indeed of the profession I had been accused of pursuing. There were five of them and they were rouged and powdered with bright-red lips and hair piled in ridiculous pompadours. One was wearing a black French corset that lifted her bosoms like overripe melons. No dress over the corset, mind you – just the corset and a shiny black skirt beneath it. The skirt was hitched up as she sat on the floor to reveal black fishnet stockings and high-heeled boots. Flossie on the bench was in a low-cut red satin dress. The other occupant of the bench had her shawl pulled around her and was trying to sleep. In contrast to the others she looked young and innocent, apart from the circles of rouge on her cheeks and the bright lips. I tried not to stare too obviously.

'So what you in for, honey?' the coarse voice asked again. It belonged to the large woman sitting on the floor in the corner, legs spread apart in a most unfeminine pose. She had an ostrich feather sticking from her hair and a feather boa around her neck.

I thought it wise not to say that I was a detective. That might cast me with the enemy and I had a whole night to spend in their presence. In the months since I had fled from Ireland and come to New York I had become adept at lying without so much as batting an eyelid. When the police officers had grabbed me, I had tried telling the truth for once and look where it got me.

'I'm afraid the officers have made a terrible mistake,' I said, trying to sound sweet and demure. 'Just because they found me sheltering from the rain on my way home from a tryst with a young man, they thought that I was – one of you.'

This caused great merriment. 'Thought you was one of us – that's a good one.' The large blowsy woman's breasts heaved as she laughed. 'You wouldn't get many clients dressed like that, dearie.'

'They must have wanted their eyes testing,' the one in the corset agreed. 'Look at you. Anyone can see you're a proper young lady and not riffraff from the streets.'

'Getting too big for their boots, that's the trouble with coppers around here,' Flossie in the red dress chimed in. 'A girl's not safe even when she's paid her protection money. Just because there's a Tammany mayor in city hall, the police think they can do what they damned-well like and nobody's gonna stop them.'

'Language, Bessy, there's a young lady present,' the blowsy one reminded her. She leaned across and patted my knee.

'Don't you worry yourself, dearie. You'll be out of here in the morning and this will all seem like a bad dream.'

I looked around the cell and found the young girl awake and staring at me. She had big dark eyes and was looking at me with such a wistful expression that it almost broke my heart. It will seem like a bad dream for you, the expression said. For me there will be no waking up in the morning.

I shut my eyes, leaned against the cold brick, and tried to sleep. But sleep wouldn't come. Now that I was over my initial fear, I was so angry I felt I could explode at the unfairness of it all. This would never have happened if I'd been a man. Men were free to walk when and where they chose in this city. But a lone female, out unchaperoned at night, was immediately suspected of being up to no good. I had already realized that there were many things that Paddy Riley had been able to do that were just not open to me. He had contacts with gangs, and with the police. He frequented various taverns. He could move freely and unobtrusively through the worst areas, and could change his appearance easily by means of a beard or a moustache. I had tried disguising myself as a young boy once and was amazed at the freedom it gave me. Of course, Paddy had seen through it right away, but maybe I should consider using such a disguise again, if I wanted to avoid more embarrassing encounters with the police.

And then again, maybe I should give up the whole idea of trying to carry on Paddy's business. Divorce cases may have been Paddy's bread and butter, but this short acquaintance with them had made me decide that they were not for me. I found them small, mean-spirited, and sordid. If I was going to stay in this business at all, then I should take up my original plan – finding immigrants who had lost touch with their families back in Europe. At least I'd be doing something positive then.

I should never have started along this train of thought. My mind moved from immigrants, to Ellis Island, to my own unpleasant experience there, and then to the little family I had brought with me when their mother couldn't travel with them. I wished I hadn't rehashed that particular worry. When I delivered them to their father, I had thought that my job was complete. It wasn't. The father, Seamus, had not been able to work since he almost lost his life in a collapse of the new subway tunnel. They had been evicted from the flat I found for them and the latest I had heard, they were back rooming with relatives on the Lower East Side. The fact that I wouldn't wish those relatives on my very worst enemy and that I had grown remarkably fond of the two little ones nagged at my conscience. I knew I should be doing something to rescue them, but I also knew it would mean leaving the most delightful circumstances in which I now found myself. My big room on the top floor of my friends' house on Patchin Place was little short of heaven. Living in a house full of artists and writers and thinkers had made it one step better than heaven itself.

I had been putting off making any decision, hoping that Seamus would be fit enough to return to work and that he'd find a good place for his family. Now it seemed that he might never be fit enough to return to hard manual labor. Which meant it was now up to me to rescue them from a Lower East Side hellhole and a dragon of a cousin. I gave a big sigh. Life seemed to be one perpetual roller-coaster – up on top of the hill one minute, then rushing downward to the depths the next.

I should never have started thinking about roller-coasters either. Instantly my mind whisked me back to happier times, when Captain Daniel Sullivan had taken me to Coney Island. I smiled now at the memory of it. Daniel had expected me to scream, faint, or cling onto him as we rushed down into the depths. Instead I had laughed, loudly. The next time we began a descent, he had kissed me and we had hardly noticed when the car reached the bottom. I turned off that memory hastily. No good would come of dwelling on that part of my past. Besides, it all seemed blurred and dreamlike, as if it was something I had read about in a book.

I glanced around the cell. Quiet had fallen. The young girl beside me slept like an angelic child. Heavy snores were coming from the bosomy lady on the floor. I closed my eyes and drifted into uneasy sleep.

The rattle of a billy club along bars woke me. First gray light was coming in through a high window. It was cold and drafty in the cell. The door was opened briefly and a tray of tin mugs full of a hot dark liquid was shoved inside. I took the mug handed to me. It was coffee, at least I think it was. I longed for a warming drink, but my gaze fell on the bucket in the corner, which one of the women was now using noisily. There was no way on God's earth that I was going to follow suit. I put the mug down untouched and wondered how long it might be before the sergeant arrived and I would be released. I opened my purse, which I had clutched in my arms all night, and took out my comb. At least I would try to look respectable when they came for me.

A little later I heard deep voices and the tread of heavy boots echoing as they came down the hall.

'The house behind Tom Sharkey's saloon, you say. They work for the Dusters then, Harry?' I heard a voice saying.

'Couldn't say, sir. Nobody's questioned them yet. You can take a look for yourself and see if you recognize any of them. Down here on the left.'

The footsteps came closer. A balding uniformed sergeant stood in front of our bars and behind him stood a taller, slimmer man with unruly dark curls that escaped from under the derby he was wearing. If I'd have had time, I would have pulled my cape over my head. His gaze fell on me as I shrank into the corner and wished myself elsewhere. 'Holy Mother – what about this one, Harry? What's she in for?'

'Not sure, sir. Found loitering on the street, late at night, as I understand it. Couldn't give a proper explanation of herself. My boys thought she might be a lookout for the Dusters, seeing as where she was stationed.'

'Did they now? Well, isn't that interesting?' The man's dark eyes flashed with amusement. 'Bring her out, Harry. I'll question this one myself.'

'Out you come then.' The sergeant motioned me to the door. 'Not you girls. Stay well back or you'll get my nightstick on your knuckles.'

'Good-bye, dearie. Good luck. Don't let that scum scare you.' The wishes echoed after me as I walked beside the sergeant down the hall. Another door was opened. I was shoved inside.

'Now behave yourself and answer the captain's questions and you'll come to no harm.'

The door shut behind us and I looked up into the captain's face.

'You hear that,' he said, his eyes holding mine. 'You'll come to no harm if you just obey me.'

'Very funny, Daniel,' I said. 'I suppose you think it's most amusing that I had to spend the night in a room full of loose women.'

I watched him suppress a chuckle. 'No, I'm sure it wasn't funny at all for you. You do get yourself into the most impossible circumstances, Molly. What was it this time?'

'I was minding my own business, observing a house on East Twelfth Street, when two of your great clodhopping constables grabbed me and hinted that I was an escaped prostitute.'

This time Daniel Sullivan did smile.

'As if I look like a floozie!' I snapped. 'I told them I was

16

an investigator, observing a house, but they wouldn't believe me. They laughed in my face. They thought I was working for some gang, scouting out a place to rob, if you please. I've never been so insulted in my life.'

Daniel put his hands on my shoulders. 'Hold your horses, Molly. They were quite within their rights, you know. They have orders to bring in any suspicious persons and I'm sure you seemed suspicious to them.'

'If I'd been Paddy, they'd have turned a blind eye and walked on past.'

'Of course they would. Everyone knew Paddy.'

'And he was a man.'

'That too.' Those big, reassuring hands squeezed my shoulders. 'Molly, when will you give up this stupid idea? Women just can't be investigators. You've seen for yourself now that it doesn't work. Last night was just an embarrassment for you. Next time it could be worse – the rumors about the white slave trade are not all exaggerations, you know. Prostitutes don't have very long lives and replacements don't exactly line up to volunteer for the job. A young woman alone on the streets at night is just what they are looking for.' A picture flashed into my mind of that young girl, looking at me with sadness and longing. I shuddered. 'And then there are the gangs,' Daniel went on. He paused, still holding my shoulders, still looking down at me gravely. 'Right now there is a war going on between two of the worst gangs in the city. The Hudson Dusters and Eastmans are fighting over territory and control of the cocaine trade. And the third gang, the Five Pointers, are hoping to expand their activities while their rivals are at each other's throats. A nasty business. There were two men lying dead in the alley behind Tom Sharkey's saloon last night. Neither gang admits knowing either of them. They've no identification on them. If some family member doesn't report them missing, they'll be buried in the potter's field and we'll never know their names. They might have been gang members, or they might have been innocent men, caught in the crossfire in the wrong place at the wrong time. Do you understand what I am telling you?'

'You're saying I shouldn't be out on the streets alone at night.'

'Precisely. And why in heaven's name didn't you have me called when they brought you in last night? I could have had you out in seconds, rather than spend the night in jail.'

'Because I have my pride,' I said. 'Because I knew you'd behave exactly as you are behaving right now.' I took a deep breath. 'And because I can mean nothing to you.'

'Nothing to me – how can you say that?'

I had been so strong all night. Now I was weary, relieved, and Daniel's hands on my shoulders were unnerving me. I had a horrible feeling that I might break down and cry at any minute. I fought to master myself. 'I haven't read in the *Times* that Miss Norton has broken off her engagement,' I said stiffly.

'Not yet, no.'

'Then I can be nothing to you, Daniel. We've been through this before. Now if you'd just let go of me, I want to go home.'

'I don't want to let go of you, Molly,' he said, with a look that made me feel even more unsteady. 'You know that. I want you to have patience until I can get things squared away.'

'You won't ever break off your engagement,' I said coldly. 'Not while your career is at stake.'

'Give me time, Molly, I beg you. I do love you, you know.'

I held his gaze. 'Not enough, Daniel.'

His hands slid from my shoulders. 'You're free to go,' he said.

I left the room without looking back.

Three

As I closed the front door at 9 Patchin Place, a voice yelled out, 'She's here, Gus, she's here!' and Sid came flying down the stairs toward me, wearing kingfisher-blue silk pajamas, followed by Gus wrapped in a large scarlet Chinese robe. Their faces were a picture of relief and joy.

'Molly, where have you been? We've been worried sick,' Gus exclaimed over Sid's shoulder. 'We've been out half the night, tramping the streets, looking for you.'

'I'm so sorry to have caused you such worry,' I said. 'I'd have let you know if I could. I got myself arrested and spent the night a mere stone's throw away at the Jefferson Market police station.'

'Got yourself arrested?' Sid asked, looking amused now and not horrified as a more respectable woman would have done. 'Molly, my sweet, what had you been doing?'

'Nothing. That was the annoying part of it. I was minding my own business, standing on a residential street and observing a house. I was picked up by the police because no decent young lady should be out alone at night.'

'The nerve of it,' Sid said. She helped me off with my cloak, which was still damp and still smelled of wet sheep. 'Your clothes are completely soaked,' she added as she hung

19

it up. 'You'd better let Gus run you a bath and I'll go along to the kitchen to make us all some strong coffee. We were so worried we didn't even think of going to the bakery for rolls yet, but I'll remedy that as soon as I've put the coffee on.'

'Come on, Molly, up the stairs with you.' Gus shepherded me up the stairs and by the time I was out of my wet clothes and into my robe, the steam was rising from the mammoth claw-footed tub that was the pride of our bathroom. 'I'll even let you use my Parisian soap to make you feel lovely and decadent,' Gus said with a wicked grin as she closed the door.

I eased myself into the water and lay back, thinking how lucky I was to have such wonderful friends. Their names, of course, were not really Sid and Gus. They had been named by their parents, rather more conventionally, Elena Miriam Goldfarb and Augusta Mary Walcott, but around Greenwich Village, where we lived, they were always Sid and Gus. They were also, for all intents and purposes, a couple – something I had not come across in my sheltered Irish existence before. At home this would have made them social outcasts, to be whispered about behind closed lace curtains. In the society in which Sid and Gus moved, there were no rules. I found this delightfully refreshing and had become very fond of them both. They, in their turn, treated me as an adored child who could do no wrong.

By the time the water had begun to cool I was feeling relaxed, energized, and ready for anything again. I came downstairs to find fresh rolls from the French bakery around the corner on the kitchen table and the wonderful aroma of Sid's Turkish coffee. I can't say I had ever learned to love Turkish coffee as much as they did, but at this moment it was clearly a symbol of home and everything being all right after all.

'So do tell all, Molly. We're quite agog,' Sid said, pulling up a chair beside me and breaking open a roll. She had changed

out of the silk pajamas into dark-gray trousers and an emer-
ald green gentleman's smoking jacket which offset her black,
cropped hair wonderfully.

'Not until she's had something to eat, Sid. The poor lamb
has been through an ordeal,' Gus said, taking the basket of
rolls from Sid and handing it to me. 'They're still warm.
Heavenly.' She was still in the red robe, her light-brown curls
still wild and untamed around an elfin face.

I sipped the black syrupy liquid and then took a big bite of
warm roll, with melting butter and apricot jam. It felt good to
be alive again.

'You'll never guess why they apprehended me to begin
with,' I said, looking up from my roll with a grin. 'They
thought I was a woman of the streets.'

'You? Were they particularly nearsighted policemen?' Sid
asked.

'It was dark and apparently they had just made a raid on a
nearby bawdy house.'

'Then why didn't they release you the moment it became
obvious that you were not that type of woman?' Gus asked.

'They decided I had to be up to no good, loitering alone in
the middle of the night. They thought I might be a lookout for
a gang.'

'Molly as a gangster's moll! This gets better and better,' Sid
spluttered through a mouthful of crumbs.

'I'm sure it wasn't very amusing for poor Molly.' Gus
patted my hand. 'A night in a dreadful jail cell. How horrid
for you, my sweet.'

'It wasn't too bad. The cell was full of prostitutes, but they
couldn't have been kinder to me. They knew as well as I did
that I'd been wrongly arrested.'

'So presumably someone with sense came on duty this
morning, took one look at you, and realized a terrible mistake

had been made.' Sid reached over to refill my coffee without being asked.

I made a face. 'The person who came on duty was none other than Daniel Sullivan – the last person in the world I wanted to see in such circumstances.'

'Daniel the Deceiver, you mean?' Gus asked. They were well aware of my story and thought very poorly of him for his actions. 'Why didn't you use his name to get yourself released last night? It's the least he could do for you, after trifling with your affections like that.'

'I refuse to ask Daniel Sullivan for help. My pride won't let me. And besides, I knew he'd only say I told you so – which is exactly what he did.'

'I take it he still hasn't broken his engagement then?'

'Let's not talk about it,' I said. I helped myself to another roll. 'And do you want to hear the ultimate annoyance of the evening? I found out when the police were leading me away that I had tailed my erring husband to his mother's house, not his floozie's.'

They both burst out laughing.

'You spent the evening spying on him visiting his mother? Oh, but that is rich.'

I had to laugh with them. 'How was I to know? All I knew was that he was visiting a woman. It never occurred to me that the woman could be his mother.'

'Poor, sweet Molly,' Gus said, still smiling. 'I wish you'd stop this highly dangerous life and become something sensible like a writer or a painter.'

'I made up my mind to stop last night,' I said. 'Stop doing divorce cases anyway. I find they leave a bad taste in my mouth. I know they were Paddy's bread and butter, but . . .'

'But they're not your cup of tea!' Sid finished for me, delighted with her own wit.

'Precisely. I'm going to go back to my original intention of helping to reunite families. I've decided to place an advertisement in the Irish newspapers, and see if that brings any customers. If not, then I'll start thinking about a change of profession.'

Sid jumped up at the sound of the morning post landing on our doormat. She came back with a big smile on her face. 'Look at this. Postcard from Ryan.'

This was, of course, our friend, the delightful, flamboyant, annoying Irish playwright, Ryan O'Hare.

'Where is he?' Gus leaped up, peering over Sid's shoulder to see the postcard. 'The postmark is Pittsburgh.'

'That's what he says. Listen. "Greetings from the land of smoke and fume. We open in Pittsburgh tonight, although what these Vulcans will think of a wickedly urbane satire, I shudder to think. After Cleveland I have come to realize that I was right. Civilization does cease outside of New York. The air here is quite unbreathable. My coughing at night rivals that of La Dame aux Camelias, indeed I may well return consumptive . . . Yours in great suffering and tribulation, Ryan O'Hare, playwright extraordinaire."'

Sid and Gus looked at each other and laughed. 'Typical Ryan. Everything has to be dramatic,' Gus said. 'Now he's dying of consumption.'

'Of course I do feel for him,' Sid said. 'It was most unfortunate that President McKinley died just before his play was due to open. It wasn't his fault that the theaters were all closed for a month of national mourning. So it makes sense to take the play on the road before tackling New York, even if that road includes Pittsburgh.'

'Let's hope he returns to triumph at Daley Theater, just like he planned,' Gus said. 'Is there a tad more coffee in that pot do you think, dearest?'

I listened to them chatting merrily but my thoughts had moved elsewhere. Something about Ryan's postcard had left me feeling uneasy. We had, of course, been together when the President was shot. That would leave anyone feeling uneasy, but it was over now. The poor President was dead and buried and life had gone back to normal again. Then I realized what it was – Ryan's mention of consumption. My nagging conscience came back to me. Poor Kathleen O'Connor was dying of consumption, back home in Ireland while I had been neglecting her children more than I should. I resolved to pay them a visit this very morning. If their conditions were not satisfactory, then I'd do something about it, however much I hated to leave this wonderful life of bohemian ease.

I got to my feet. 'I should go out,' I said.

They were instantly at my side, the postcard from Ryan forgotten. 'You'll do no such thing,' Gus said. She could be quite forceful in spite of her delicate appearance. 'You've just spent a night in damp clothing in jail. You need a good long rest.'

I tried to protest, but Sid took my arm. 'No arguing. Now up you go and we'll wake you for lunch.'

I thought it best not to protest further. I went up the two flights to my room, opened the windows, and lay down on the bed. Delightful autumn sunshine streamed in through my window, along with the chirping of busy sparrows in the bushes outside. I could have been miles from the city. How could I possibly give this up? I tried to sleep but my mind was coiled tighter than a watch spring. In the end I gave up, put on my business suit – since my dark skirt was still sodden around the hem – then crept down the stairs like a naughty child. Out of Patchin Place, diagonally across Washington Square until I met the Bowery. Then I headed south to the Lower East Side where Seamus and his family were now again living.

I stopped at a butcher to buy a chicken, and at the green-grocer to buy grapes, remembering how Seamus had enjoyed them before. Then I added two lollipops from a street stall. If you're wondering where the money came from, seeing that I wasn't making any yet, I was paying myself a modest salary from the money Paddy had left in the business – or more accurately, the money I had found hidden in the bottom of a filing cabinet drawer. I had not been naive enough to hand it over to the police but had opened a bank account with it until a next of kin claimed it. So far no next of kin had come forward.

As I went on my way, the streets became noisier, dirtier, and smellier, the buildings taller, crammed together, shutting out the sunlight, giving me the feeling of being hemmed in. Memories of my own arrival in New York and my first unpleasant days on these streets came flooding back to me. How long ago it seemed. Was it really less than a year ago that I was walking these streets, penniless, afraid, with nowhere to go? I took stock of how far I had come and felt more cheerful right away.

As I passed through the Jewish quarter, crossing Hester Street then Rivington and Delancey, the streets became clogged with humanity – pushcarts everywhere, laden with every kind of merchandise. Vendors shouted their wares in tongues I couldn't understand. Chickens and geese hung by their necks in rows. Strange foods sizzled on makeshift stoves giving off exotic, spicy smells. I looked with interest at a pickle vendor, producing fat green pickled cucumbers from a barrel like a conjurer bringing rabbits from a hat. I wondered what they tasted like and was tempted to stop and buy one. There were so many things in the world that were still new to me. One day I should take the time to try them all. But the suspicious looks I was getting from bearded men

25

in tall black hats, from women who passed me with baskets on their arms, dragging serious, dark-eyed children let me know clearly that I was an outsider with no business in their territory. My bright-red hair and Irish complexion were definitely a disadvantage for a budding detective. Paddy could blend in anywhere. I'd find it hard to look anything but Irish.

It was the same as I moved into the Italian section to the south. Streets echoed with men in animated conversation, laundry flapped above our heads, old women in black sat on stoops in the morning sunshine, babies cried, children played, more pushcarts with different wares – jars of olives, jars of olive oil, jars with what looked like thin sticks in them which I guessed might be uncooked spaghetti – and me with the definite feeling of being the outsider.

A group of street urchins with dark, close cropped hair came running past me, the steel tips on their boots creating sparks on the cobbles. They leaped up at me and tugged at my long red hair. 'Hey, where's the fire, lady?' one of them shouted in accented English. He grabbed at my hair ribbon. I had grown up with brothers. I reacted instantly, caught him off guard and sent him sprawling backward. They didn't bother me again.

There was no mistaking when I came to Fulton Street. The fish market announced its presence long before I was anywhere near it. The smell of fish was heavy in the air, making me bring out my handkerchief and hold it to my nose. There were fish scales floating in the gutters and men hurried past pushing carts piled high with boxes of fish. I passed the market itself and was glad to turn onto South Street where a good, strong breeze from the East River made it possible to breathe again. Out of all of New York City, why on earth had they chosen to live right here?

Of course, I had to grant them the view. Over our heads the Brooklyn Bridge soared majestically across to the far shore, suspended, it seemed, by the frailest of strands. The East River was dotted with sails, ranging from tall-masted ships from across the ocean to squat, square-sailed barges going upriver. It painted a charming, lively canvas and I would have lingered longer to admire, had not the whiff of the fish market caught up with me. I crossed South Street and passed open shop fronts where sail-makers and woodwrights plied their trades before I turned into a narrow side alley and found the building I was looking for.

It was another dreary tenement building, even worse, if anything, than my first home on Cherry Street. The dark, narrow staircase smelled of urine, boiled cabbage, and fish. I made my way upstairs, past landings cluttered with prams and old boxes, hearing crying babies, voices raised in anger, a woman singing. I started when something scurried across the floor in front of me. Too big for a mouse. It had to be a rat.

I was out of breath by the time I had reached the fifth floor and prayed that Seamus would be at home. How did he manage to climb so many stairs with his damaged lungs? I knocked on the door and prayed this time that Nuala might not be at home. I had no wish ever to see her again. My prayer was not answered. Nuala herself opened the door, her bloated shape blotting out any light that might have come from the room behind her.

'Saints preserve us,' she said. 'Would you look what the cat dropped on our doorstep.'

'Lovely seeing you again too, Nuala.' I tried to get past her and into the apartment but she remained blocking the doorway.

'I didn't think you'd be turning up again, like a bad penny.

So your fancy man finally threw you out, did he? I knew it would happen in the end – didn't I tell you so, Seamus? Wasn't I saying that she'd come a cropper, for all her airs and graces? Well, it's no use thinking you're going to bunk here – packed like sardines, we are.'

'I have absolutely no wish to move in with you, Nuala,' I said. 'I have a very comfortable apartment, which I share with two female friends and not a fancy man in sight. I came to see how Seamus was getting along.'

Grudgingly she stood aside and let me enter. It was a hell-hole of a room with no windows, lit by one anemic lamp. Seamus was sitting in the one armchair and the lamplight made him look like a pale shadow of himself.

'Molly, my dear,' he said, rising awkwardly to his feet. 'It's so good to see you. How kind of you to come and visit us.'

'I was concerned about you, Seamus. I heard that you'd found a new place so I thought I'd come and pay you a call.'

'Yes, well it's not exactly what you'd call homely, is it, but it will have to do for now, until I can get back on me feet again.'

'Why on earth did you choose to live here of all places?' I blurted out before I realized it wasn't exactly a tactful remark.

'Beggars can't be choosers, can they?' Nuala answered for him. 'And seeing as how I'm the only breadwinner in the family and I'm working at the fish market there, I'm not risking walking home alone in the dead of night past all those drunken men. This city's not safe for a woman.'

I thought privately that the men would have to be very drunk indeed to have intentions on Nuala, but I nodded agreement.

'So Finbar isn't working?' I asked.

'That idle, no good bag o' bones? Who would hire him? When he worked for the saloon he drank more than he earned. I tried to get him a job as a porter at the market but he couldn't lift the loads.' She sniffed in disgust. 'He's sleeping in the next room.'

'I heard that,' came Finbar's voice and the person himself appeared in the doorway, looking like Marley's ghost in a white nightshirt and nightcap, his face pale and gray as the cloth he was wearing. 'And if I've told you once, I've told you a hundred times, woman, I've got meself a fine job lined up for the election.' He smiled at me, revealing a mouth of missing teeth.

'The election.' Nuala sniffed. 'We'll believe that when we see it.'

'Ask the Tammany boys yourself,' Finbar insisted. 'They told me they'd pay me for every man I lead, push, or drag to the polling place – who puts his cross for Shepherd, of course.'

'Pay you in liquor,' Nuala said. 'You'll drink yourself stupid and then be out of work again.'

I shifted uncomfortably at this brewing fight. 'And where are the children – in school?' I turned to Seamus.

'We haven't got them into a school yet,' Seamus said. 'Bridie's out running errands, and the boys – well, I don't quite know where they are.'

'Speaking of errands, I stopped off along the way and brought you a chicken and some grapes.' I found space for them on the table between dirty dishes, yesterday's *New York Herald* and some socks that Nuala had been darning. 'I thought you maybe could use some nourishment.'

'Most kind of you,' Seamus said. 'You're a good woman, Molly Murphy.'

I watched Nuala sidling up to whisk away my offering.

'Any news from Kathleen?' I asked, beating Nuala to the grapes and handing them to Seamus.

'Yes, but it's not good. She's fading, Molly. She keeps up a brave front, but I can tell she's fading. If only I could be with her. It fair breaks my heart. I tell you, Molly, there are times when I'm ready to take the risk and borrow the money for a passage home.'

'It must be very hard for you,' I said, 'but you know you'd be thrown in jail or even hanged if you go home. Think of the children. What good would it do to have a father in jail and a mother who's deathly sick?'

'What good am I here to them?' he said. 'Another useless bag of bones like Finbar. Not able to earn my keep at the moment.'

As he spoke I heard the sound of light feet running up the stairs. The door burst open and Bridie stood there. When she saw me, her face lit up. 'Molly. You've come back to us. I was praying in church on Sunday that you would.'

I put my arms around her thin little body. 'How have you been keeping? And how's your brother?'

She looked up, a big smile on her face. 'He's become a junior Eastman.'

'A what?'

'He and our cousins. They've joined a gang. They're called junior Eastmans, and they go around busting stuff up. And sometimes they get to do stuff for real big gang members and the big guys give them a quarter each.'

'Seamus, did you know about this?' I asked.

He shrugged. 'There's no harm in it. Just talk. Boys always run in herds, like young ponies, don't they?'

But I couldn't take this news so lightly. I had heard enough last night about violence and protection rackets to make me believe that there was indeed harm in young Shamey running with a gang. And I knew it was up to me to get him out of it. I'd just have to find a place of my own and bring them to live with me, at least until Seamus was on his feet again. I felt deep depression settling over me at the thought of leaving the little heaven on Patchin Place, but it had to be done. I was only alive now because the children's mother had given me a chance to escape. Giving up a few months of my life was the least I could do in return.

Four

I walked home with heavy steps, deep in thought. How could I afford a place of my own, big enough to take in Seamus and the children? I wouldn't want it to be in a neighborhood like this, either. I wanted to stay in Greenwich Village, where I had made friends and where I loved the exuberance of the lifestyle. Somehow I needed to make money. I did have the means in front of my nose – I'd just have to overcome my repugnance and get on with the Tomlinson divorce case – if I wasn't arrested every time I tried to follow Mr T.

I gave a big sigh. I wasn't the sort of person who liked going against her principles, which was the reason that I was not prepared to spend the tidy sum of money that I'd discovered in Paddy's filing cabinet. It was sitting in the bank, waiting for an heir to claim it. So far no one had, which probably meant it was my money. But I still couldn't bring myself to use it for anything but official business.

I stepped back from the curb, hastily, as a carriage went past, its wheels and the horses' hooves spraying up muck from the gutter. I supposed I'd have to go back to spying on Mr Tomlinson. I just prayed he didn't have aged female relatives all over the city. Next time I'd find some excuse to check out who owned the houses he visited. It was all so complicated.

Why couldn't the wretched man just agree to give his wife a divorce and save me all this trouble? I was half tempted to go to his office and beg him to grant her wish, so that I was spared any more of this sordid business. I paused on a street corner, one foot in midair. Why not? Why did it always have to be furtive and sordid like this? We were, after all, civilized human beings.

Having made up my mind, I turned on my heels and, instead of catching the trolley up Broadway, I went in the other direction, down to Wall Street. I knew where Mr Tomlinson worked. I had stood outside waiting for him enough times now. It was right next door to the magnificent columns of the stock exchange where there was always such a hustle and bustle that I could blend nicely into the crowd. This time I didn't lurk in the shadows. I went up the steps, through the front door, and up a flight of marble stairs. I passed an impressive mirror and glanced at myself. I was glad that I had elected to put on my one respectable garment, a beige tailored business suit which had been made for me when I decided to become a female investigator. But I wished I'd put my hair up. With it tied back in a ribbon I looked ridiculously young and most unprofessional. I stepped into a recess and attempted to twist it into a knot. If only I could learn to wear hats like other women, then I'd never be caught out like this. But I'd grown up without wearing a hat and only wore one when strictly necessary. I didn't like the feel of my head being restricted any more than I liked the restriction of a corset on my body.

J. BAKER TOMLINSON III, STOCKBROKER, was on the second floor. A hollow-eyed young man wearing a large starched collar greeted me and tried to wheedle out of me why I wanted to see Mr Tomlinson. I was suitably enigmatic and, shortly afterward, I was shown into a tastefully furnished office with mahogany desk and thick carpet on the floor.

'Miss Murphy?' Mr Tomlinson waved me to a leather padded armchair. 'My secretary didn't make it clear what your manner of business was. Are you here for financial advice?' I saw him summing up the quality of my costume and the hair, which was probably already escaping from its makeshift bun.

'I'm here on a very different sort of matter, Mr Tomlinson,' I said. 'One which causes me considerable embarrassment.'

'Really?' He was looking interested, not guilty. 'Please proceed. I am quite intrigued.'

I handed him my card. 'My company was hired by your wife.' I met his gaze. 'She wanted us to provide proof for her to file for divorce.'

Mr Tomlinson sat back in his chair with a thump. 'Good God.' He hadn't even noticed the profanity spoken in my presence. 'Lillian wants a divorce? I can't believe it.' His eyes narrowed. 'So if you are working for my wife, why exactly have you come to see me?'

'Because I don't like it, that's why,' I said. 'I'm not the sort of person who enjoys snooping for sordid details. I've been watching you for a couple of weeks now, and you seem like a gentleman to me. Quite the opposite of another chap I was watching who was with a different floozie every night. So it seemed to make sense to lay it out straight in front of you. If your wife wants a divorce, why not behave like a gentleman and agree to give her one? That way we will all be spared a lot of embarrassment.'

He continued to look at me through narrowed eyes then he started laughing. 'You're a rum one all right, Miss Murphy. I have to admit you've caught me completely off guard. I had no idea that Lillian wanted a divorce. We haven't had the happiest of marriages for some time, owing to her illness, of course.'

'Mrs Tomlinson is ill?'

He sucked through his teeth before answering. 'She thinks she is. She takes to her bed at the slightest excuse and we have a constant procession of doctors coming to the house. I know she thinks I'm not sympathetic enough but God knows I've tried. She complains I'm never home, but who'd want to stay home with a wife who spends the evening taking patent medicines and then retires for the night at eight?' He stopped suddenly, as if he realized he had said too much. 'I've stuck it out so far because I was raised to do the right thing, but by God, if she wants a divorce, I will be happy to grant her one.'

'Is there anyone – another woman?' I couldn't resist asking. 'I've been following your movements and I've not found one yet.'

'So now you're getting me to do your work for you?' A spasm of annoyance crossed his face, then he laughed again. 'You really are delightfully refreshing, Miss Murphy. They always say your countrymen have a touch of the blarney, don't they?' He straightened a pile of papers on his desk before he looked up again. 'If you really want to know, there is one young woman I would have approached, had circumstances been different. But, as I say, I was brought up to do the right thing. I have thrown myself into my work and put thoughts of other women aside.'

I left John Baker Tomlinson's office with a warm glow of success. Now both the Tomlinsons would get what they wanted. Lillian would be free of a husband who paid no attention to her and John would be able to court the woman he admired. I always knew that the forthright approach was best. All that time Paddy had wasted, lurking in dark alleys and trying to take incriminating pictures, while I had brought my first divorce case to a happy conclusion without any effort!

I stopped off at the post office on the way home to buy a stamp, so that I could send my advertisement to Dublin. I was about to leave when the postal clerk, a florid man with mutton chop whiskers, called me back. 'Aren't you the young woman who worked for Paddy Riley?'

'That's right.'

'Letter just came for J. P. Riley and Associates,' he said and produced it. I thanked him and put it in my purse, although I was dying to open it. Once I was safely in the street, I ripped it open.

The letter was typewritten. 'Mr Max Mostel requests that you call on him at your earliest convenience, regarding a matter of great delicacy and confidentiality.'

The address was on Canal Street – a seedy area of commerce, factories, and saloons. Another divorce case? In which case, a strange address for a client. But he had called it a matter of some delicacy. The difference was that a man had written to me this time. And in all the other divorce cases in Paddy's records, the clients had been women. This in itself made it appealing. More appealing was the fact that it represented the possibility of enough money to rent a place of my own.

Sid and Gus were out when I returned to Patchin Place, probably doing the morning shopping at the Jefferson Market opposite. I hurried up the stairs with a sigh of relief. I sat at my desk and wrote a letter to the *Dublin Times*. 'Lost touch with your loved ones in America? Private investigator will make discreet inquiries. Reuniting families is our specialty.' I didn't mention the sex of the private investigator, nor that I had never actually reunited a family. I asked for long-term advertising rates and promised to send payment by return of post. Then I went downstairs again and deposited the letter in the mailbox at the end of the street. I looked up to see Sid and Gus bearing down on me. Gus's arms were full of flowers. Sid carried two overflowing baskets.

'Look, Gus, she's up and awake and looking so much

better. We have been having such fun, Molly. Gus has been buying up the entire market.'

'I wanted oysters, but Sid wouldn't let me, even though I told her there was an R in the month so it should be fine.'

'They didn't look fine to me, they looked decidedly peaky,' Sid said. 'I had an uncle who died after eating a bad oyster. I'm not taking any chances with you.'

'So I had to settle for lobster instead. Even Sid had to agree they were still swimming around with great vigor and positively radiated health. So I'm going to prepare a true Boston lobster feast tonight. Whom should we invite?'

'Someone who won't mind plunging the damned things into boiling water,' Sid said, laughing.

They swept me along Patchin Place, caught up in the excitement of frivolous living. It was moments like this that reminded me how very hard it would be to leave them and move to a place of my own.

That afternoon, while Sid and Gus were in a flurry of preparation for tonight's lobster feast, I made myself look respectable and businesslike, secured my hair in a bun with twenty or more hairpins, perched my one respectable hat on top of it, and set off to present myself to Mr Max Mostel. As I followed the Bowery southward, and then turned onto Canal Street, my confusion and curiosity grew. This was not a respectable residential area – it was full of factories, run-down saloons, the occasional seedy boarding-house. Certainly not the kind of area in which I expected my clients to live. When I came to Number 438 it wasn't a residence at all. The bottom floor was half open to the sidewalk and I could hear the sounds of hammering and sawing going on inside. A newly made chair was being varnished just inside the doorway. I asked for Mr Mostel and was directed up the staircase around the corner.

A business then, not a home. I went up the dark and narrow stairway, one flight, two flights, then a third, until I came to a doorway with a sign on it: MOSTEL AND KLEIN, LADIES FASHIONS. I knocked and entered a packing and shipping area. Men were staggering around with large boxes and depositing them on a primitive platform outside a back window to lower to the street. I asked for Mr Mostel.

'In his office. Up two more flights. Go through the sewing room and you'll find the stairs at the end,' an elderly man gasped as he paused to mop his brow.

Up another flight that ended in a closed door. I knocked on this and eventually was admitted into a long gloomy room full of young women sewing, row after row of them, their heads bent low over their work. I had been in a room like this before, when I had briefly tried my hand at any job I could get. I hadn't liked it then and I didn't like it now. The room resounded to the clatter of the machines. A hundred pairs of feet worked the treadles while one hundred needles flew up and down. There were bolts of cloth piled along walls. It was airless and lint rose from under my feet, causing me to sneeze. This made several of the girls glance up, look at me, and then go back to their sewing again, as if they begrudged the second they had wasted. Nobody said a word as I walked the length of the room until a male voice roared out, 'Hey, you – where do you think you're going?'

I imagine that every sweatshop employs at least one male bully to strike fear into its female workers. This one – sallow, sagging, and with the sort of face that had a perpetual leer – was rather more repulsive than the one I had encountered before. Luckily I was in a very different situation this time. I eyed him coldly.

'I am on my way to see Mr Mostel. Would you kindly find out if it is convenient to see me at this moment?'

'You want to see Mr Mostel? Miss Hoity Toity, ain't we! If it's about a job, I'm the guy you see. The boss don't see no stinking girls.'

'Fortunately I bathed this morning and don't happen to be a stinking girl,' I said, hearing the titter of laughter from some of the workers who understood English. 'But I received a letter from him this morning, asking me expressly to call upon him.' I was about to hand him my card, when I remembered that I should be discreet and confidential. No need to let this greasy man or any of these girls know who was calling on the boss. 'If you would direct me to his office, please.'

'Follow me,' he said, 'and don't blame me if you get your head blown off.'

He led me up another flight of stairs, negotiating boxes of thread and trimmings on almost every step. He knocked on the door and opened it gingerly. 'Young lady to see you, sir. Says you wrote her a letter.'

I stepped past him into a cluttered little office. There were more bolts of cloth stacked in the office and a dressmaker's dummy displaying a frilled blouse and black skirt. Max Mostel was seated at a cluttered desk. He was a big podgy man with heavy jowls, sweating in a pinstriped three-piece suit. A cigar stuck out of one corner of his mouth.

'Yeah? What do you want?'

I handed him my card. 'You wrote to me. Here I am.'

He looked at it, glanced up at his foreman. 'What are you hanging around for?' he growled in heavily accented English. 'Get down there again before one of those girls shoves a few yards of my ribbon into her blouse. Go on. *Raus!* And shut the door behind you.'

The foreman went, closing the door none too gently. Max Mostel continued to scowl at me. 'You're the one I wrote to?'

I nodded. 'I am Miss Murphy. Junior partner. I'm sorry if

39

you were expecting a man, but I assure you I am most efficient and do excellent work.'

'No, I wasn't expecting a man,' he said. 'It's a woman I need for this job. I was asking around and a little bird told me that you were doing this kind of thing. Am I right?'

'What kind of thing was that, Mr Mostel?'

'Snooping. I need someone to do some snooping for me.'

'I see. Would you care to elaborate?'

He leaned across the desk toward me, even though the door was shut and we two were alone in the room. 'We've got a plant.'

I looked around the room, also, trying to locate this particular piece of flora.

'A plant?' I asked.

'A spy in the camp, Miss Murphy. A traitor in our midst.' He looked around the room again. 'You see this design—' he handed me a page from a catalog showing a sleek, long dress with high collar and sweeping skirt.

'It's very nice,' I said.

'And it was on the racks in all the major department stores a week before ours was finished, with the Lowenstein label on it. My design, mark you. My garment. With his filthy label on it.'

'Are you sure that it wasn't an unhappy coincidence?'

He shook his head so that his chins quivered. 'Stolen, from under my very nose. And not the first time it's happened either. Someone in this building is a plant, Miss Murphy, secretly working for Lowenstein. Getting their hot little hands on my latest designs and running them across town for him to copy in a hurry.'

'And you would like me to discover who this person is?'

'Exactly. Have you ever been involved in the garment industry, Miss Murphy?'

'Only very briefly.'

'But would you know how to operate a sewing machine?'

'With only moderate success. I haven't had much practice.'

'No matter. We'll take you on here and train you, until you get up to speed. Then I want you to apply at Lowenstein's. Keep your ear to the ground in both places and see who turns up where he or she shouldn't.'

I nodded. 'I can do that. Who has access to your designs?'

'Not many people. The cutters and finishers would see them when they are in the process of being made, but the girls at the machines – they only do piecework, whatever is put in front of them. Their only concern is a sleeve or a pocket or a collar. They never see the finished garment.' He tapped the side of his nose. 'That's not to say that a smart girl couldn't do some snooping if she'd a mind to, but I don't see how. I'm usually here in my office most of the day. The designs are kept in this drawer. And I lock my office when I go out.'

'Are you the only one with an office up here? What about Mr Klein?'

'Mr Klein?' He looked surprised. 'Dead, Miss Murphy. Dropped dead two years ago – may he rest in peace.'

'I'm sorry to hear it, Mr Mostel. So who might come up to your office during the course of the workday?'

'My foreman. My two sample hands – who are completely trustworthy, by the way. The samples are made in the little back room up here, behind me, so nobody has a chance to see the garments before they are ready to be shown. Apart from that – I usually come down if there is a problem with an employee. They don't come up here.'

'And buyers?'

'I go to them, Miss Murphy. Buyers are not going to climb up five flights of stairs.'

'Could anyone get in when everyone has gone home at night?'

41

'I take the designs home with me.'

'So it has to be someone who works here during the day.'

He nodded. 'A nice little problem we've got for ourselves, eh? So will you take on the job, Miss Murphy? I'll make it worth your while.'

'This could require several weeks of work,' I said. 'Shall we say a retainer of one hundred dollars, plus the regular wages I would earn if I worked here?'

He put his hand to his chest. 'One hundred dollars? Miss Murphy, I asked you to help me, not bankrupt me.'

'I assure you this is the sort of fee my clients expect to pay, Mr Mostel. If you think you can find someone who can do the job more cheaply . . .' I got to my feet.

He shrugged. 'If it will allow me to sleep soundly in my bed at night, then I suppose I have no choice – even if the children will have to live on rye bread and cabbage soup for a few months.'

'I understand cabbage soup is very healthy, if properly prepared,' I said and I saw a smile twitch his cigar up and down.

'So it's a deal then, Miss Murphy.' He held out a meaty hand. I shook it.

'I will enjoy the challenge, Mr Mostel.'

Five

I came home bubbling with enthusiasm. Now this was a real case, one I could sink my teeth into with no twinges of conscience about catching illicit couples. It would be easy enough to blend in and pass as an ordinary working girl, since I was one. Not in such dire circumstances as most of them, but still struggling to earn my way in a new country. Of course learning to be an efficient seamstress was another matter. Skill with a needle has never been one of my greatest attributes.

The front door at 9 Patchin Place was open, revealing a veritable hive of enthusiasm and industry. Exotic, herby smells wafted down the hallway toward me. Gus was studying an enormous cookery book in the kitchen, while Sid was stringing paper lanterns out in the garden. The kitchen sink teemed with scrabbling lobsters. I didn't even have time to spill the news of my new commission before Gus pounced upon me.

'Molly, you're just in time. I need someone to slice onions.'

I was given an apron and dragged into the frantic preparations. By eight o'clock the house was ready and started to fill with writers, painters, poets, and freethinkers. There were many more people than there were lobsters, but it didn't seem to matter. There was plenty of wine and ale, so a good time was had by all. Myself, I was content to sit back and take it all in. I was still such a newcomer to the world of artists and free-thinkers that I felt a little awkward taking part in their witty badinage, but I soaked it all in like a sponge. The discussion moved from women's rights to birth control to anarchy. Then the talk moved on to New York politics and the upcoming mayoral election.

'It really seems that Tammany might be losing its grip,' Lennie, a painter friend, said, waving an ear of sweet corn – a delicacy I had just discovered. 'There's little love for this Shepherd fellow. Everyone says Seth Low is the man to get rid of Charlie Murphy's corruption.'

'I see little point in discussing an election in which half of us can't participate,' Sid said angrily. 'Whoever wins it will be the same – more jobs for the boys, more kickbacks under the table.'

'And what do you say, Mr Clemens?' Gus asked an elderly gentleman with bushy white hair and a drooping mustache who had come to join the group. He looked too old to be part of Sid and Gus's artistic set and I wondered how he had been invited.

The old man smiled. 'It should be perfectly obvious what you have to do. Give women the vote. That will do away with tyrants and dictators instantly. Women will always opt for sensible and compassionate over warlike and corrupt.'

There was loud applause from the whole room. I began to think that he must be a politician of sorts. I nudged Gus who was standing beside me. 'Who is that man?'

She looked at me in amazement. 'You haven't heard of Samuel Clemens?'

I shook my head.

'He's one of our most distinguished writers. He's just come back from Europe and he has chosen to live in our little neck of the woods. Isn't he magnificent?'

I had to agree that he was and resolved to go out and buy one of his books forthwith. Any man who was a champion of votes for women was definitely worth reading.

As the talk went on late into the night, I found myself becoming philosophical. This group and those factory girls I had witnessed just a few short blocks away were so far removed from each other that they might have been circling two different suns. I knew that some of these people also struggled to survive. That chubby painter in the corner only ate when he sold a painting. And yet survival was not at the core of their existence. If they had to choose between paint and food, they would choose the former. Whereas those girls at the sweatshop worked their lives away in those dreary conditions to pay for food and rent and probably thought that they had no choice. But didn't each of us have a choice in what we did? Then I decided that it was the unaccustomed wine that was making me think this way.

The last reveler didn't leave until the wee hours of the morning. We collapsed into our beds, only to be woken at first light by a hammering on the front door. I heard Sid's slippers flip-flopping down the stairs, a conversation, then up again, calling softly, 'Molly, are you awake? A man is outside with a message for you.'

My head was throbbing from the effects of alcohol. I reached for my robe and hurried downstairs. A young boy grinned at my disheveled appearance. 'Compliments of Mrs Tomlinson,' he said and handed me a letter. I had to race upstairs again to find a dime to tip the boy, then I opened the note. I hoped it would contain her check and grateful thanks. Instead it requested that I present myself in person at the Tomlinson house as soon as possible. Obviously the good woman wanted to pay me and thank me in person.

So after breakfast, suitably businesslike in my attire, I

made my way to the East Side. I was shown to an upstairs room where Mrs Tomlinson reclined on a daybed. She looked pale and languid, but she sat up easily enough as I came in.

'Miss Murphy,' she said.

'I came as soon as I got your message, Mrs Tomlinson.'

'You went to see my husband yesterday—'

'I thought it better for both parties. Your husband seemed like a gentleman. I didn't feel right trying to expose him. So he agreed to do the gentlemanly thing, did he? That must be a relief for you.'

'A relief? You stupid girl! I asked you to find me facts, not to interfere. Now look what you've done!'

'He won't grant you the divorce?' I was puzzled.

'Of course he'll grant me the divorce.' She spat the words out. 'He came to my room last night and told me he'd be only too happy to set me free from a restricting marriage.'

'But isn't that what you wanted?'

She glared at me. 'It is not at all what I wanted. I had no intention of actually getting a divorce. I hoped my actions would spur my husband into paying me more attention and realizing how shamefully he was neglecting me. But now—' she put her handkerchief up to her mouth and gave a little sob – 'now he sees a divorce as a liberation for both of us. I've lost my husband, Miss Murphy, all because of you and your meddling ways!'

'I'm truly sorry, Mrs Tomlinson,' I said, 'but I was instructed to find evidence for a divorce case. And if you really want to know, I came up with no blot on your husband's character.'

This only made her cry harder.

'If you tell him your true motive, maybe there will be a hope of your reconciliation,' I suggested. She didn't answer. I thought it best to make a retreat, and I hadn't the heart to ask her for my fee. That's it, I decided. The last divorce case that

I shall ever tackle. I resolved to do a better job when I went spying at the factory.

A loud jangling noise woke me. I sat up in darkness, my heart thumping. Fire. It must be a fire bell ringing. I had to get out. Then my foot touched the cold oilcloth and I remembered that I had borrowed Sid's alarm clock to make sure I woke at six A.M. I had to report to work at Mostel and Klein by seven. As I went down the stairs to the bathroom I remembered that I had been dreaming about a fire before the bell woke me.

I came back upstairs, shivering in the early morning chill and dressed with care in my old white blouse and the plaid skirt that I had worn when I fled from Ireland. I tied my hair back instead of putting it up. I had to look as if I was a newly arrived immigrant. I would have to watch my mouth too. Last time I had worked in a similar sweatshop I had told the foreman what I thought of him, which had brought me dismissal within a week. That and having sewn a whole pile of sleeves inside out.

I tiptoed down the stairs, trying not to wake Sid and Gus, and helped myself to some of yesterday's stale bread and jam. As the reality of what I was doing hit me, I began to question yesterday's enthusiasm. Stale bread and twelve hours of toil ahead of me instead of a leisurely breakfast of fresh hot rolls and Sid's strong coffee – if this was what an investigator's life was like, couldn't I find a more civilized job?

I let myself out into cold gray dawn. The Jefferson Market was in full swing, but as I crossed Washington Square it was still deserted. Too early for students or artists! But as I followed the Bowery southward, the city came to life – trolley cars clanged as factory workers dodged past them to cross the street. Delivery wagons rumbled past, pulled by huge stocky horses. I reached Canal Street with ten minutes to

47

spare and had time to collect my thoughts before I entered the building. Mr Mostel had given me my instructions. Nobody was to know that I wasn't an ordinary worker. I was to blend in and keep my eyes open. But not at the expense of my work. I couldn't be seen to be minding other people's business. And I'd be treated just like any other girl – not a pleasant prospect when I remembered the leering foreman. Still it was only for a few weeks. I could stick it out for that long, couldn't I?

A parade of girls was now making its way up the stairs. I joined them, getting some odd stares. I listened to the conversation going on around me and realized I couldn't understand a word of what was being said. The girls in front of me were speaking Yiddish, those behind me were gabbing away in Italian. It suddenly hit me that this assignment was not going to be easy. If there were any kind of conspiracy, I'd have no chance of overhearing any whispered messages. I'd just have to rely on using my eyes and my instincts.

The other girls hung up their hats and shawls on a row of hooks then took their places at their machines. I stood looking around, not knowing what to do next.

'You are new, *ya*?' one of the girls asked in broken English. I nodded shyly.

'You must wait until Seedy Sam gets here,' another girl said. She was tall, slim, and attractive with a smart white blouse and a cameo at her neck. 'He'll tell you where to sit.'

'Seedy Sam?' I asked innocently.

She grinned. 'It's what we call Sam Walters, the foreman. Only don't let him hear you call him that, or you'll be out on your ear.' She looked at me with interest. 'You're not Jewish or Italian – are you English?'

'No, I'm Irish.'

'That's very funny.'

'What is – being Irish?' I stuck out my chin and felt my fists clench. Nobody made fun of the Irish when I was around.

'Sorry. I don't mean funny. Strange. It is strange. The girls who speak good English don't stay long, and they talk back to the bosses. That's why Sam likes to hire newniks like us who can't talk back. I'm Sadie. Sadie Blum.'

'Molly Murphy,' I said, shaking her hand politely. 'Pleased to make your acquaintance. You seem to speak pretty good English,' I added.

'Yes, well I'm here two years now and I learn quick.'

Several other girls had clustered around listening to this exchange. One of them tapped my shoulder. 'Weren't you here the other day, visiting the boss?'

She was eyeing me suspiciously.

'That's right. I was bringing him a message from an old friend in Europe. Then I decided I might as well ask him for a job while I was here.' I saw a glance pass between two of them. 'Oh, don't worry,' I said. 'The boss made it very clear to me that I could expect no special treatment if I worked here, just because my great-uncle knew him.'

'Whassamatter, did they declare a public holiday that I didn't know about?' a big male voice boomed and Seedy Sam came into the room.

'If they did, we wouldn't get it off,' Sadie muttered in my ear.

'Get to it then. It's already one minute past seven. To your machines and no talking. You know the rules!' Then he noticed me. 'And what have we here?'

'My name's Molly Murphy. Mr Mostel said I might start work today.'

'I remember you, all right.' Sam sneered. 'All that garbage about delivering letters to the boss, when you were really after a job here!'

'That was true,' I said. 'I was delivering a message from an old friend. I just decided to ask him for a job when I was talking to him.'

'Don't think you're going to be treated any different from the rest of these girls,' Sam said with his usual leer.

'Why would I be? I have no connection with your boss, other than delivering him a message. Now where would you like me to sit?'

'What skills do you have? You know how to sew, don't ya?'

'I can operate a machine, but I'm a little out of practice. Mr Mostel said I could start out on something simple until I get up to speed.'

'Collars then. Go and sit next to Golda. She's in charge of our learners. She'll show you what to do.'

A large middle-aged woman in a high-collared black dress beckoned and patted a stool beside her. 'Sit your heiny down there and we'll get started,' she said, giving me a friendly smile. 'Did you bring your needle?'

'Needle?'

'Oh yes, girls have to supply their own sewing needles in this shop. And your own thread too. You can start off with one of mine, but during your lunch break you pop across to the dry-goods store and get yourself a medium-point needle and a spool of white thread.'

'They make us buy our own needles and thread?' I burst out before I remembered that I was supposed to be shy, withdrawn, and not attract any attention to myself.

Golda looked shocked. 'But they do at all the shops. Where were you working last?'

'At a little place in Ireland,' I said. 'It was different there. Just a few girls. Friendly atmosphere.'

'How nice,' she said wistfully. 'You won't find the atmosphere too friendly here, thanks to Seedy Sam over there. He makes sure we're always miserable. We're not supposed to talk at all. If a girl is found talking, he docks five cents off her wages. We get away with it now, because I'm showing you what to do. Now watch carefully.' She took two pieces of collar, put them together, and the machine clattered as it flew around the edges of three sides. 'Smooth sides facing out. Get it?'

I nodded and demonstrated for her, rather more slowly.

'*Ach ya*, you'll do just fine,' she said a short while later. 'She's a quick learner, Sam. She's ready to start out on her own.'

Sam motioned me to an empty place beside Sadie, who gave me an encouraging grin as I sat down. A large pile of pre-cut collars was put on my right side. I started sewing. As I finished each piece a small girl darted up with a large pair of scissors to cut the ends. As fast as the pile went down, Sam was there with another huge pile. It was never ending. I thought I was doing well until he said, 'If you go at that speed, you'll be here all night. Step it up, will ya?'

I glanced at my fellow workers. Their needles were positively flying up and down. How was I going to be able to observe who might be sneaking around when I obviously wouldn't have a moment to breathe? The morning dragged on. Nobody spoke, unless Sam left the room and then there were whispers. One girl got up and walked down the room toward the door.

'Where do you think you're going?' Sam demanded.

'Washroom,' the girl said. 'I need to go.'

'You were up and down all day yesterday,' Sam complained. 'Think you've found a way to slack off, do ya? Well, I'm docking ten cents from your pay packet. That'll teach you.'

'Give her a break, Sam,' Sadie said. 'She's expecting.

Everyone knows you have more calls of nature when you're in that condition.'

'You girls should think more about your duty to your boss and less about populating the world with more stinking kids,' Sam growled. 'Go on then. Go to the washroom, but you're staying late if you don't meet your quota. I don't care how many brats you got squalling for you.'

Sadie looked at me and shook her head.

At last a bell rang and everyone jumped up.

'Half an hour, remember,' Sam yelled. 'Not no stinking thirty-five minutes. We don't pay you good money to waste the boss's time.'

'They don't pay us good money, and that's a fact.' Sadie fell into step beside me as she reached for her shawl.

'You talking again, Sadie Blum?' Sam's voice echoed down the room. 'Better watch that mouth or you'll owe me more than you earn by the end of the week. Okay, line up for inspection if you want to go out.'

'What is this, the army?' I whispered to Sadie.

'He has to inspect our bags and pockets to make sure we're not stealing any of the trimmings,' she whispered back. 'Sometimes they even lock the doors when we're using expensive stuff.'

Sam came charging up to us. 'Some people never learn, do they, and now you're teaching the new girl bad habits. I'm docking you each ten cents from your pay packet. And next time you talk, it will be a quarter. Your fancy airs and graces don't work around here.'

He searched my purse then he put his hands on my waist and ran them down my sides. 'Hey, watch it!' I said, slapping his hands away from me. 'You can search my purse if you like, but you're not touching my person.'

'I'm only checking your pockets, sweetheart. Nothing to

get your dander up about.' He grinned at me with that insulting leer. 'If I was really feeling you up, I'd do a much better job of it.'

At last he opened the door and we filed down the stairs. 'That man is awful,' I muttered to Sadie as we passed through the door and started in a procession down the stairs. 'Why doesn't somebody do something about him?'

'Do what? If we complain, we're fired. The boss doesn't care how we're treated as long as the work gets done. And there are plenty of girls stepping off the boat every day waiting to take our places.'

'And it's better than some of the shops,' another girl commented, coming up to join us as we stepped out into the fresh air of the street. 'My sister only gets five dollars a week if she's lucky, and they dock her pay for the use of the firm's power supply, and an extra five cents for the use of the mirror and towel in the washroom. She says the mirror is so small you can hardly see to powder your nose. She tried bringing her own towel from home too, but they still docked her the five cents a week.'

'None of these bosses care about their workers, Sarah. It's all about money,' Sadie said. She turned back to me. 'Girls are always getting sick because there's not enough air to breathe and too many of us crammed into one room, but they won't let us have the window open, even in summer.'

'So why do you stay?' I asked.

'What else can *newnik* girls like us do?' Sarah, the second girl, said with a shrug of her shoulders. In contrast to Sadie, who was tall and carried herself with a certain air of grace, Sarah was frail and hollow looking, as if she hadn't had a good meal or been out in the fresh air recently. 'Nobody's going to hire immigrant *newniks* outside of the sweatshops.'

'I'm educated, but it don't matter,' Sadie said. 'Back at

home I had a good life. I was taking piano lessons and French. Too bad it wasn't English. Now I just pick up gutter English.' She slipped her arm through mine. 'You speak nice. You help me to speak more educated, okay?'

'So why are you here, if you had such a good life?' I asked.

Sadie and Sarah looked at each other as if I was rather stupid. 'When there's a pogrom, they don't care which Jews are rich and which are poor. They destroyed and burned our house. They threw my piano out of the upstairs window.' She turned away, biting her lip. 'And what they did to my big sister was unmentionable. My mother was thanking God that she died. I was hiding under the straw in the henhouse, but we could hear her cries for help.' She pressed her lips together and turned her face away from us.

'They killed my father,' Sarah added. 'They ran a bayonet through him while we watched. My mama brought us to America with money she had sewn into the hem of her skirt.'

I had had no idea that such things went on in the world. I looked at tall, elegant Sadie and frail little Sarah and was amazed how calmly they were telling me this. No wonder these girls put up with such bad conditions in America. At least they didn't have to fear for their lives every day.

I should do something to help, I thought. I speak English. I could make the bosses listen. Then I reminded myself that this was not my struggle. I was only here as a spy. In a few short weeks, I'd be gone again.

Six

By the time I had been at the garment factory a week, I had almost come to believe that I really did work there and that this terrible life of drudgery was all I had to look forward to. My feet ached from working the treadle. My fingers were raw from handling the cloth. I prayed to get the assignment over quickly, but my sewing still wasn't good enough to guarantee that another firm would hire me. In addition to this, the designs for the new spring collection wouldn't be ready until the middle of November, at least three weeks away. The plan I had hatched with Max Mostel was as follows: I should work for him until I was up to speed, which would give me time to observe his workers. I would then apply at Lowenstein's and start work there at least a week before Max Mostel finished his designs and passed them to the sample hands, so that I was familiar enough with the routine at the new factory to be able to know who was who and what was what. That meant about two more weeks at this hellhole.

I think it was the lack of air that got to me most. That and the lack of light. As the autumn light faded and one gray day followed another it became harder to see what we were sewing. The row of girls closest to the window had a slight advantage, but not much because the windows were small and badly needed washing. Those of us three rows back had to rely on anemic gas lamps. No wonder the girls bent low over their work and several of them were wearing glasses.

And of course for me the hardest thing of all was holding my tongue and not getting myself fired. Those girls were so submissive and browbeaten that it riled my fighting spirit. Every time one of them was docked money for going to the washroom too often, or coming in one minute late from lunch I was itching to jump up and tell that leering monster Sam what I thought of him. On the last day of my assignment I'd let him have it all right! I spent those long hours at the machine thinking up choice phrases to hurl at him when I made my grand exit.

By the end of a week I had received a pay packet containing four dollars and ninety cents. The other dollar and five cents had been docked for various sins – twice back late from lunch, once whispering, once dropping a collar on the floor and once getting up to stretch out my back. On the way home I thought gloomily that I hadn't foreseen how hard this assignment would be. I couldn't imagine any of those downtrodden females having the nerve to slip upstairs to the boss's office and steal his designs from under his very nose, even if they could ever get past the fearsome foreman.

A whole week had gone by and I hadn't even started my investigation. At this rate the new designs would come and go and I'd still be trying to get up to speed on collars! I should be sounding out the other girls with cleverly phrased questions. If only Paddy had still been around, he would have known what to ask. Why did he have to die before I had had a chance to learn from him? There was so much I still didn't know. In fact every time I set out on a case, I felt like a lone traveler, floundering through a blizzard.

My only chance to talk to the other girls was at lunch,

when some of them went to the little café across the street and got a bowl of stew or at least a coffee to go with their sandwich.

'So what are we actually making here?' I asked, like the bright new learner that I was. 'I only get to see collars.'

'Right now it's ladies' dresses – latest fashion for the big stores,' someone said.

'Latest fashion, eh? That sounds very exciting,' I said. 'So I'll get some tips on what to wear if I see what comes out of this shop?'

'You won't ever see the finished garment,' Sadie said. 'They have finishers who put the pieces together.'

'So who designs these latest fashions? Do they come from Paris or something?'

'Listen to her! Paris? Such ideas.'

I laughed. 'Well, I don't know anything about it. I'm new. I always thought that fashions came from Paris.'

'I think old Mostel designs his own, doesn't he?' The girls looked at each other.

'Yes, and he thinks he's the cat's whiskers too.'

'I can't imagine him designing ladies' dresses.' I grinned at them. 'He doesn't look like a fashionable kind of man.'

'You should see his family,' Golda said, leaning confidentially close. '*Oy vay*, but do they live like kings. He's here working away at the business every day, making sure nobody steals a yard of his precious ribbon and his wife and children are out spending his money as fast as he can make it. And when you see them, they go around with their noses in the air, like they were born aristocrats and not just arrived from a stadtl, like the rest of us.'

'They're immigrants too?'

Golda nodded. 'Only they came here twenty years ago. He arrived with nothing but the sewing machine from his father's tailor shop – and look what he's made of himself. You have to hand that to him.'

'On whose backs, though, Golda?' Sadie asked. 'With our sweat and our labor.'

'Hush, Sadie, you shouldn't talk like that. You never know who might be listening,' Golda said.

'You mean there might be spies?' I asked innocently, looking around me for any face that might have betrayed shock or embarrassment. 'Tattletales who report back to the boss?'

Golda touched the side of her nose. 'You never can tell.'

What did that mean? I asked myself as we went back to work. Did she know that one of the girls present was a spy for the boss – in which case did she have any idea if any of the girls might be a spy for someone quite different? I'd have to make friends with Golda and see if she'd divulge any of her secrets.

At home in my room that night I made a list: Befriend Golda. Get to know the sample makers. They have the means – see designs first. But motive? Old women. Rheumatism. One is Max's cousin.

The trouble was that stealing designs from under Max's nose required courage and bravado. I couldn't picture any of those downtrodden girls taking such an appalling risk. Of course, the most likely suspect was our foreman Seedy Sam. He looked to be the type who wasn't above shady behavior and he had access to Max's office. Maybe I'd eat my sandwiches at my machine in the future, so that I could keep an eye on him.

The sweatshop had become my life so completely that I had almost forgotten the advertisement I had placed in the Irish newspaper. I was therefore stunned when, in the middle of my second week, I received a letter from Ireland.

Collingwood Hall
Castlebridge
County Wexford, Ireland

Dear Sir,
I saw your advertisement in the Dublin Times.
I am trying to locate my only daughter Katherine.
The foolish child has run off with one of our estate
workers, an undesirable young man called Michael
Kelly, and it appears that they took a ship to New York.
Naturally I want her found and brought home as soon
as possible, although I fear it is already too late where
her reputation is concerned. As you can imagine, this
is breaking her mother's heart. My wife is bedridden
and of very delicate constitution. I cannot leave her or
I would have undertaken this assignment myself. Please
advise by return of post whether you will take on this
commission and the fee you would require.
Yours faithfully,
T. W. Faversham, Major, Retired

Now this was just the kind of job I had imagined when I made the absurd decision to become an investigator. I wrote back immediately to Major Faversham, telling him that I would be delighted to find his daughter for him, that I needed as many details and photos as he could send me, the amount of money she might have taken with her, plus the names of any friends or relatives she might contact in the United States, and that my fee would be one hundred dollars plus expenses. My conscience got the better of me and I had to add, 'In matters of extreme delicacy such as this, our junior partner, Miss Murphy, usually handles these cases with the required finesse and discretion.'

It was only when I posted the letter that I stopped to wonder how I would manage to juggle these two assignments. If I was in a sweatshop from seven until seven every day except Sundays, I wasn't left with any time for finding missing heiresses. I didn't actually know whether she was a heiress, but the English who had settled in Ireland had mostly done very well for themselves – unlike the Irish who had either starved or been driven from their homes during the potato famine.

I decided to start making inquiries right away. It should be possible to find out when a Mr and Mrs Michael Kelly had arrived in New York. I presumed they would claim to be married. I'd have to find out if the records were kept over on Ellis Island, and if they'd let me go over there to check them. But in the meantime a splendid notion had come to me. If Miss Faversham had any connections among New York society, then my acquaintance Miss Van Woekem would hear about her. I resolved to visit her this coming Sunday and sent her a note to that effect. Miss Van Woekem liked things to be done correctly.

On Sunday morning, at an hour when all good Christians would have returned from Sunday services and less good Christians like myself had finished taking coffee and pastries at Fleischmann's Vienna Bakery, I took the trolley car up Broadway, alighted at Twentieth Street, and walked to the charming brownstone on South Gramercy Park. In case you are wondering how an Irish immigrant girl like myself should have friends who live in such exalted parts of the city – I had briefly held the post of companion to Miss Van Woekem. For once I was not fired, but resigned from the position myself, for personal reasons. We had sparred considerably, the old lady and I, but had forged a mutual respect. She admired my decision to strike out on my own and had invited me to drop in from time to time.

The maid showed me into the first-floor drawing room,

overlooking the park. Miss Van Woekem was sitting in the tall-backed armchair by the fire.

'Ah, Miss Molly Murphy, what a delightful surprise.' She held out her hand to me. 'To what do I owe the honor of this visit? Not coming to reapply for the position, I fear. My current companion is a feeble little creature who cringes when I shout at her. No fun at all.' Her beaky, birdlike face broke into a wicked smile. 'Come, seat yourself. Ada will bring coffee, or would you prefer tea?'

I took the armchair indicated on the other side of the fireplace. 'Coffee would suit me very well, thank you.'

She was looking at me, head cocked to one side in another remarkably birdlike posture. 'You're looking well,' she said, 'and more . . . established. You're more sure of yourself since the last time we met. So tell me, is your detective business flourishing?'

'Hardly flourishing yet, but I am currently engaged in two interesting cases.'

She leaned forward in her chair. 'Do tell me – all the details.'

She listened attentively while I told her about the garment factory, making annoyed tut-tutting noises as I described the conditions there. 'If anyone can sort them out, then you can,' she said. 'Now, about this missing girl.'

'Her name is Katherine Faversham. English landed gentry, living in Ireland. I thought that if she was staying with society friends anywhere in the city, you might hear of it.'

Coffee arrived and was poured. Miss Van Woekem took a sip, then looked up. 'Faversham,' she said thoughtfully. 'Faversham. The name doesn't ring a bell. Of course, if she has married a penniless scoundrel, she might not wish to make her presence known to friends of the family. Although if she is married, her family presumably has lost authority over her and can do nothing.'

'My job is to locate her,' I said. 'How they persuade her to come home is not my concern. When I find out under what financial circumstances she left Ireland, I'll know where to start looking, but in the meantime I decided it couldn't hurt to put my spies to work.'

Miss Van Woekem cackled. 'Your spies. I like that. I have always wished to be a spy. In fact, if I had not been born a woman, I might well have volunteered my services to the government. I will keep my ear to the ground, my dear, and report back to you.'

'Thank you,' I said. 'I knew I could count on you. I am really glad that—'

I broke off at the sound of voices in the hallway outside. Before I could finish my sentence the door was flung open and a young woman burst in with a great rustle of silk.

'I've caught you at home, how wonderful!' She stood with arms open, a vision of loveliness in lilac silk, with a white fur wrap flung carelessly around her shoulders and an adorable little bonnet, also fur trimmed. 'I wasn't supposed to come to town this weekend, but Alicia Martin dragged me to a concert at Carnegie Hall last night and I'm so glad we went because it was an Italian tenor. You know how I feel about Italian tenors because you've promised to take me to hear Mr Caruso the moment he comes to New York – and then we spent the night with Alicia's aunt in a really interesting apartment in the Dakota. I'd always thought only poor people lived in apartments, but Alicia's aunt isn't at all poor and summers in Paris. Then this morning we were about to go strolling in Central Park but I said that I had to surprise my darling godmother first – are you suitably surprised?'

'Oh yes,' Miss Van Woekem said. 'Most surprised.'

'You don't seem overwhelmed with delight at seeing me.' The young woman pouted.

'I am very pleased to see you, of course, Arabella, but, as you may notice, I already have company.'

'Oh.' The girl's mouth formed a perfect circle and she appeared to notice me for the first time. I saw her taking in the cut and quality of my clothes. 'Oh, I didn't realize. Have I burst into the middle of an interview for a position in your household? I'm awfully sorry.'

'I am entertaining a good friend,' Miss Van Woekem said calmly. 'Allow me to introduce you. Miss Murphy, this is my goddaughter, Arabella Norton. Arabella, this is Miss Molly Murphy, a famous private detective who was actually trying to capture that odious man when he shot President McKinley.'

'Really? How amazingly exciting. I think I've seen you before, haven't I?'

'Maybe.' I knew exactly where I had seen her before but I didn't trust my mouth to utter more than one word. Luckily she kept on babbling.

'A woman detective – how frightfully interesting and brave. You should meet my intended. You two would have a lot to talk about, although I don't know what he will think of a woman doing his job.'

Then, to my horror, she turned back to the door. 'Daniel, do stop sulking out there and come and say hello. I promised you we'd go walking in two seconds, but you have to meet this fascinating female detective.'

I took a deep breath as Daniel Sullivan stepped into the room. He was wearing a smart black-and-white check suit I hadn't seen before with a white carnation in his buttonhole. His unruly dark curls were slicked down and parted. His derby was clutched in his hands. His face said clearly that he also wished himself anywhere else but here at this moment. 'Miss Van Woekem,' he said, bowing slightly. 'I trust you are well.'

63

'In better health than you at the present, I surmise, Daniel.' Although I had told her nothing, the old lady had been very quick to grasp the situation when I left her employment. 'And this is Miss Murphy.'

'Miss Murphy.' Daniel's eyes didn't meet mine as he bowed.

'And she's a detective, Daniel. Did you ever hear of such a thing?' Arabella slipped her arm through his and drew him close to her. 'You two must have a lot to talk about.'

'Arabella, we are interrupting a private conversation,' Daniel said. 'I really think we should be going.'

I got to my feet. 'No, it is I who should be going. We have already concluded a most delightful coffee hour and I have friends waiting for me at a restaurant. Please excuse me.' I took the old woman's hand. 'Thank you for the coffee and for an enjoyable morning.'

'Do come again soon, my dear.' She patted my hand, a gesture that was most unlike her. 'I hope to have news for you.'

I stumbled from the room, down the hall, and out of the front door. Arabella's high, clear voice floated after me. 'Where on earth did you meet her, Aunt Martha? What extraordinarily dreary clothes.'

I kept walking fast until I came to Park Avenue, then I turned and started walking south. The wind in my face was bitter, but I kept on walking. If I slowed down then I'd have to think, and if I thought, then the conclusions I'd come to would not be pleasant. I knew that Daniel was engaged to another woman, but he had sworn that he loved me and planned to break that engagement as soon as possible. And so I had kept hope in my heart. Now, seeing them together, I was forced to admit that such hope was ill founded.

Seven

I came into the front hall at Patchin Place to find most of it taken up by an enormous hat stand made of the antlers of some unknown giant beast.

'What in heaven's name?' I asked.

Sid poked her black, cropped head around the drawing room door. 'Don't you adore it?' she asked. 'Mrs Herman across the street is going to live with her sister in South Carolina and was getting rid of items that were too big to move. This was so wonderfully ugly that we just had to have it. Gus is going to hang her painting smock on it up in the studio.'

My mind was already moving beyond painting smocks. 'Across the street, you say?'

'Yes, you know, the old lady at Number Ten. With the cats – who are all travelling to South Carolina in baskets, you'll be pleased to hear.'

'So Number Ten will be vacant? Will she be selling it, do you know?'

'I don't think she owns it. Gus will know better than I. She's the one who takes an interest in the neighbors. Help me carry the monstrosity up to her studio and you can ask her.'

We picked up the hat stand between us and womanhandled it up two flights of stairs.

'Look what your devoted servants have done for you,' Sid said, pushing open the studio door. 'We have risked life and limb bringing the monstrosity up the stairs for you. I hope you are duly grateful.'

Gus looked up from her painting. To me it was a lot of red streaks and black dots, but then I hadn't yet learned to appreciate the intricacies of modern painting. Sid went over to it and put an arm around Gus's shoulder. 'It's one of your best yet, Gus dear. It speaks to the heart. A true representation of the chaos of war.'

I smiled and nodded agreement without actually having to say anything.

'Do you know what is going to happen to the house opposite when Mrs Herman moves out?' I asked, before I was drawn into a discussion on the merits of the painting.

'It will be rented to someone else, I imagine.' Gus slashed another great daub of red across her painting.

'You don't happen to know who the landlord is, do you?'

'What is this?' Gus laughed. 'Have you tired of our company and are seeking to make an escape?'

'Not tired of your company,' I said, 'I could never do that, but I have been plagued with guilt about the little family I brought over from Ireland. I can't leave them living in deplorable circumstances any longer. Now that I have two commissions and I'm well on my way to becoming a successful businesswoman, I could consider renting a place of my own if the rent were not too high.'

'We would hate to lose you, Molly,' Sid said. 'But across the street would be better than nothing. And I have to admire your philanthropic attitude.'

'Across the street would suit me just fine,' I said. 'It would be perfect, in fact. I could wave to Gus as she does her painting, and come over for Sid's Turkish coffee.'

'Of course you could,' Gus said. 'And we can help you look after those two poor, dear children.'

It was sounding better by the minute. I resolved to write to the landlord immediately. As yet I had no money of my own, apart from the pittance being paid me for my work at the sweatshop, but J. P. Riley and Associates had money in the bank, from which I could loan myself an advance on my salary. It would be an enormous risk, renting a whole house on such a flimsy promise of future income, but if worse came to worse, I could always take in boarders or even start my own small school. There was no limit to the things I could do with my talent and enterprise! I was resolved to forge ahead with my life without Daniel Sullivan, one way or another.

I dropped the letter in the mailbox on my way to work on Monday morning and got a reply on my return home the very next day. The landlord was prepared to rent the place for forty dollars a month. Forty dollars a month was twice as much as I was making in the sweatshop right now. Although I had the expectation of a handsome fee at the end of my assignment, I had come to realize that not all cases were resolved success-fully and not everybody paid. In my case nobody had paid so far! Four hundred and eighty dollars a year – I went hot and cold all over at the thought of it. My family had never owned that much money. I wasn't at all sure I could earn that much in a year, but I wasn't about to let this chance slip away. I wrote the check with trembling hand to pay the deposit. I had already taken some fairly large risks in my life, but this counted among them. Like most of my risks, I had little choice if I wanted to rescue Seamus and his family. Afterward I was so excited and full of nervous energy that I went straight to Fulton Street to deliver the good news.

Nuala let me in, grudgingly, her eyes darting to see if I had come with more chickens or grapes. The children had already bedded down for the night, curled up like puppies on top of some crates that still smelled of their fishy origin. They all scrambled up as I came in and Bridie ran to my side.

'Greenwich Village,' Nuala said with a sniff as I told them my news. 'No respectable person would want to live there – a lot of students and rowdies and Negroes and anarchists from what I've heard.'

'Which suits me just fine, because you surely won't be welcome, Nuala. Not you nor your children.' You don't know how long I'd been waiting to say something of the kind. It gave me enormous satisfaction. I looked at Seamus, sitting pale and white in his chair. 'So it's up to you, Seamus. If you want to move into your own room, with heat and running water, then I'm offering you a place. But no relatives. Take it or leave it.'

Bridie rushed to hold my skirt. 'I want to go and live with Miss Molly,' she said.

Seamus smiled weakly. 'We'd be honored,' he said, then turned hastily to his cousin's wife. 'No offence, Nuala, but I have to do what's best for the children.'

Nuala smoothed down her apron over her wide hips. 'You don't see me crying my eyes out, do you? Crammed in like sardines we were with the three of you. I'll be glad to see the back of you and that's God's truth.'

I beat a hasty retreat from what could turn into an ugly scene.

I arranged with the landlord to take up residence at the end of the week. In the meantime my days would be more than full with twelve hours spent at the sweatshop, and hopefully enough time and energy to pursue my first inquiries into the whereabouts of Katherine Faversham. I was really rather annoyed that I found myself trapped in such a lengthy and demanding assignment when this Irish case was just what I had dreamed of when I decided to become an investigator.

How would I possibly be able to comb New York when I was chained to a sewing machine until dark?

I hadn't yet heard anything from Miss Van Woekem, so my first step was to ascertain that Katherine and Michael Kelly had indeed come to New York. If they had access to Katherine's money, they could have crossed the Atlantic in a second- or third-class cabin, which would mean that they stepped ashore with little or no formality and might well have already left the city. If they were penniless, on the other hand, they would have entered through Ellis Island and there would be a record of their arrival.

I wasn't sure how to go about checking the Ellis Island records. I knew a record of each ship and its passenger manifest must be stored on the island, but I didn't believe I'd be allowed to look at them. The general public was kept well away from the island buildings. Relatives who came to meet their loved ones were kept waiting at the dockside. If things had been different with Daniel I could have used his influence, but there was no point in thinking about him anymore.

Then it occurred to me that bribery and corruption had been very much in evidence when I came through Ellis Island. One of the inspectors or watchmen might do the job for me, if I offered to make it worth his while. Which was why I was standing on the dockside long before first light the next morning, waiting for the six o'clock government boat that would take the day shift over to the island and bring the night guards back. Several watchmen were standing together, impressive in their blue uniforms. I hesitated to approach a group such as this. The fewer people who knew of my plan, the better. Then I noticed a young inspector, dressed in a dark suit and stiff white collar, heading for the boat slip alone. I hurried to intercept him.

'If I might have a word with you, sir?'

He stopped and regarded me nervously. I could see him trying to decide if I was a criminal or a woman of the streets about to accost him. I gave him a big smile. 'I'm Molly Murphy just come over from Ireland, and I'm trying to trace my cousin Katherine. I know you're an inspector on the island and I wondered if you'd know how to look up the records and find out if Katherine ever got here.'

'You could write a letter to the governor, requesting such information,' he said stiffly. Wonderful – out of all the corrupt inspectors on the island, I had picked the only stiff shirt.

'I daresay I could, but it would take so long,' I said, 'and I'm worried about my poor cousin Katherine, who may be living in a slum with no money when I could be helping her get a good start.' I gazed up at him appealingly. 'If you'd be willing to put yourself out, I'd make it worth your while. I'm not rich, but I do have a little put by, and my cousin is very dear to me.'

I saw his Adam's apple go up and down. 'What exactly would you require me to do?'

'Nothing illegal. Just check the entries for the last few months to see if a Mr and Mrs Michael Kelly from Wexford arrived in New York. She ran off with this Mr Kelly, you see, and the relatives at home suspect that they headed for America.' I touched his arm lightly. 'If you are prepared to do that for me, I've got five dollars saved up that I'm willing to pay you for your trouble.'

I saw him glance around. Other inspectors were now hurrying past us to the dock. I heard a boat give an impatient toot.

'I have to go,' he said. 'How will I find you again?'

'I'll meet you here, shall we say on Friday morning, to give you enough time. And I'll have the money with me.'

He glanced at the men now boarding the government launch. 'I don't know . . .'

'Do your best anyway,' I said. 'I'll understand if you can't go through with it, but I'll be forever in your debt if I can find my dear cousin. Michael and Katherine Kelly. They would have sailed from Queenstown.'

He nodded and had to sprint to jump onto the boat as the gangplank was being pulled away.

On Friday morning I was up before dawn, and waited in swirling fog for the young inspector. I cursed myself that I hadn't thought to find out his name. If he hadn't managed to do what I asked, then I'd have to start all over again, or I'd have to write to the governor and wait for the wheels of bureaucracy to turn. Then at last I saw him, hurrying through the fog.

'Miss Murphy?' he said with a little bow. 'This is for you.' He handed me an envelope.

'Thank you kindly. And this is for you.' I, in my turn, handed him an envelope. Neither of us checked our envelopes as we went our separate ways. Once around the corner, however, I ripped it open.

Michael and Katherine Kelly. Sailed from Queenstown on the S.S. Britannic. *Admitted to the United States August 18, 1901.*

A big smile spread across my face. I had bribed an official, passed money, and got information I wanted. I was turning into a real investigator!

Eight

That Sunday I took up residence in my own home across the street. Even though the houses looked the same from the outside, my new abode had not benefited from Sid and Gus's loving and artistic care, or from any of their modernizations. There was no beautiful claw-footed bathtub and the W.C. was in a little room outside the back door. The old lady had lived there for thirty years without giving anything even a lick of paint – or a good spring cleaning. So Sunday was spent with sleeves rolled up, scrubbing linoleum so dirty that the roses on it only came to light after hours of elbow grease. Seamus and the children arrived early in the morning and tried to help with the cleaning, but to be honest I'd have done a better job on my own. Seamus was weak after pushing their belongings from the Lower East Side and the two little ones saw an opportunity to play with water.

After we'd moved my meager possessions across the street, we had an impromptu party. Sid and Gus brought over food and wine and we ate at the kitchen table by candlelight (the gas having been turned off when Mrs Herman left).

'To Molly's ventures, may they all flourish, and may she stay in one piece,' Sid said, raising her glass. I fervently seconded this. If my current ventures didn't end in success, I'd not be able to make the rent.

Now that I had good reason to believe that Katherine and Michael Kelly might indeed be in New York City, I had no idea how to start looking for them. Talk about looking for needles in a haystack! How many Irish lived in the Lower East Side alone, not to mention over in Hell's Kitchen or any of the other tenement districts? And how could I begin to hunt for them in the dark, at the end of my working day? I'd discovered already that being out alone after dark was not wise for a woman. For a lone woman who would be asking questions in run-down boarding-houses and taverns in the worst slums of town, it would indeed be asking for trouble. I've attracted enough trouble in my life so far, but I've never actually asked for it!

Of course I could do nothing until I knew who I was looking for. I had to wait to receive full descriptions from Katherine's father. In the meantime, I would just have to be patient and concentrate on the bird in the hand and Mostel's spy.

That Tuesday was election day in New York. I made my way to work through a city draped with bunting and banners. Men I passed in the streets were wearing rosettes with the likeness of either Edward Shepherd or the Fusion party candidate, Seth Low. I knew little of what either of them stood for, and cared even less. If I didn't get a say in choosing them, then what did it matter?

When I came out of the garment factory twelve hours later, I found the streets full of drunken men singing, laughing, and fighting. It seemed that both parties had lured voters to their side with the promise of drink, or even of a dollar, which had now been spent in the nearest saloon. I passed a polling booth, still in operation. It was decorated with American flags and it looked decorous enough, but the area outside was patrolled by the toughest-looking louts I had ever seen. They swaggered around, swinging blackjacks and pouncing on any unsuspecting man who came past them.

'Have youse done yer votin' yet?' I heard one of them growl at a thin little fellow in a derby hat.

'Not speaking good English,' the fellow replied, spreading his hands imploringly.

'No matter. Youse go in there and put yer X next to Shepherd, you hear? The one that starts with S – dat's the one. And when you come out, there will be a whole dollar for ya. If you vote for the wrong one, I'll break yer head. Understand?'

The little chap scuttled inside fast. I passed the polling booth without meriting a second glance. I was a woman and therefore no use to them. I did, however, have to fight off several amorous attempts as I made my way to the trolley.

The next morning the *New York Times* proclaimed that the Tammany candidate had lost, in spite of the bully boys' intimidation and bribery tactics. The editorial hoped for a brighter future in a city free from corruption. Unless they'd elected St Patrick himself, I doubted that would come to pass. The gutters were full of discarded rosettes and trampled bunting.

The world went back to normal and work went on at Mostel and Klein, one day blurring into the next. Each night I came home wondering how much longer I could keep going and why the heck I was putting myself through this torture. Then the next Monday's post brought a second letter from Major Faversham (retired). It was a fat packet containing a photograph of a lovely girl in a ball gown. The photo had been tinted so that the gown was light blue and her hair was a soft light brown. The gown was low cut and she wore a locket on a velvet ribbon at her neck and carried a fan – every inch the daughter of privilege. Another photo fell out of the envelope, this time of Katherine in hunting attire, on horseback. The young man holding the bridle was looking up at her – a good-looking example of Black Irish, not unlike Daniel's appearance. He was younger, taller, and skinnier than Daniel but with similar unruly dark hair and rugged chin. It didn't take a genius to guess that I was looking at Michael Kelly.

I read the accompanying letter:

I have enclosed two good likenesses of my daughter. The groom is, of course, the scallywag Michael Kelly. He is the most reprehensible young man. When he was caught poaching on my estate I took pity on his youth and had him trained to work in the stables. He proved himself good with horses and could have made something of his life if he had learned to be content with his station. Instead he became a rabble-rouser, a so-called freedom fighter, and was arrested for attempting to blow up the statue of Queen Victoria in Dublin. Again I spoke for him, and hoped that my lecture would make him mend his ways. It did not. Again he was implicated in civil unrest and, not content to flee the country, persuaded my young, impressionable daughter to flee with him. Heaven knows if he plans to make a respectable woman of her or if she is ruined forever.

You can see why my case is so desperate. If we could bring her home and manage to hush up this whole sordid business, she would still have a chance of a normal life in society. She is but nineteen years old.

I can only presume that he took her with him, hoping to get his hands on her fortune. She will, indeed, inherit a considerable sum when she turns twenty-one, but at present she is as penniless as he is. If she has any money at all with them it would be from the sale of some minor pieces of jewelry she took with her.

As to friends in America – we have none. Most of Katherine's life has been spent in India, where I had the honor to serve Her Majesty in the Bengal Lancers. She

75

*is completely unused to fending for herself and I am in
grave fear for her. I urge you to put the full facilities
of your enterprise to this commission and find our
daughter as soon as possible.*

*I am in this matter, your obedient servant,
Faversham*

I reread the letter with satisfaction. At last I had something
to sink my teeth into. Katherine had come to New York penniless. That meant there was a good chance that she was still
here in the city. Now that I had photos I would start to track
her down. My main problem was when. How could I track
down Katherine Faversham if my days were still spent in
a dreary sweatshop, with no end yet in sight? Indeed Max
Mostel hadn't even completed the designs in question, so
there was nothing to steal. And every day my frustration was
boiling up, ready to explode. I wasn't at all sure how much
longer I could continue to hold my tongue.

That very day Paula Martino, the young pregnant woman,
had risen from her chair and was creeping toward the exit
when she was spotted by Seedy Sam. 'Where do you think
you're going now?' he demanded.

She gave him a shrug and an apologetic smile. 'Sorry. I
gotta go.'

'You gotta go, all right,' Sam bellowed. 'Get your things.
You're outta here. The boss don't pay no stinking girls to
waste his time powdering their noses.'

'No, please,' she begged, her face white and strained. 'I'm
sorry. It's only until the baby – it presses down so and then I
can't help it.'

'Listen, kid, I'm doing you a favor,' Sam said. 'You wouldn't
be allowed to bring no squalling baby in here anyway. Buy
yourself a machine and start doing piecework from home.'

'Buy myself a machine?' Paula demanded, her face flushed and angry now. 'How you think I buy myself a machine, huh? You think I got gold hidden under my bed, huh? I got two kids to feed and a husband who can't find work and you say buy myself a machine?'

I could stand it no longer. I jumped up and grabbed Sam's sleeve. 'You can't fire her for heeding the call of nature. That's just not fair. And it's not as if she's paid by the hour, so she's not wasting your time. She's paid by the piece and she stays late to finish her work if she has to.'

Sam shook himself free from my grasp and eyed me with a distasteful leer. 'I remember now why we don't hire no Irish. They stir up trouble. Ain't none of your damned business. Go and sit at your place and get on with your work if you don't want to follow her out of the door.'

The encounter might well have ended with my being fired but at that moment there was a diversion. The door opened and a young man swept into the room. He was wearing a top hat and a silk-lined cape and carried a silver-tipped cane. He looked at our little scene with amusement.

'Are you bullying people again, Sam?' he demanded. 'What's the poor girl done this time – dared to sneeze when the filthy lint got up her nose?'

Sam managed a weak smile. 'I'm just trying to keep 'em in line, Mr Benjamin. Making sure they don't waste your pa's time and money, that's all.'

'My father's in his office, is he?' the young man said, his amused gaze sweeping the room until his eyes rested on me. I saw him register surprise at my Irish freckles and red hair. When I didn't look down demurely, as most of the girls here would have done, he gave me an outrageous wink. Fortunately I was used to winks too. I smiled politely, nodded my head graciously, and didn't blush. As he walked toward the doorway that led to the stairs I saw him glance back at me. 'I hope he's in a good mood,' I heard him say to Sam. 'The automobile just had an unhappy meeting with a streetcar and the front fender is no more.'

Sam turned back to us. 'Well, what are you waiting for, get back to work. The boss don't pay you to sit around gawping.' He jerked his head at Paula. 'You, out.'

I went back to my machine wondering what I could do. The boss's son had seemed interested in me. Could I appeal to him to override the foreman's decision? Then I had to remind myself that I was not here to make trouble. I was just playing a part. I would help nobody by getting myself fired. When the boss's son came down from his father's office again, he walked past us as if we didn't exist.

'I expect he got a ribbing from his old man for denting the automobile,' Sadie whispered to me.

'That's Mr Mostel's son? Is he part of the business too?' I whispered back.

She shook her head. 'Goes to some fancy university – studying to be a doctor.' Her eyes became dreamy. 'Imagine that – less than twenty years in this country and already a son who'll be a doctor. We should all be so lucky.'

'Sadie Blum and Molly Murphy – five cents docked for talking,' came the voice from the other end of the room.

I sat, treadling away furiously, and fumed. Somebody should do something for these girls. Their lives shouldn't be like this. At the end of the day, we took our wraps from the pegs on the wall and I walked down the stairs with Sadie and Sarah.

'I could hardly wait for seven o'clock to come around,' Sarah whispered, even though work was officially over and we were allowed to talk. 'I was near to bursting, but I was too scared to ask if I could go to the W.C. after what happened to Paula. In the future I'm just not going to drink anything at lunchtime.'

'You wouldn't have a problem, Sarah.' Sadie looked at her kindly. 'You're quiet and shy and you do what you're told. And you're a dainty worker too. It's girls like you that they like.'

'That's my aim,' Sarah said softly, 'to stay invisible and pray to get through each day.'

My annoyance boiled over at the thought of little Sarah, too frightened to ask to relieve herself.

'It's not right,' I said. 'Why doesn't somebody do something? If you all got together, you'd have strength.'

They looked at me with pity. 'You think nobody has tried?' Sadie said. 'We've had girls here who are all fired up like you and try to do something to make things better, and what happens? They disappear. One day they are here, next they don't come to work. And if we all joined together and demanded better treatment, Mr Mostel would just fire us all, send Sam down to the docks and pick new girls straight from the boats. We are at the bottom of the heap, Molly. We have no one to speak for us. We work here with one thought in mind – that one day there will be something better.'

I should be doing something, I thought. I could speak up for these girls. Then I had to remind myself severely that good investigators do not allow themselves to become emotionally involved in their cases. So far I wasn't being too successful in this area. My assignment, for which I was being paid, was to find a spy – and the sooner the better, as far as I was concerned. I wanted this assignment to be over for various reasons, not the least was the bad taste it left in my mouth.

But I was also itching to move on to my other case. How could I track down Katherine Faversham and her scallywag companion while they were still in the city when I had no time and no energy? As things stood, I only had Sundays to devote to finding Katherine and Michael. If I didn't find them soon, they might be out of the city and far away and I would have lost them for good.

I stood in the cold, dank street as the other girls wrapped their shawls around their heads and scurried off into the night. I hesitated on the sidewalk. This is ridiculous, I thought. The Katherine Faversham case was important to me, important to my whole future as an investigator. Was I going to let it slip away because I was sewing collars all day? I'd just have to take some risks and find enough energy to hunt for them at night. I wrapped my shawl around my head and started toward the dock area.

I only got as far as the first corner tavern before my resolve faltered. A couple of drunken men staggered out and made a grab at me. I fought them off easily enough and crossed the street with their ribald comments and laughter ringing in my ears. The next street was dark and I was scared to enter it. I hated to admit I was giving up, but clearly this wasn't going to work. Reluctantly I made my way back to Broadway and the trolley, trying to put my racing thoughts in order. Exactly why was I slaving away at a sewing machine all day? I was proficient enough now, so what could I achieve until Max's designs were ready? By the time I reached the trolley I had come to a momentous decision. I had wasted enough time working for Max Mostel. I was going to take a few days off.

As soon as I got home I sat at the table and started to write a letter.

Dear Mr Mostel,
   I have been at your garment factory just over three weeks. This has given me ample opportunity to observe

*your workers and to get my sewing up to speed. I now
plan to apply at Lowenstein's, so that I am completely
familiar with his workers and operation by the time
your designs are complete. Please keep me apprised of
the status of your designs and send me a copy of them
by messenger the moment they are complete. You can
always leave a message for me at my new address, 10
Patchin Place.*

Bridie came to look over my shoulder. 'You write pretty,' she said. 'All curly.'

'You'll learn to write like that too if you study hard at school,' I said. 'Your pa should enroll you in a new school this week – one close by.'

'I ain't going to no school,' Shamey said, standing in the doorway and scowling at me. 'School is for sissies.'

'You're going whether you like it or not,' I said. 'Everybody needs to know how to read and write.'

'I know how to read and write already,' he said. 'My cousins don't go to no sissy school and they earn money.'

'Running errands for a gang, Seamus? I don't think your father would want you doing that.'

He glared at me defiantly. 'I want to earn money too so I can take care of my pa and my sister.'

I looked at his skinny young face and realized that the scowl had not been of defiance, it had been of worry. He had decided that he must take over the duties of head of the family. I went over to him and attempted to put an arm around his shoulder. 'That's a very noble thought, Seamus,' I said, 'but you'll be able to take care of them much better if you educate yourself first.'

'I don't have time.' He shook himself free from me. 'I can get a job as a newsboy right away.'

'Of course you have time. You have a place to live and enough to eat.'

He looked at me scornfully. 'Nuala says it's accepting charity.'

'Charity? Of course it's not charity.'

'You ain't a relative. Only relatives are supposed to help each other. That's what Nuala says.'

'Your Nuala talks a lot of rubbish.' I smiled at him. 'But I'll tell you what – if you need to earn money now, then I'll employ you. Promise me you'll go to school and then you can run messages for me when school is out. I need a messenger tomorrow morning, as it happens.'

'You do – where?'

'To take this letter to an address on Canal Street.'

'I know where that is.' His face had lit up.

'Good. Then you're hired. When you take it, make sure it goes directly to Mr Mostel. Tell them it's important. Oh, and Shamey – don't tell them it's from me.'

I finished the letter and addressed the envelope from J. P. Riley and Associates. When I handed it to Shamey the next morning, I felt a great sense of freedom and relief. No more sweatshop for a few days. I was off to find a missing heiress!

Nine

I started the trail for Katherine and Michael at the very tip of Manhattan Island where the ferry from Ellis Island lands the new immigrants. If they were penniless and knew nobody, then their first priority would be finding themselves a place to stay. I remembered clearly my own arrival from Ellis Island. I had been with Seamus, of course, and he had led me directly to his apartment on Cherry Street, but we had run the gamut of touts, waiting to prey on the newcomers. Those same touts were already lined up, bright and early in the morning, waiting for the first ferry from the island. Some of them clutched signs, some wore sandwich boards: The messages were written in Italian and Yiddish and Russian and God knows what else. A few, however, were written in English. MRS O'BRIEN'S BOARDINGHOUSE, CHEAP AND CLEAN. ROOM TO LET. GOOD SAFE NEIGHBORHOOD . . . as well as the more ominous, PETER'S PAWN SHOP, 38 THE BOWERY, GOOD PRICE PAID FOR YOUR VALUABLES. Some men carried no signs. They lurked in nearby saloon doorways and watched and waited. Maybe they were hoping to find unaccompanied young girls, or even young men, but you could tell just by looking at them that they were waiting to prey on the weak and the unprotected.

I walked among the signs, taking down the addresses of

the various boarding-houses and rooms for let. Then I started to visit them, one by one, beginning with those closest to the ferry dock. If they had arrived late in the day and were tired, they'd have chosen the closest.

Several hours later I was tired and footsore, and none the wiser. I had visited ten boarding-houses, God knows how many rooms for let, and none of them had heard of Katherine and Michael Kelly.

From what I knew, the Irish slum areas were along the waterfront, facing the East River, stretching from Cherry Street, where I had first lived with Nuala, down to Fulton Street where she now lived. There was also an area on the other side of the island, also along the docks, where my former employer, Paddy Riley, had lived, and then further up there was Hell's Kitchen – although I didn't look forward to going back there. I'd just have to start on the Lower East Side and work my way around. A daunting task, but I couldn't think of any way around it. Again I was reminded how little I knew about being an investigator. Paddy would have probably been able to locate the missing couple with a few well-placed questions. He had the contacts on both sides of the fence – the police and the underworld. I had no contacts, anywhere. Everything I did was by trial and error.

I decided to start on Cherry Street and comb the area methodically. It was now midday and commerce was in full swing. The saloons were open and a parade of men drifted in and out. It was likely that Michael Kelly had slaked his thirst in one of these. He was, from his photo, an attractive young man, with the ability to charm both Major Faversham and his daughter. He'd have been noticed. But women did not go into saloons. Again I was reminded how much easier this job was for a man.

I had to be content with stopping women on the street

and asking about local boarding-houses or landlords who let cheap rooms. At each of these establishments I gave the same emotional plea about my dear lost cousin Katherine and her husband Michael. I asked about other boarding-houses nearby. Usually the answer was similar, 'There's herself down at Number Eighty-nine on the corner. Calls herself a boarding-house but it's so dirty even the mice won't stay there.' I worked my way down Cherry Street, up Water Street, and then I moved inland – Monroe, Madison, Henry, and their cross streets. It was hopeless. In this area of crowded tenements almost every building had rooms that were let, sublet, and sub-sublet. Half the families took in boarders. And there were enough people called Kelly to send me on several wild-goose chases.

In the end I gave up and went back to the ferry dock, realizing that I should have questioned the touts and shown them the photos. They were a striking couple. Someone might well have remembered them. I came back to find a three-ring circus in full swing – a boat was just unloading, children were screaming, touts were shouting and trying to herd hapless immigrants in the direction of their establishment, small boys were trying to earn some coppers by carrying baggage, which the frightened owners were not going to release, and among the crowd I spotted enough criminal element to make the immigrants' fears justified. Pickpockets were doing a lively trade in the crush and some more brazen crooks were simply snatching bundles and boxes and dodging off with them into back alleyways. What a welcome to the land of the free! And where were New York's finest when you needed them? I'd have to tell Daniel – forget that right now, Molly Murphy, I told myself. I wouldn't be telling him anything again.

I was cursing myself for coming all this way for nothing when I saw something that made me grin from ear to ear. At the far side of the crowd a tall lugubrious fellow was walking up and down with a sandwich board with the words, MA KELLY'S BOARDINGHOUSE. JUST LIKE HOME. CHEAP AND CHEERFUL. The address was on Division Street, a mere half block from where I had stopped my search.

Of course they would have gone there if they'd seen the sign. How could Michael Kelly have resisted going to someone who might even have been a distant relative? I hurried to the Third Avenue El and rode it up to Canal Street where it was a mere hop, skip, and jump to 59 Division Street. A dreary tenement like all the rest – five stories of dingy brown brick. I knocked on the front door and it was opened by an enormous woman wearing a dirty white apron over a faded black dress. 'Yes?' she asked, folding her arms across the monstrous shelf of bosom.

'I'm looking for my cousin and her new husband who recently arrived from Ireland. I'm wondering if they might have stayed here, seeing that their name is also Kelly.' I gave her a hopeful smile. 'Michael and his wife Katherine – a young couple, just married, they are.'

I had hoped that her granite face might have softened when she heard the Irish accent, but she continued to glare at me. 'Don't mention them to me, the no-good pair,' she said.

'Then they were here?'

'They were here all right. Treated them like me own son and daughter, didn't I? Him with his blarney about us being related.' She hoisted up the bosoms and sniffed. 'No more related to him than the man in the moon.'

'So they're not here any longer?' I asked cautiously.

'Upped and left without a by your leave or a thank you, didn't they?' she demanded. 'Waited until I was doing me shopping then simply upped and left. When I came back there was no sign of them, and they left owing a week's rent too.'

'How long ago was this?'

'Going on for a month, I'd say. Good riddance to bad rubbish.'

'I'm sorry they treated you so badly,' I said. 'It's Katherine who's my cousin, not this Michael Kelly. I understand from the folks at home in Ireland that he's a bit of a rogue.'

'A bad lot if you ask me.' She bent toward me. 'I think your cousin married beneath her. Always behaved like a real lady, that one, and talked all highfalutin too – although she could be a proper little madam if she'd a mind to. Had the nerve to criticize my housekeeping, she did. She told me her dogs at home wouldn't want to eat off my floor. Can you imagine? The nerve of it.'

I swallowed back the smile. From what I could see of the grimy lace curtains and pockmarked linoleum, Katherine was quite right. I nodded with sympathy. 'She was brought up rather spoiled,' I said. 'But she's a sweet nature and I'd like to help her if I can. You've no idea where they went, have you?'

She shook her head. 'It wasn't as if they said more than two words to me. Kept themselves to themselves, they did.'

'Were they around the house much when they lived here? Did they find jobs?'

'She did. She was out all day and every day, but that great lummox of a husband of hers, he lazed around doing nothing half the day. He didn't perk up until the saloons opened and then he was out half the night.'

'So he could have been working a night shift then?'

She leaned closer to me again. 'You don't come home from the night shift on unsteady legs, smelling of beer.'

'Do you happen to know where Katherine was working?' I asked. 'Maybe I could trace her through her job.'

Ma Kelly sniffed again. 'Like I told you, we hardly exchanged more than two words. Kept herself to herself, that one, but with her fine airs and graces you'd have thought that she'd have had no trouble landing herself a refined job.'

I tried to think of more questions to ask, but couldn't. 'I'm sorry to have troubled you then, Mrs Kelly. If any post arrives for them from home, maybe you could have it forwarded to my address. It's Ten Patchin Place, in Greenwich Village. Molly Murphy's the name.'

'I can do that,' she said. 'I hope you find your cousin. Like I said, she was no trouble at all. He was a typical Kelly. Just like my late husband – couldn't trust him farther than you could throw him. Went and inconvenienced everybody by dying when all he had was the influcnza.' She sniffed again.

'If you do hear anything about Michael and Katherine, please let me know then,' I said. 'I'll be offering a small reward for information.'

'I've just given you information,' she said, a gleam coming into her eyes.

'So you have.' I reached into my purse. 'Here's fifty cents for your trouble. If the information leads to finding them, it will be more, of course.'

'I'll keep me eyes and ears open for you, my dear,' she said, smiling at me most benignly now.

I left Ma Kelly's unsure what to do next. Katherine and Michael had been living there until recently. Then they had left in a hurry. Had they found a better place to live – a room of their own? If Katherine was working, then it was entirely possible. But how would I ever trace them in a city this size? Paddy's words came back to me – always start from what you know, however unimportant you think it is. What did I know? I knew that Katherine had found a job, and that Ma Kelly had suggested it might be a job suiting her refined airs and graces. A shop maybe? I knew that ladies sometimes worked in hat or dress shops, but how many of them would there be in the city? Too many for me to check out all of them.

I knew that Michael lounged around most of the day and came back at night smelling of beer. So the next step would be to find out where he did his drinking. If his step had been not too steady, then the saloon wouldn't be far away. I'd start with the saloon on the corner and work outward.

I knew I'd be asking for trouble if I went into saloons, but I had to follow up on my only lead at this point. I'd just have to put on my most haughty expression and keep a hat pin ready. I slipped it out of my hat, held it between my fingers, and made my way to O'Leary's Tavern on the corner of Division and Market. It was now around one thirty and the lunchtime trade was in full swing. Through the open door I could see men lined up at the bar, each with a bowl of hot food and a roll in front of him – all for the price of a beer. These free saloon lunches were most popular, especially with single working-men. At least this looked like an honest workingman's bar and I thought I'd be fairly safe.

I had scarcely passed in through the open door when one of the wags at the bar called out, 'Careful, boys, here comes someone's old woman, wanting to get her hands on his wage packet.'

The bartender came hastily around the bar to me. 'Sorry, miss. No women allowed.'

'I'm not intending to stay, sir,' I said. 'I'm trying to locate a missing cousin of mine and I understand he might frequent this saloon. I wonder if you might have seen him.'

'Lady, I get a hundred men a day in here. Unless they get rowdy and smash up the furniture, I couldn't tell them one from another and that's the truth.'

'I just thought you might have noticed this young man. He lived just down the street, until a couple of weeks ago. His name was Michael Kelly – tall, dark haired, good looking, straight from Ireland, had the gift of the blarney, so they say.'

The barman shook his head, then I saw his expression change. 'There was one fella used to come in here for a while. Liked to talk big. Boasted about blowing up things and escaping from under the noses of the English police.'

'That would be the one,' I said. 'Any idea where I might find him now? He left his boarding-house a few weeks ago.'

The man shook his head. 'I can't help you there, I'm afraid. Some of these gentlemen are in the bar of an evening – they might know more than me.' He raised his voice. 'Young lady here is looking for her cousin. Remember that young fellow name of Mike Kelly – did a lot of talking about being a Fenian and a fighter for home rule? Whatever happened to him?'

An older man in dirty overalls looked up from the roll he was eating. 'Last time I saw him, he was talking to Monk.'

'Monk?' I asked.

'Monk Eastman,' the man said, lowering his voice so that the words were barely audible.

'And who's he?' I asked.

Some of the men looked at each other. 'He's the local gang boss, miss,' one of them said, lowering his voice and his gaze.

'You think Michael might be involved with a gang?' I looked directly at the older man. He shrugged.

'I mind my own business, miss. I don't get mixed up with the likes of Monk Eastman. I'm just telling ya what I saw. I saw him in front of the Walla Walla, talking with Monk.'

'He better have been in Monk's good books, because if not he'd be floating in the East River by now,' someone else chimed in.

'What is this Walla Walla?' I asked.

'It's the nickname for the Walhalla Hall – a local social club.'

90

'A social club? And where would that be?'

Again I saw the men exchange glances.

'Just around the corner on Orchard Street, just off Canal, but I wouldn't go there yourself, miss. It's a regular gang haunt. Not a place for nice young ladies, like yourself.'

'Don't worry, I don't intend to do anything stupid,' I said. 'Thank you for your time and trouble, gentlemen.'

'Not at all, miss.' Several hats were raised. I left like departing royalty. I stood on the street corner, enjoying the sun that had appeared from between the clouds. Several men followed me out of the saloon and one of them took off at a run. I wondered if I had made him late back to work.

My, but that stew smelled good. My growling stomach reminded me that I hadn't eaten since breakfast. Yet another disadvantage of being a woman was that I couldn't get myself a nourishing lunch for the price of a beer, but would have to seek out a café. Not wanting to stop when I was now hot on a trail, I bought myself a bag of hot roasted chickpeas from a pushcart. I had never tried them before, or even heard of them, but they were salty and crunchy and satisfied the hunger pangs very nicely.

I was in a quandary about what to do next. I knew that it would, indeed, be foolish to go asking questions at a gangland haunt. I needed to tread very carefully. But what harm could there be in walking along Orchard Street in broad daylight, just to get a look at the place? Mostel's factory was only a block or so around the corner, on Canal Street and I had never felt myself in danger when I walked from the Broadway trolley car. I picked up my skirts, stepped off the curb, and struck out along Canal Street, looking a good deal more confident than I felt.

The Walhalla Hall was a solid-looking brick building with an imposing front door and marble ornamentation. It was, unfortunately, completely deserted, closed and shuttered at this time of day. I even crossed the street and examined it. From the outside it looked respectable enough, apart from the bars over the downstairs windows. There were posters on a billboard in front, advertising coming dances and social events. A perfectly respectable community hall, by all appearances.

I wasn't sure what to do next. Clearly there would be no activity at the building during daylight but coming here at night would be a big risk to take. I surely didn't fancy myself coming face-to-face with Monk Eastman or one of his cronies in the dark! I walked up and down the block once more and was wondering whether I might show Michael's picture to any of the neighbors on the street when I heard the clatter of boots on cobbles. Three small figures came hurtling down Orchard Street and dodged into an alley on the far side of the Walhalla Hall. I thought I heard a police whistle blowing in the distance. With grim determination I set off after the boys down the alleyway. And in case you think I needed my head examined, let me just say that there was more at stake here than just getting information. I had recognized one of the boys. In fact I had put that black cap on his head myself this morning.

Ten

The alley was dark, narrow, full of garbage, and stank. I picked up my skirts to negotiate rotting food and turned the corner with heart pounding. I heard a scurry of boots and a voice whispered, 'Someone's coming.'

'Someone's coming all right,' I said loudly. 'Come out here this instant, Seamus O'Connor, or you won't be able to sit down for a month.'

'It's her,' I heard a small voice whisper and by and by three small faces appeared from out of a coal bunker. They belonged to Shamey and two of his cousins, Malachy and James. I grabbed Shamey by the neck before he could escape again. 'Holy Mother of God, I thought you and I had a bargain,' I said. 'I thought we agreed no more hanging around with the cousins, no more gangs. You promised you'd go and enroll yourself in school.'

'She's not your mother,' Malachy said. 'She can't tell you what to do.'

'No, I'm not your mother,' I replied, 'but we both know what your dear mother would think of the way you are behaving right now, don't we? She'd want you to be doing the best for yourself. Do you want to make her worry if she hears that you're getting yourself into trouble? Do you want to break her heart if she finds out you've got yourself killed or thrown into jail?'

Shamey's lip quivered. 'No,' he said, looking down at his boots.

'Well then, remember in the future that a promise is a promise,' I said. 'You're coming home with me right now. And these boys better run home to their own parents if they've any sense.'

I took him by the hand and led him away.

'I'm sorry, Molly,' he whispered when we were clear of the cousins. 'I came down here to deliver your letter like you said and I met them. They told me I was a sissy and they said that the men would give us a whole dollar for going to smash up a fruit stall on the Bowery. A whole dollar, Molly.'

'A whole dollar – is that a good trade for a life in jail? It's a crime you know, breaking up someone's property. Is it a gang member that's telling you to do these terrible things?'

'It's the Eastmans.' He looked proud and defiant. 'They rule this part of town. They're going to rule the whole of the city when they've shut down the Dusters and the Five Pointers. They're going to take me on when I'm bigger. I'm going to be a junior Eastman. They say I'm a fast runner.'

'You are not joining any gang, Seamus, so put that out of your mind right this minute. People who join gangs wind up dead. If you really want to help your family, you go to school and study hard and better yourself. And in the meantime you can make yourself some money by being my messenger and right-hand man.'

This perked him up a little. 'I delivered your letter, just like you told me,' he said. 'I told them I had to hand it straight to the boss because it was important so they took me up and I gave it to him.'

'Did he say anything when he saw who it was from?'

'No, but he nodded and put the letter in his jacket pocket right away.'

'You did well, Shamey. I can use you again, if you're going to be trustworthy. But if you think of running off with those no-good cousins, then forget it.'

'You can use me again,' he said. 'Are you really a detective?'

'How did you know that?'

'Nuala said. She said you told her but she didn't believe you. She said you had a fancy man who beat you up.'

'Like I said, Nuala talks a lot of rubbish.'

We had reached Broadway and joined the line waiting for a trolley car.

'If you're really a detective, I could help you,' Seamus whispered. 'I could go and find out things for you.'

A thought had struck me. I tried to dismiss it. I wrestled with it. Seamus knew the Eastmans. They had employed him. Would I be putting him in harm's way if I sent him to ask a simple question of them? I pulled him back from the trolley queue into the shadow of an awning.

'Could you do a real job for me? I don't like to ask you, but I don't have a way of finding out myself. It's about the Eastmans.'

His eyes lit up. 'I know plenty of Eastmans.'

'Listen, I don't want you to get yourself into any danger, but I need to know if a man called Michael Kelly is part of the Eastmans gang. Could you find out for me? Tell them it's his cousin from Ireland who wants to know. A girl cousin. I'm trying to find him.'

'I can do that. Easy as pie. Do you want me to run down there now?'

'Is anyone around during the day? The hall was closed up.'

'I know where to find them.' Shamey looked grown up and proud. 'They're only around the hall when there's a dance or something going on. Otherwise they're at their headquarters.'

'Which is where?'

'On Chrystie Street, around the corner.'

'I don't want you going to any gang headquarters,' I said. 'Forget that I even asked you.'

'Some of the Eastman guys might be at the saloon,' Shamey suggested. 'I've been there before with my cousins, delivering messages.'

'I'll come with you then. I'm not having you going to any saloon by yourself.'

He looked horrified. 'They wouldn't tell me nothing if you came along. It's a saloon. Full of people. I'll be safe as houses.'

'Very well,' I said hesitantly. 'Ask the question and come straight home then. Here.' I reached into my purse. 'Here's a quarter. That will take care of your trolley fare and in case you get hungry.'

'Gee. Thanks.' His eyes lit up.

'Be home before it's dark, and no running off with your cousins again.'

'I will. Bye, Molly.' He waved and set off back in the direction we had come. I watched him go with considerable misgivings. I had just used an innocent child to do work I was afraid of doing myself. That couldn't be right – what had I been thinking of? I started to run after him, but he had completely vanished.

I went home on the trolley and prepared a big plate of sausage and mash, which I knew was Shamey's favorite. The dinner was ready, it got dark, and still he didn't come.

I told myself it was early yet. He may have had to wait around until some of the gang members showed up. I told myself that he was accepted by them. He ran their errands. But none of this took away the worry that gnawed at the pit of my stomach.

'That smells good,' Seamus senior said, looking more

sprightly than I had seen him recently. 'I think I'm getting my appetite back. Where's the boy? Out running around again?'

'He'll be back soon,' I said. 'I'll put this in the oven until he gets here.'

Darkness fell. I served the food to Seamus and Bridie but I was too sick of heart to eat it myself. At last I could stand it no longer. 'I'm going looking for him,' I said. 'That young scallywag has no idea of time.' And I tried not to let my face betray my worry to them.

Back down Broadway on the tram, then along Canal Street. It was poorly lit after the bright lights of Broadway and the Bowery and seemed empty and deserted. No pushcarts here, no street life going on – no movement at all except for figures who slunk through the shadows and men who emerged from corner saloons. Why hadn't I thought of changing into boy's clothes? I had done this once and was delighted how I could pass invisibly through the city. Now I felt horribly vulnerable and was annoyed at myself. I was no better than the helpless females I so despised. I'd be reaching for my smelling salts and wearing a corset if I wasn't careful! I pulled out my trusty hat pin and curled my fingers around it. Now ready and armed I turned onto Orchard Street.

The front door of the Walhalla Hall was still closed, but I could see some lights on inside. I hesitated, unwilling to rap on that formidable door. I walked past, trying to find a window I could peek through, but they were all too high. I crossed the street to observe it from the other side. Nothing much seemed to be going on. I continued down the street, annoyed with myself that I had not asked Shamey the name of the saloon the Eastmans were known to frequent. I really had no idea where I was going or what I was looking for. On the corner I paused and spotted the street sign. Chrystie Street! That name rang a bell. Shamey had said that was where the Eastmans had their headquarters. I was about to take the plunge and walk in that direction when I heard footsteps behind me.

I tried to remain calm and nodded a civil good evening as a man passed me. Instead of passing, however, he stopped.

'Can I help youse, lady?' he asked in a strong Bowery accent. 'Dis ain't no neighborhood for a lady like yourself to be out alone. Youse lookin' for someone?'

He was young and skinny, a harmless-looking little chap with a fresh, clean-shaven face, dressed in a smart black suit with a jaunty derby on his head.

I felt a sigh of relief escaping. 'Why, thank you, sir. Actually I'm looking for a small boy. I sent him to this neighborhood before dark to run an errand for me and he hasn't returned. He's nine years old – Irish like me. Skinny and dark haired. You wouldn't have seen him by any chance, would you?'

'You know I tink I did,' he replied. 'A whiles ago now.'

'Oh, thank heavens. If you could show me where you last saw him . . .'

'He was talking to some guys outside the Walhalla Hall. Come on, let's go and see if he's still there.'

He gave me a reassuring smile. We crossed the street together and headed back to the Walhalla. The area around the hall was still deserted.

'Dey might have gone in,' my rescuer said. 'Let's go ask inside.'

He pushed open the front door. I hesitated. 'Are you sure it's all right to go in there? I mean, isn't it a dangerous place where gangs hang out?'

He laughed. 'It's just a neighborhood social club, miss. They hold parties here – weddings and wakes, all that kinda stuff. Even church socials. And you'll be safe enough wid me.'

I stepped inside. He closed the door behind us. We found

ourselves in a large, dimly lit room with chairs around the walls and a large expanse of floor.

'Not much happenin' tonight, is there?' he asked. 'Dead as a doornail. Let's check the back.'

He strode across that big floor, his boots making loud tapping noises on the wood floor, his white spats flashing. Beyond the hall was a long dark hallway. Light was coming from under a door at the far end. The young man sauntered ahead and confidently rapped on the door, opened it, and went in. Emboldened by his apparent lack of fear, I followed.

'Hey, Monk,' he said. 'You know that dame you wanted? I got her for you.' And he shoved me inside, slamming the door shut behind us. The man standing in front of me was no thin and harmless-looking little chap this time. He was also quite young, big-boned but not very tall, with a large pudgy round face, a lot of dark hair on top of it, and a derby a couple of sizes too small for him perched on top of the hair. Where the other fellow was neatly dressed, this one was scruffy, with suspenders over rolled-up shirtsleeves and – I started in surprise as my eyes took in the shape – a live pigeon sitting on his shoulder. His appearance verged on the comical until I noticed some kind of club sticking out of his waistband. 'Who's dis dame, Kid?' he demanded, also with a strong New York accent.

'You know how Bugsy said some redheaded dame was asking questions at O'Leary's today and then she was poking around the hall? And you said we should bring her in. Well, I tink she's the one what you want. I caught her snooping around again now – says she's looking for a kid dis time.'

I had recovered from my shock just enough to realize that I was face-to-face with Monk Eastman himself. Not a pleasant thought. I just hoped he had a finer nature I could appeal to. 'Yes, sir. I'm only trying to find my lost nephew, sir. Seamus

O'Connor. I sent him down to this part of the city with an errand and he should have returned hours ago – but he's very smitten with your gang and I know he's hung around you in the past, with his cousins, that is.' I knew I was babbling, but I was watching his face for a sign that he might be softening toward me.

'And today you wanted to know about Mike Kelly, right? Doing too much snooping altogether, if you ask me.' He stepped toward me, eye to eye with me, but intimidating in his bulk. 'Okay, so who sent ya? Because whoever it was is going to find out dat Monk don't like no snoops.'

'Nobody sent me,' I said.

'Then youse don't got nothing to worry about, have ya?' He opened the window behind him, brushed the pigeon from his shoulder, and it took off into the night with a loud flapping of wings. I saw the flash of something bright on his fingers. A lot of rings, maybe?

'Whatta youse want me to do wid her, Monk?' Kid asked.

'Take her to my place. I'll be along as soon as Lefty gets back from dat little errand.' He grinned. It was in no way a charming grin.

'Okay, girlie. Get going and no fuss.' Kid went to grab one of my arms. I am not used to doing anything without making a fuss. I twisted sharply and stuck at him with the hat pin.

'Will you let go of me! This is no way to treat a perfectly respectable lady.' Kid yowled and sucked at his hand. For a moment I had broken free. I grabbed the door handle.

'Watch her, she's got a knife,' I heard Kid shouting.

Before I could wrench the door open, Monk had grabbed me and held me with one giant paw. 'Youse is lucky I don't use me nucks on women, or you'd be lying dere with a smashed face,' he said pleasantly enough.

'It wasn't a knife, it was just a hat pin, like any lady would use in her own defense,' I said. 'I don't know what's the matter with you people, but if this is the way you treat ladies then I'm glad I'm not married to one of you.' The words came out as an angry torrent, masking the fear that was rushing though me. All of Daniel's warnings about white slavery had come back to me. I was determined not to let them see I was afraid. 'And if you can't answer one simple question about a little lost boy, then in heaven's name just let me go.'

'Youse ain't going nowhere,' Monk said. 'Not until you tell us who sent ya. Coppers or Five Pointers or Dusters? Which one youse working for, huh? Take her upstairs instead, Kid. I'll get to her in a minute.'

I was vacillating between playing the weak and helpless female and doing my Queen Victoria impersonation, haughty and aggrieved. I thought the second might have more chance.

'Will you get it into your heads that nobody sent me? You are making a horrible mistake,' I shouted as Kid twisted my arm behind my back and shoved me out of the door. 'I'm an ordinary Irish girl – the name is Molly Murphy. I was asking about Michael Kelly because he's married to a sort of cousin of mine and I understood they had arrived in New York recently, and the young boy who lives with me, Seamus O'Connor, offered to come down to this part of town and try to find Michael for me. That's all. Nothing complicated about it.'

We were halfway along that hallway when doors burst open. Whistles were blown and suddenly the hall was full of blue uniforms. 'Cops!' I heard someone shout. I could hear the crash of chairs turning over and hasty footsteps up above our heads.

The hand released my twisted arm.

'What the hell do youse tink you're doing busting in like this?' I heard Monk behind me shouting. 'Dis is a respectable social club.'

'And I'm the President of the United States,' the policeman said. 'The chief would like a word, Monk, if you can spare the time. All nice and friendly like.'

'Your chief is asking for trouble.' Monk almost spat out the words. 'Youse guys know youse can't touch me. Bring me in and Tammany's going to hear about it, I promise you. Then you'll see what heads are going to roll.'

'I told you, it's a friendly chat, Monk. Nothing more. Nobody's talking about arrest.'

'Then get the damned cuffs off me.'

'Just making sure you don't do a bunk on us. Now into the wagon nice and easy and you'll be back home in no time at all.'

Monk was manhandled out the front door, followed by a squirming Kid. I heard feet on the stairs and saw officers bringing down more men. It was only then that they appeared to notice me.

'What about the dame?' one of them asked.

'Bring her too.'

'I'm not one of them,' I said angrily. 'In fact you've just rescued me. They dragged me in here.'

I saw two of the constables exchange a grin. 'Out you go, girlie, and no tricks.'

I was escorted out to a waiting paddy wagon and shoved into the back with five or six members of the Eastmans.

'Whoever did this is going to be very sorry,' Monk said as the horses got up to speed and we were thrown around. 'Who do they tink they're messing with? Why do they tink I pay them protection money, huh?'

It was a mercifully short ride. As we were taken out, I saw that we were at Mulberry Street headquarters. Up the steps and into the building.

'What have we got here?' a bewhiskered sergeant asked.

'Five Eastmans and one of their molls. Chief wanted a word.'

'I am not anyone's moll,' I said, stepping away from the column of men. 'They dragged me into their building and the coming of your men actually rescued me.' I weighed up whether to use Daniel's name, and decided that he owed me a favor. 'You can ask Captain Sullivan if you like. He'll vouch for me.'

'Is Captain Sullivan in the building?' one of the arresting officers asked.

'I think he just stepped out for a bite to eat,' the sergeant said. 'Put her in a holding cell until he gets back. Oh wait, speak of the devil . . .'

Daniel Sullivan had come in through the front door. 'What's going on here, O'Malley?' he asked. He recognized the largest of the prisoners. 'To what do we owe this honor, Monk? Gracing us with your presence?'

'Go to hell, Sullivan, and tell your chief he'd better watch the way he picks on innocent citizens or he's going to be sorry. Tell him next time to send a hansom cab for me. The seats in your Black Maria are too hard – besides, I got my reputation to consider!'

'Please escort Mr Eastman and his friends upstairs and let the chief know they're here,' Daniel said.

'And the girl, sir. Says she knows you.'

Daniel looked at me and I saw his eyes open wide in astonishment. 'Molly – what in heaven's name have you been doing with yourself now?'

'Minding my own business, until these gentlemen pounced on me and dragged me into their building.'

'You know her then, sir?' the sergeant asked.

'Oh yes, I know her,' Daniel said, glaring at me angrily. 'Take her up to my office. I'll talk to her later.'

I tried to protest. I was escorted up the stairs and sat on the hard chair in Daniel's glass-fronted cubicle, waiting for him. At least Monk Eastman and several of his men were now in custody. Maybe they could be persuaded to reveal if they had done anything with Shamey. I tried not to think what might have happened to him. Now that all the excitement was over, I found I was shivering. I had never seen Daniel look so angry.

At last he came storming up the stairs. 'What in God's name have you been doing, woman?' he shouted at me. 'Do you know who those men are?'

'Yes, I do. Monk Eastman and his gang.'

'And didn't I warn you about gangs? Didn't I tell you about the turf war going on at this moment and the struggles for the cocaine business, not to mention the white slave trade? What on earth possessed you? You're lucky to be alive.'

'I know that,' I said.

'If you don't give up this absurd notion of yours, I'm going to have you arrested and shipped back to Ireland as a public nuisance – do I make myself clear?'

I knew this was a threat he wouldn't carry out but, all the same, it brought me up with a jolt. I could never go back to Ireland, where there was a price on my head.

I decided to try humility for once. 'I'm sorry, Daniel. I knew I was asking for trouble, but I was looking for young Seamus O'Connor. He's been running errands for the Eastmans and I was worried about him.'

'Seamus O'Connor – the boy you brought over from Ireland?'

I nodded. 'His no-good cousins got him mixed up with a gang.'

'And Molly, the champion, took it into her head to go and find him, single-handed? Sometimes I think you were born with a death wish.'

'I had no option, Daniel. I acted because I thought the boy was in danger – the boy is probably still in danger.'

'You could have come to me.' His voice was quieter now. He was gazing at me steadily.

'When will you get it into your head that I cannot keep running to you for help?'

'Are we not still friends?' he said. 'And friends can ask each other for a favor.'

'Oh yes, and I can picture Miss Arabella allowing you to have friends like me,' I said angrily. 'For one thing, I don't wear the right sort of clothes.'

I saw him try to stifle the grin. 'I'm really sorry about the other Sunday,' he said. 'It must have been very unpleasant for you.'

'No more pleasant for you, I'd warrant,' I said, smiling also now.

'You behaved perfectly. I was most grateful.'

'And you could have taken the opportunity to tell Arabella the truth. You could have said, "This is the woman I love. I can't marry you." But you didn't.'

'No, and I despise myself for it. I suppose you are right. My career does mean a lot to me. If Arabella felt I had betrayed her, she would not rest until she had ruined me completely.'

'And yet you could end up married to such a woman? Certainly a pleasing prospect.'

He shrugged and looked away. 'I will tell her, I promise. The time has to be right.'

'This is no time to be discussing our unhappy situation,' I said. 'Not while young Shamey O'Connor may be in danger.' I got up from my hard chair. 'I must go, Daniel, if I'm permitted to do so and not to be charged as a gangster's moll. I must continue looking for the boy.'

He put his hand on my sleeve. 'Molly, I thought we'd been through this before.'

'All right,' I said. 'Seeing that you owe me a favor for my good behavior and for holding my tongue that Sunday – you find the boy for me.'

'I will do that. Where was he last seen?'

'He went to get some information from the Eastmans for me.'

'You sent a child to the Eastmans?'

'Hold your horses – all right, I'm not feeling so wonderful about it myself now, but it seemed like a good idea at the time. This child has been used by them as a messenger. I thought he'd come to no harm and he might get more out of them than I would. I've been trying to locate a man called Michael Kelly, newly come from Ireland. I have reason to believe he may have joined the Eastmans. Young Shamey was going to find out for me, seeing that he knew about their haunts.'

Daniel made a tut-tutting noise but said nothing and got out his pad. 'Description of the boy?'

I gave it to him. 'And while you're about it, I've got a picture of Michael Kelly. You could make inquiries about him too – find out if he is known to the Eastmans.'

I fished for it in my bag.

Daniel studied it. 'Not unlike me,' he said. 'Not quite as good looking, of course.' I went to slap him playfully and withdrew my hand at the last second. 'And why are you looking for him?'

'Part of my missing person's business,' I said. 'He ran off with a girl of good family. Here is her picture – her name is Katherine Faversham, or was before she married Michael Kelly. The father wants her found.'

'I'm not surprised if she's run off with a gangster.' He took the portrait from me, stared at it for a moment, then handed it back. 'Not a bad-looking girl either. A little haughty for my taste.'

I was about to remind him that Arabella Norton spent her life looking down her nose at the rest of us, but I decided to concentrate on more important matters. 'All I've been able to trace so far is that they lived on Division Street until about three weeks ago, when they did a bunk, leaving rent unpaid. I heard a rumor that he might have joined the Eastmans.'

'And how did you hear that?'

'Local tavern,' I said breezily and watched Daniel sigh again.

'All right,' he said. 'I'll do what I can. I don't think the Eastmans would stoop to killing children – although who knows? They've been pretty violent in their actions recently. We've had a body brought into the morgue almost every day, although they've all been men. They have a different fate for women.' He frowned at me again. 'But for that police raid, you might never have been seen again, my dear.' He turned away. 'Can I make you swear to me that you will never do such a foolish thing again?'

'I'll try to behave more sensibly,' I said, moved by his emotion.

'I couldn't bear it if anything happened to you.' He reached out and stroked my cheek. I wished he hadn't done that. Any other gesture and I could have handled it. This was so tender that tears welled to my eyes. Instinctively I covered his hand with my own and held it to my cheek. Then I controlled myself, brushed his hand away, and rushed from his office. 'I've got a lost boy to find,' I said.

Eleven

I was not looking forward to going back to Patchin Place and telling Seamus that I had lost his son, but I didn't want to worry him just as much by staying away.

I turned back to Daniel, who was guiding me down the stairs. 'You will do what you can, won't you? He's just a little boy. He may think he knows his way around the city but he really hasn't been here long and . . .' I let the 'and' hang in the air.

Daniel put his hand on my shoulder. 'I'm sure he'll be all right. You know boys. He's found a pal and gone off with him, or he's gone back to his cousins' place.'

The latter hadn't occurred to me. Nuala's place was not too far away. If Shamey had found himself in a spot of bother, he might well have run there for protection. I should have thought of that.

'I'll try the cousins myself,' I said. 'I can do that without getting myself into any kind of trouble.'

Daniel's lips twitched in a smile. 'Yes, I imagine so. I'll put men out onto the streets straight away, and I'll have a little talk with Monk and his friends too, just in case they know something they are not telling you.'

'Thank you,' I said.

'And Molly, please—' Daniel began.

'I know, take care of myself,' I finished for him. 'I'll have to, won't I, since I've no one else to care for me.'

At that moment a great voice boomed up from the basement beneath us.

'Why don't you pick on someone your own size, you big bullies? Frightening tender young children to death like that!'

I recognized the voice and broke away from Daniel, hurrying down the stone stairs into the darkness. I heard a policeman shout, 'Hey, you, where are you going?' but I didn't stop.

At the end of a dark, dank hallway Nuala was standing, arms folded in defiance over a considerably smaller police constable.

'Let them out of there this minute, or I won't be responsible for me actions, so help me God,' she said, unfolding her arms and giving every indication of winding up to take a swing.

'Nuala!' I called, relieved for the only time in my life to see her. 'Have they got the boys down there? Is Shamey with them?'

'Locked them away like hardened criminals and all for a bit of boyish fun,' she said.

I ran toward her. Shamey's scared face peered out at me from behind the bars.

'What's all this about?' I asked the constable, who now looked doubly scared at having to confront two angry women.

'They were identified as the gang that broke up a fruit vendor's stall this morning,' he muttered.

'A gang you call them?' Nuala's beefy arm tensed again. 'Nothing more than boyish high spirits. Have you got nothing better to do with your time or are you afraid to go after the real criminals?'

Daniel had come to my side. 'What's going on?' he asked.

I pointed to the cell. 'Shamey is in there,' I said. 'Apparently he helped his cousins to smash up a fruit stall.'

'We didn't mean no harm,' Malachy, the oldest cousin, said.

'Honest, Officer, we was just foolin' around,' James, the second cousin, added.

'Of course you meant harm,' Daniel said coldly. 'You were being paid for it, weren't you? You don't have to tell me. I know. The Eastmans like to pay kids to do their dirty work, then you get caught, not them. They had you smash up the stall because the owner wouldn't pay his protection money, didn't they?' He walked up to the bars. 'Take a good look around you, boys. Do you like the look of this place, because it's not half as bad as some of the cells in the Tombs down the street, and that's where you'll be spending most of your lives, if you are foolish enough to mix with gangs. If you live long enough, that is. Would you like to see how many bodies I've got lying on a marble slab in the morgue right now? Gang members, every one of them.'

He nodded to the constable who produced a key. 'I'm going to let you out this time, but if I find you in here again, then you'll be very sorry.'

The door was opened. Nuala's two boys ran into her arms. 'He said he'd throw away the key, Ma,' Malachy sniveled.

Nuala hugged them fiercely. 'Let's go home, boys, before these no-good bullies change their minds. But if I ever hear about you working with a gang again, I'll knock your blocks off, so help me God.' She drove them like sheep ahead of her up the stone steps. Shamey stood there outside the cell, looking up at me with big, frightened eyes.

'And as for you, Seamus,' Daniel said, glaring at him. 'You remember me, don't you?'

Shamey sniffed and nodded. 'You're Captain Sullivan. You used to come visiting when we lived with Molly before.'

'I'm a very important policeman, Seamus, and I've got my spies all over the city. If I ever hear that you've had anything to do with gangs again, then you're going to be very sorry indeed. We've even worse prisons than this, you know. This one's like Coney Island compared to the Tombs. So do I have your word that you'll not make Molly worry about you again?'

'She asked me to go and talk to the Eastmans,' Shamey said, a hint of defiance returning.

'She didn't realize how stupidly dangerous that was. Now she does. She'll not be asking you to do a foolish thing like that again, I can promise you. Now go home, the both of you, and let me get on with my work.'

'Let's go, Shamey,' I said gently. 'There's sausage and mash keeping hot in the oven.'

He nodded. I spared his dignity by not taking his hand as we walked up the stairs. At the top I looked back at Daniel. He was watching me with such an intense look of longing on his face that it gripped at my heart. For once he was the one suffering. Good.

Once outside I put my arm around Shamey. 'You've had quite a fright, haven't you?' I said. 'I blame myself for sending you to do something that was stupidly dangerous. I'll never do that again. I'm sorry.'

'The police were watching the place and they grabbed us,' he said. 'I'm sorry I didn't get to ask about that guy for you, Molly.' Then, a few steps later, 'Does my father have to know?'

'I don't think we need to worry him, do you?' I said. 'We'll tell him that you went home with the cousins and Nuala invited you to stay to supper.'

A beaming smile spread across his face. 'And it was so good I forgot to come home,' he finished for me, then burst out laughing. It is hard to keep the young downhearted for long. I, on the other hand, had some serious thinking to do. My thoughtless behavior today had brought me to the notice of the Eastmans. They had been looking for me, maybe they'd come looking for me again. I would have to tread very carefully in the future.

The next morning I took Shamey and his sister and personally enrolled them in the local school. 'And if I hear you've been playing truant, it will be bread and water for a week,' I said, giving Shamey my severest stare.

As I walked home, I was unsure what to do next. I had to hope that Daniel would keep his promise and find out about Michael and Katherine for me. Until then, I had nothing to do. After those weeks at the sweatshop, it was a strange feeling. I went to have coffee and rolls with Sid and Gus and recounted my adventure with the Eastmans. They were suitably impressed.

As the weekend approached and still no word from Daniel, I realized that I could wait no longer – I would have to apply at Lowenstein's on Monday morning, or I'd miss the crucial moment when the new designs were finished. And if Daniel hadn't found out any more about Michael and Katherine for me, then I'd just have to do it for myself, even if I was putting myself in danger.

I was walking the children to Washington Square on Saturday afternoon to play with a new whipping top Sid had bought for Seamus when I saw a young police constable striding up Patchin Place.

'Miss Murphy?' He stopped and saluted. 'I was told to deliver this by Captain Sullivan. He told me to apologize that he hasn't the time to deliver it himself, but he said to tell you that he's had no sleep all week, what with this gang business.' He handed me a slim envelope, saluted, and went back the way he had come. I stood fighting back the disappointment that Daniel himself hadn't delivered the note. I kept making splendid resolutions never to see Daniel again, then was down in the dumps when I didn't. This had to stop.

I tore open the envelope. It contained a few lines scrawled in Daniel's sloping script, obviously written in haste:

Sorry that the news is not happier for you: Michael Kelly was indeed loosely connected with the Eastmans for a short while. They claim to have no knowledge of where he is now or what happened to him. However, one of the cadavers found in a gangland back alley certainly bears a resemblance to your photograph. I cannot give you positive proof, as the skull was smashed with great force, but he was of the same height, build, and coloring. Of course he had no identification on him and nobody has come forward to claim the body.

I fear the news on Katherine is no better. A young woman was pulled from the East River three weeks ago. She also had no identification on her, but was described as fair skinned, light brown hair, blue eyes, about five feet, four inches. She was also pregnant – do you know if this was the case?

It seems likely that Michael was killed and Katherine threw herself into the river in a fit of despair. Both were buried in the potter's field so we have no way of verifying either identity.

It was signed simply, Daniel.

I stood staring at it until Shamey pulled at my jacket. 'Aren't we going to play in the square, Molly? You promised to show me how to make my top go fast.'

I came out of my reverie. 'Yes, of course. We're on our way.' I thrust the letter into my pocket and took Bridie's hand as we crossed the street. So the case was closed. I was not looking forward to writing to Katherine's father with this worst of all news.

We reached the park and I demonstrated how to whip a top with great expertise.

'There. Now you do it,' I said.

'Let's play tag, Molly,' Bridie yelled. 'You catch me!'

'Not right now, sweetheart,' I said. 'Molly doesn't feel like playing at this moment.'

I stood watching them run through dead leaves, hearing their whoops of exuberance and started the letter to Major Faversham in my mind. 'It is with deep regret that I have to inform you that your daughter appears to have met an untimely end.'

It was a pity that I couldn't confirm the awful truth. It would leave the parents never being completely sure. It did seem to be the most logical answer, however. Either Michael had crossed the Eastmans or run afoul of a rival gang and wound up dead in an alleyway. But I couldn't believe that Katherine had drowned herself in despair. That girl in the photograph with the proud stare and determined chin didn't look as if she would give in so easily. She had, after all, dared to leave a life of privilege to run off with a family servant. That took spunk. Being pregnant and alone in a strange city, and in grief for her new husband too, might have driven her over the edge, but I just couldn't see Katherine flinging herself into the East River. If she truly had wound up in there, then somebody else threw her in. Which meant that I should look into this a little further.

Hold your horses, I told myself severely. I had promised myself never again to get involved in a criminal case. I was not the police. I could share my suspicions with Daniel and he could look into it or not as he chose. My work on this case was done. I had located Michael and Katherine and now all I had to do was report the sorry news and collect my fee. It left a bad taste in my mouth, but that was that. On to Lowenstein's in the morning and back to a life of drudgery.

'You're no fun today, Molly,' Shamey said, tugging at my skirt.

Twelve

Whereas Mostel and Klein's garment factory had been in a loft, up several flights of narrow stairs, Lowenstein's was in a basement just off Houston Street, at the northern boundary of the Jewish quarter. From the heights to the depths, I thought as I stood outside the building on a cold, damp morning and peered down into a narrow well area. The first chill of winter was in the air and the horse that pulled a wagonload of barrels past me was snorting with a dragon's breath. I felt frozen to the bone and wished I had worn Paddy's lovely long wool cape. But sweatshop girls couldn't afford capes. They wore shirtwaists and skirts and wrapped themselves with whatever might pass as a shawl.

I picked my way down a flight of broken steps and ducked in through a low doorway. I found myself in a long dark room with a low ceiling, lit only by two high windows up at street level, through which some railings and the base of a lamp were visible. The ceiling was strung with pipes and festooned with cobwebs. There were gas mantles hissing away, but they did little to dispel the gloom. The clatter of fifty sewing machines echoed back from the brick walls. I had arrived just after seven and it looked as if everyone here had been working away for hours. Not a good sign. I had thought that

Mostel's had crammed in as many machines as possible into that one room, now I saw I was wrong. The girls here were working, crammed so closely together that they could barely move their arms without hitting each other, and there was hardly any space between the tables. It suddenly occurred to me that there might not be a vacancy for me after all, in spite of Mostel's insistence that I'd get a job here with no problem.

I stood in the doorway and looked around for the boss. Not one of the girls looked up from her work to notice me, but a little child – a thin little scrap who couldn't have been more than ten, who was squeezing her way down the table, cutting off threads from finished piles with an enormous pair of scissors – looked up, saw me, and reacted with a start, jogging the elbow of the nearest girl.

The machinist yelled something in Yiddish, and slapped the child around the head. The child started to cry and pointed at me. Heads turned in my direction.

'Hello,' I said brightly. 'I'm here about a job – whom would I see?'

It turned out I didn't have to ask. At this outburst of noise a man had come out of a room at the far end. 'What is it now? Can't I leave you lazy creatures to work for five minutes while I get the books done?' he shouted. He had a heavy European accent but he spoke in English.

'It's a new girl, Mr Katz,' someone at my end of the room said.

The man forced his way toward me. He was younger than Seedy Sam, thin, angular, good looking almost in a depraved sort of way, with heavy-lidded dark eyes, a neat little black beard, and a sort of half smile on full lips. He was wearing a formal black suit and white celluloid collar, although the black suit was now well decorated with pieces of lint and thread.

'So this young lady thinks she can disrupt the work of a

117

whole room, does she?' He stared at me. 'And for why should I hire you?'

'The child was startled when she looked up and saw me, that's all. And I'm here because I'm a good worker and I was told you are about to hire more workers for the busy season.'

He was still gazing at me with a hostile sneer. 'What accent you speak with? Irish? And for why should I want to hire an Irish girl when most of my workers speak Yiddish?'

'Since we're not allowed to talk when we're working, what difference would it make?' I demanded, looking him straight in the eye. 'And if you're not hiring, just say so, and I'll take myself elsewhere.' I turned to go.

'Wait,' he shouted. 'I didn't say we weren't hiring. I can always use a good worker. Where have you worked before?'

I had decided it would be wise not to mention Mostel and Klein. 'I'm just arrived from Ireland, sir. I worked for my auntie who ran a dressmaking business. We did everything – bride's dresses, latest fashion, and always in a hurry. I'm used to hard work, sir.'

It was hard for me to address this obnoxious fellow as sir, but it obviously worked, because he nodded. 'I'll give you a trial. You'll get five dollars a week if you do your quota. You bring your own needles and thread.'

I nodded. 'I have them with me.'

He looked annoyed that he hadn't had a chance to catch me out. 'You pay us ten cents a week for the use of power.'

Power? I thought. Those pathetic gas brackets counted as power? I certainly couldn't feel any form of heating.

'And five cents for the use of mirror and towel in the washroom.'

It struck me that I had heard that one before. Someone at Mostel's had told me about it. I wondered if it was common practice in the garment sweatshops.

'The rules are simple,' he said. 'Do your work on time and you get paid what you're due. You don't leave your seat without permission. You don't talk. Obey the rules and you get your full paypacket. Got it?'

'Yes, sir.' I looked suitably humble.

'All right. Get to work then. What are you working on, Lanie?'

'Sleeves,' a voice from the middle of the room said.

'Start her on sleeves too then. What's your name, girl?'

'Molly, sir.'

'Go and sit next to Lanie. She'll show you how we do things around here. And the rest of you, get on with it. Mr Lowenstein is not going to be happy if he comes in and finds you're behind with this order. If those dresses aren't ready to be shipped by Friday, I'm docking everyone a dollar's pay. Understand me?' For the sake of those who didn't, he repeated the whole thing in Yiddish. I then heard someone passing it along in Italian, then maybe Russian or Polish, with a gasp each time.

I squeezed my way between the rows of girls until I came to a plump girl with a magnificent head of dark hair, coiled around her face. She looked at me with big, sad eyes and a rather vacant expression.

'I'm Lanie,' she said. 'Pleased to meet you, I'm sure.'

I squeezed myself onto the vacant chair beside her. The chair had a broken back and rickety legs. I hadn't been told to remove my shawl and now I was glad to notice that most of the other girls wore theirs too. Some of them wore gloves with the fingers cut out. The atmosphere was decidedly damp and chill. From the depths of the room came the sound of coughing.

'You've worked a machine like this before?' Lanie asked over the noise of the treadles.

Luckily I had. It was identical to the ones at Mostel's. I nodded.

'We're doing sleeves,' she said, pointing at the huge stack of dark-blue bombazine. 'All you have to do is the side seam, then pass them on to Rose. She's setting them in the bodice.'

I turned to the girl on my other side. She was petite with red curly hair and she gave me a bright smile. 'Another redhead. Now I won't feel so much like a freak.'

I smiled back. 'We redheads must stick together.'

I started sewing. By the time the clock on the wall rolled around to lunch, my fingers were stiff and cold and my back was aching from sitting on the uneven chair with no support. A bell rang and chairs scraped as we got to our feet.

'Did you bring your lunch with you, Molly?' Rose asked as we joined the throng of girls making their way to the exit.

'Not today. I wanted to see what the other girls do.'

'As you can see, we all leave,' Rose said. 'Nobody wants to be down here, breathing this rotten air, for a second longer than necessary. When it's nice we eat our sandwiches in a churchyard – only don't tell my father. He's a rabbi. He'd die of shock to hear that his good Jewish daughter was hanging around a church.'

I laughed. 'And when it's not nice, like today?'

'Then we go to Samuel's Deli on the corner over there. You can get a bowl of soup with matzoballs or liver dumplings for a nickel. It's good and filling.'

We joined the line waiting to be served, then carried bowls of clear soup with what looked like three small dumplings in it to the counter that ran around the wall. It was already lined with girls standing and eating.

'Can you make room for two hungry people, Golda Weiss?' Rose said, shoving another girl in the back.

'There's no room, Rose. We can hardly breathe here.'

'Then hold your breath, we're hungry and there's nowhere else to go.' Rose elbowed her way in to a few inches of counter, then grinned at me.

'So how do you like it so far?' she asked. 'Isn't it fun? Like being on holiday, huh?' She rolled her eyes.

'Beggars can't be choosers,' I said.

'Ain't that the truth. I tell you, Molly, if I could find something else to do, I'd be out of here like a shot.'

'What else is there for poor girls?' I asked.

'Only walking the streets, which makes more money, so I hear, and I understand it may even be more pleasant.'

'Rose Levy – if your father could hear you talking like that!' The girl Rose had elbowed aside spun around to look at Rose in horror. 'You ask for trouble, you know. You and your mouth.'

'Just joking, Golda. For God's sake we need to joke sometimes, don't we?' Rose rolled her eyes again and looked back at me. 'They all take life too seriously. Most of them just try to keep going until their parents make a match for them – hopefully with a guy who can afford for them not to work.'

'Their parents make a match for them? They don't choose their own husbands?'

'That's how it's done in the old country.'

'So will you marry someone your parents choose for you?' I shuddered as I thought of the great, clodhopping louts that my parents would have chosen for me.

'Not me,' Rose said with a look of bravado, 'only don't tell my father. I aim to be a lady writer and support myself.'

'You do? Then you must—' I had been about to say that she must come and meet my friends in Greenwich Village, before I remembered that nobody must know I wasn't a poor Irish girl just off the boat.

'I must what?' she asked with interest.

'You must keep going until you succeed,' I said lamely. 'Have you written anything yet?'

'Lots of things, but mostly just for me. But I'm hoping to get a weekly column in the *Forward* someday soon. I'd like to write articles exposing the injustices in this city.'

'Like the treatment of girls in sweatshops?'

She looked at me curiously. 'You've only been here one morning and already you notice that we're not justly treated?'

'Paying for the company's power and the use of the company's mirror?' I said. 'And that cold, damp room. Do they bring heaters in when it gets really cold?'

'They brought in two oil stoves last winter, but what good were two stoves for a room that size? The W.C. froze. That's how cold it was. I tried complaining to Mr Lowenstein himself, but it didn't do any good. He told me if it was too cold, he'd shut down the place until the weather warmed up again. None of us can afford not to work.' She chopped off a big piece of matzoball and chewed it with satisfaction. 'I'm the only breadwinner in my family.'

'Is your father sick?'

'No, just religious.' Again that wicked smile. 'I told you, he's a rabbi. In the old country he was well respected. He ran a big shul and we lived well. Here there are too many rabbis and no one earning enough money to make donations.'

'So he won't try and get a real job, just until you're settled here?'

'You haven't met my father. God will provide, like Moses in the desert. I tell you, Molly – if I didn't work, we'd all starve and God wouldn't care.'

I looked at her with admiration. She was clearly younger than I, probably still not even twenty and yet she had taken the responsibility for her family on her young shoulders.

'I'm just not good at keeping my mouth shut,' she went on.

'This is the third shop I've worked in. I can't seem to shut up when the foreman is being mean to a girl or they are cheating us again.'

I found that I was staring at her in amazement. It was like looking at myself.

'What?' she demanded. 'Have I spilled soup down my chin?'

I laughed. 'I think you and I are going to get along just famously.'

On the way back from lunch, our stomachs satisfied and our bodies warm, I had to remind myself that I must not become too intimate with any of the girls, even Rose. Least of all Rose. Because one of them could be a link in the chain that smuggled designs out of Mostel's and into Lowenstein's and I ultimately would have to expose her.

As we made our way down the slick, crumbling steps and ducked into the workroom the foreman was waiting for us, hands on hips and an indignant expression on his face. 'Late again! Won't you girls ever learn?' He pointed at the clock on the wall behind him. It showed twelve thirty-three. 'That will cost you ten cents. At this rate you'll end up paying me by the end of the week.'

'We can't be late,' I blurted out. 'I looked at the clock at the deli and we had five whole minutes to cross the street.'

I felt Rose dig me in the ribs.

'Late on your first day and argumentative too? Dear me, that's not a good sign, Miss Murphy. I'll have to dock you twenty cents so that you learn to keep your trap shut. Now get to your machines, all of you!'

As Rose and I made our way down the line of machines she whispered to me, 'I should have warned you – if you oppose him, he fines you, so it's not worth it.'

'But I'm sure we weren't late. How can we have taken eight minutes to cross one street?'

123

'We weren't late. He puts the hands forward on the clock. He does it all the time. And he turns the hands back when we aren't looking so that we work later at night.'

'Jesus, Mary, and Joseph. That's disgusting. Does the owner know?'

'Oh, I'm sure the owner knows all about it,' Rose said. 'He turns a blind eye, if he didn't order it in the first place.'

'It's terrible. We should do something. They can't treat us like that. It's just not fair.'

Rose smiled and shook her head. 'You're new,' she said. 'You'll learn that a lot of things aren't fair.' She leaned closer to me. 'Oh, and another word of warning – don't let Katz get you into the backroom alone. He'll claim there is something wrong with your work, or pretend he needs to give you a talking-to. All he wants to do is to force himself on you. He's tried it with a lot of girls.'

'I still hear talking!' Katz's voice shouted. 'Someone want no pay this week?'

We got down to work. I watched the clock carefully all evening to make sure that Mr Katz didn't try to move the hands backward. I was dying to catch him at it. But he didn't go near it.

It was raining and a cold wind was blowing as we staggered up into the fresh air at seven o'clock.

'I'll see you bright and early then,' Rose said. 'He likes us in our seats at six thirty, although our day officially starts at seven.'

'If that was one day, I don't know how I'll manage a whole week,' I said. 'My back is so stiff from that broken chair. I pointed it out to Katz and he told me I could bring my own if I wanted.'

Rose waited for a group of girls to go past, then pulled me closer to her, under an awning out of the rain. 'If you really want to help change things, some of us are trying to get a union going. There's a meeting on Wednesday night.'

I had promised myself I wouldn't get involved. I shook my head. 'I'd really like to, but . . .'

She nodded. 'I understand. It's a big risk. If someone snitches on us and the bosses find out, nobody would hire us again, but I'm willing to take the risk. I'm educated. I can think for myself. If someone doesn't speak out for these girls, nothing will ever change.'

'You're very brave.'

She laughed. 'Maybe I'm just stupid. Me and my big mouth, huh? But I feel it's up to me – most of these girls are peasants, they can't even read and write. They don't speak English well, and their families are desperate for money. So they shut up and put up with all of this. We won't get nothing unless we unionize. My brother was with the Bund in Poland.'

'The Bund?'

'It's a radical socialist group, working to change the old order – justice, freedom, equality for all people. Many Jewish boys were involved, even though it meant possible prison or even death. My brother had to keep his work secret from my father – my father would never have approved.'

'What does your brother do now?'

'He lies in an unmarked grave. He was executed when one of their group betrayed them to the secret police.'

I touched her arm. 'I'm so sorry. So many tragedies in the world.'

'That's why I'm doing this work with the union. Someone has to make sure my Motl didn't die for nothing. Someone has to make sure this country is better than the last one.' She draped her shawl over her head. 'Think about it and let me know if you change your mind. You'd be a real help, because you speak good English.'

'So do you.'

'*Ya*, but I sound like a foreigner – a *newnik*. Nobody's going to take me seriously. The union loves English-speaking girls. There was this English girl who came a few times. You should have heard her talk – *oy*, but she talked real pretty. Just like the queen of England. "We're going to make these petty tyrants sit up and listen to us," she said.' Rose did a fair imitation of upper-class English speech. Then she laughed. 'Real hoity-toity, she was. I got a kick out of her.'

'She's not there anymore?'

Rose shook her head. 'Nah. She only came for a few weeks, then she didn't show up no more. I expect she'd found something better – a girl like her from good family. I don't know what she was doing working in no lousy sweatshop to start with.'

I was getting a chill up my spine and it wasn't from the drips that were falling on us from the awning.

'What was her name?' I asked.

'Kathy,' Rose said. 'I remember it because none of us from Europe can say that "th" sound proper. We called her Katti and she kept correcting us.'

'And when did she stop showing up?'

Rose put her hand to her mouth, thinking. 'Must have been about three, four weeks ago.'

'I've changed my mind,' I said. 'I think I will come to this union meeting with you after all.'

Thirteen

There were lots of girls called Kathy in the world, I told myself. I shouldn't read too much into this – but it did sound a lot like her. I would try to ask for a description, without seeming too interested, of course. And at the union meeting maybe I'd find out more. In the meantime I had to remind myself that I was being paid to discover a spy. Sometime in the next few weeks, someone was going to deliver stolen designs to Lowenstein's.

By the time Wednesday night rolled around, I was more than ready to attend the union meeting, and not just because I wanted to find out if the English girl called Kathy was the Katherine I was seeking. As I watched injustice after injustice going on at Lowenstein's, I realized that I couldn't just sit quietly and do nothing. I had promised myself that I wouldn't get involved, but I wasn't very good at following my own advice. Someone had to do something and that someone was me.

If Mostel's had been purgatory, then Lowenstein's was hell itself. The dark, dank cold went right through clothing and bones to the very soul. To sit hunched over machines, eyes straining in the gloom, fingers numb and chilblained, with the constant sound of coughing over the clatter of the treadles was enough to break even the bravest of spirits, and these girls had been through so much before that their spirits were already broken.

On Friday evening the bully Katz wound back the clock hands twenty minutes so that we'd stay to finish the workload and he wouldn't have to pay us overtime. I saw him. So did several other girls, but nobody said a word. I also watched him smirk to himself as he passed by to his office. I sat there fuming, longing for a chance to get even with him. I'd help get these girls unionized if it was the last thing I did!

The bell rang to signal seven o'clock, which was really seven twenty. Tired girls stood up, stretched cramped limbs, stamped cold feet, snatched up belongings, and got out of there as fast as they could. As I followed Rose to the door, a hand grabbed my arm. 'Not you, Murphy. I want a word with you.'

I looked around to find Katz smirking at me.

'What have I done?'

'These sleeves,' he said. 'Call yourself a seamstress, do you? I don't know what the standard of work is like in Ireland, but it must be pretty bad.'

'There's nothing wrong with my sleeves,' I said angrily. 'I stitched a nice straight seam and I finished my quota.'

'Not what I've been seeing,' he said. He turned and disappeared through the door into the back room. 'Call this a nice straight seam?' He held up a sleeve and waved it at me.

I stomped into the back room after him. 'Let me see that. I'll tell you if it was my work or not.'

I snatched the sleeve from him. 'Why, this isn't even my sleeve. I don't start my work that way, and look, the threads aren't even cut. Little Becky cut every one of my threads today.'

I looked up and he was still smirking. I realized then that I had been tricked. The sounds in the workroom were dying away.

'I like 'em feisty,' he said, coming toward me. 'A good fight makes the conquest all the sweeter, and you look like a lusty girl who enjoys it, am I right?'

I was so frozen in horror that I didn't react quickly enough. He pushed me against the cold wet brick wall and pinned me with his body, his knee thrust between my legs. As I opened my mouth to scream, he forced his mouth onto mine, his tongue into my mouth, his hands groping at my body.

I didn't know what to do. I hadn't believed he could be so strong. I tried to shake myself free from him, but he held me pinned like a butterfly to a board. Revulsion flooded over me as I felt him getting excited and impatient but I fought to remain calm. If he wanted to take this amorous attack one stage further, he'd have to move to lift my skirt and then I'd go for him where it hurt. I was finding it hard to breathe. Then I felt him trying to shift me along the wall to where bolts of cloth lay piled on the floor. If he got me that far, he could throw himself on top of me. I wasn't going to let that happen. I managed to get my hands up to his face. I couldn't reach his eyes, but I grabbed his long, curling hair, and I yanked as hard as I could.

He reacted just enough for me to break free of his mouth.

'Let go of me or you'll be sorry!' I gasped. 'I killed the last man who tried to rape me.'

'I don't kill so easy,' he said, laughing. 'Like I said – the harder the struggle, the sweeter the conquest.'

'Molly? I've been waiting for you. Are you ready yet?' Rose's voice echoed behind us, unnaturally loud.

Katz spun around. 'What the hell are you doing here?'

'Keeping an eye on Molly and making sure she gets home safe and sound,' Rose said calmly. She walked over to me, linked her arm through mine, and dragged me away. 'Let's go home now, Molly,' she said. Then she walked with me calmly out of that door and down the long, empty workroom.

'Thank you,' I stammered. 'If you hadn't come back for me, I don't know what might have happened.'

'I hung around,' she said. 'I thought he might try it. I've noticed him looking at you. He tries it with all the pretty new girls.'

'He's disgusting,' I said, wiping my mouth with my hand and fighting back a desire to vomit. 'The owner should be told. He shouldn't be allowed to get away with it.'

'Mr Lowenstein doesn't care about anything except quick profits,' Rose said. 'How often do you think he even shows up here? Hardly ever. And Katz gets the work done on time for him. That's all he cares about.'

'I'm putting a knife in my skirt pocket in the future,' I said, 'in case he tries it again.'

'He won't,' Rose said. 'He'll go on to someone who's easier. That's one thing you can count on around here – a never ending supply of girls.'

'Not when we get the union going,' I said.

Rose chuckled. 'Another redhead just like me. We're all born fighters, Molly. I'm so glad you came here. We'll show 'em, won't we?'

'We'll set the dogs on Mr Katz!'

We linked arms and left the building smiling.

On Monday morning an old gentleman with a neat white beard came into our workroom. He wore a long black coat and top hat and he carried a silver-tipped cane. The effect was rather like an elderly wizard.

'*Guten Morgen*,' he said in German. 'Everyone working hard. That's good. Where is Katz?'

Katz came flying out of the back room at the sound of the voice.

'Mr Lowenstein – such a privilege that you should visit us,' he said, groveling. 'Everything is going well, sir. The order will go out today like you wanted.'

'*Gut. Gut.*' Lowenstein rubbed his hands together. 'And think about taking on some more girls. Busy season coming up. I should have the new designs in the next week or so and then it's full speed ahead, *ja*? A bonus for everybody if we get the first batch of new dresses in the stores two weeks before Christmas.' He rubbed his hands together again. 'It's cold in here, Katz. How can these girls do their best work if it's cold? Get the oil stoves out, man.'

'Papa, are you coming?' A slim, dark-haired beauty made her way gingerly down the outside steps and poked her head through the door. She was wearing a fur-trimmed bonnet and a big blue cape, also trimmed with white fur. The cape was open and she wore a black velvet ribbon around her throat on which hung a silver locket, sparkling with precious stones. She posed in the doorway, conscious that all those eyes were on her.

'It's too cold waiting out in the carriage,' she said. 'Hurry up, please or we'll be late for our lunch appointment.'

'Coming, my dearest.' Mr Lowenstein looked up at her and smiled. 'Sorry I can't stay longer. Keep working, everyone. Good-bye.'

He waved and joined his daughter.

'How about some of us help you carry the oil stoves, Mr Katz?' Rose asked, not wanting him to be able to wriggle out of it while the boss was in earshot. 'Come on, Molly and Golda and Lanie. Let's help him.'

'Very well. Come on, then.' He stomped into the back room and finally unearthed two oil stoves from a storage closet. We picked up one between two of us and carried them out.

'So that was the boss?' I whispered to Rose as we staggered out with the stove.

She nodded. 'He might look like a nice old gentleman, but he's hard as nails. When Gussie died of consumption right before he gave out the Christmas bonus last year, he wouldn't even send the bonus to her family. And how do you think she got sick in the first place? Sitting in this damp hole, that's how.'

'And that was the boss's daughter, I take it?'

She made a face. 'Letitia, her name is. Only child. Spoiled rotten.'

We set down the stoves and waited for Katz to come with the can of kerosene. I couldn't get the picture of the boss's daughter out of my mind. There had been something disturbing about her, something that made me uneasy. I thought some more, but couldn't put my finger on it.

'Be happy that the boss has such a kind heart,' Katz announced as he poured in kerosene and got the stoves going. There was no room for them between the rows of girls so one stood at the doorway to the street and one at the doorway to Katz's back room. Most of the girls felt no effect at all.

I was looking forward to the union meeting on Wednesday. I had written a list of grievances that I couldn't wait to share with union organizers. Maybe with two of us, Rose and myself, we could light a fire under those girls at Lowenstein's and get them to speak up for themselves.

Rose and I had a bowl of soup together at Samuel's and then we made our way to Essex Street where we went down the steps into another basement. This one was quite different – brightly lit, warm, and filled with benches, most of them already occupied.

'Here's Rose, at last,' one of the young women called as we stood hesitantly in the doorway. 'I thought things had been too quiet until now.'

'Yes, and look what I've brought with me,' Rose said,

dragging me inside. 'A new warrior for our struggle. This is Miss Molly Murphy, come from Ireland.'

'Welcome, Molly. Sit yourself down.' A place in the back row was indicated for me. I sat and looked around the group. I was interested to see an equal number of men and women in the group – serious young men in workers' garb, with dark beards and dark eyes. There were plenty of young women like ourselves, dressed humbly in shirtwaists and skirts with shawls around their shoulders, but one or two stood out, the cut and fabric of their dress announcing them to be not of the working class. What were they doing here?

Three men and two women sat at a table in front of us. The women were better dressed than the rest of us and one of them looked familiar. I stared, trying to place her. Had I seen her picture in a newspaper? She had dark and rather angular features, a long thin nose, and hair swept severely back from her face. She wore a black fitted coat, trimmed with astrakhan, and a neat little black velvet bonnet sat on the table beside her, decorated with a stunning black ostrich plume. Obviously not one of us, then.

'Right then, let's get started.' A young man banged a gavel on the table. 'For those of you who don't know, I'm Jacob Singer of the United Hebrew Trades, and we're here to help you form a ladies garment workers union.' He spoke with the slightest trace of a foreign accent. He was slim with a neatly trimmed beard and expressive dark eyes, framed with round wire-rimmed spectacles, which gave him a boyish, owlish look.

A slim girl in black rose from my left. 'We've had such a union for a year now, Mr Singer.'

'Yes, I know that, Miss Horowitz, but it has only existed on paper, hasn't it? It hasn't sprung into action yet.' Jacob Singer smiled. His face had been so grave and earnest before that it came as a shock to see his eyes twinkling. It quite changed his appearance.

'No, but it will.' The girl thrust out her chin defiantly.

'I don't doubt it, but first it needs members. How many members are on your books so far?'

'Twenty-five.' The girl's voice was little more than a whisper.

There were some titters from around the room.

'So it would appear, ladies, that our first task is to grow your membership,' Jacob said.

'How do we do that?' Rose got to her feet. 'How can we persuade girls to join us when they fear for their jobs? Where I work, at Lowenstein's, we are treated worse than animals. We have no rights. There are constant abuses. But if a girl speaks up, she is dismissed. So all remain silent and the abuse goes on.'

Jacob nodded his head gravely. So did the others at the top table. 'We can do nothing without solidarity,' another man at the top table said. He looked more like a student, with straggly beard and Russian worker's cap on his head. 'I represent the cloak-makers union, and we have had some small successes with strikes in the past. But only if we get one hundred percent participation. All for one, one for all. We cannot hurt them until we are united. If there is to be a walkout, then all must walk out.'

'If we walk out, then they just hire new girls,' Rose said.

'If the walkout is only at one shop,' the straggly young man agreed. 'If all shops walk out at the same time, then they have a problem.'

'It will never happen,' a voice behind me said.

'We have to let them see that it can happen,' the slender young woman at the top table said. 'Maybe there will have to be some sacrifices, but we must let the owners see that we are prepared to strike and lose our jobs if we want progress.'

'Begging your pardon, miss.' A girl with a luxuriant coil of hair, wound around her head like a halo, rose to her feet. 'But you keep on saying "we" and "us". It won't be you who loses your job. You have a nice house uptown to go home to after these meetings. I know you mean well, but you can't know what it's like to live in a stinking tenement and never have enough to eat.'

The girl at the top table flushed, then nodded gravely. 'You're right. I can't know exactly what it's like for you, but I do have some experience with confronting the enemy when it comes to the suffrage movement. I have been to jail twice, and believe me, I was not treated like a lady there. There are many of us, all of good families, willing to go to jail, to make nuisances of ourselves, if we can obtain the right to vote for our sisters.'

There was scattered applause from the audience. The young woman from uptown bowed her head again. 'But I admit that I know I will have a home to go to and food on the table when I am let out of jail. I know you will be asked to make enormous sacrifices, but somebody has to, or nothing will ever improve. Every generation of immigrants who steps off the boat will go into conditions like the ones you are enduring right now.'

'So what can we do?' Rose asked.

'You must recruit members where you work,' Jacob said. 'Plant seeds in the minds of your fellow workers that you can change things, that you can make your employers fear you. I know that for many of you the busy season is approaching – the rush to get items into the stores for the holiday shopping and then the new spring lines after the January sales. This is when the shops make their biggest profit. If you walk out now, you will cost them valuable time while they find and train replacements. Maybe they are not so willing to lose that time. Maybe they are willing to negotiate.'

Rose looked at me, her eyes shining. 'It might just work,

Molly. If we walked out the moment Lowenstein wanted us to start on the new designs, maybe he would listen.'

'It's worth a try,' I said.

Rose got to her feet. 'We are willing to try. Mr Lowenstein prides himself on getting his garments into the store first. Maybe this will be a way for us to make him listen.'

'Good for you, Rose,' the dark girl at the table said. 'Do you have someone to work with you?'

'I have Molly,' Rose said. 'She has just arrived from Ireland. Stand up, Molly, and let them see you.'

I rose to my feet.

'Two redheads, *oy vay*,' someone near me said. 'I pity poor Mr Lowenstein.'

There was good-natured laughter.

The meeting progressed. It was decided that Lowenstein's should be a test case. We would try to bring all of the girls into the union so that we could conduct an effective walkout the moment the new designs were produced. I knew better than any of them that this might work. Lowenstein counted on getting his stolen designs into the stores before Mostel had his ready. If he couldn't corner the market first, then he would lose. A good bargaining tool indeed.

When the meeting concluded, refreshments were served – cookies and hot tea and a big plate of sandwiches. The girls fell upon them with gusto. I took a cup of tea, then joined a group of girls.

'So you're from Ireland, are you, Molly?'

I agreed that I was. 'And I understand that there was another Irish girl here not too long ago? Didn't you say so, Rose? By the name of Kathy?'

'Kathy? But surely she was English,' one of the girls said.

'I thought someone said she was from an upper-class English family, only she lived in Ireland.'

'I don't think she ever said where she was from, did she?' The girls looked at each other.

'No, very tight-lipped about herself, she was. But outspoken when it came to union matters. You should have heard her talk. My, but she could have talked the hind leg off a donkey.'

'Remember you told her that, Fanny? And she laughed and said something about being good at blarney, whatever that means.'

'Too bad she stopped coming to meetings.'

'So where did she go?' I asked. 'Did she move away?'

The girls looked at each other and shrugged.

'I don't know what happened to her,' one said.

'Which company did she work for?'

Again the girls shrugged. 'She only came a few times, then she stopped. Too bad because I'd have loved to hear her tell those bosses what she thought of them. Real haughty she was, and kind of looked down her nose when she spoke to you.'

'Did she have light-brown, sort of wispy hair and very light eyes?' I asked.

'Yes, did you know her?'

'I thought she might have been a friend from back home,' I said.

'So you just arrived from Ireland, did you?'

'That's right.' As I said it, I found myself looking at the upper-crust young lady from the top table. She was standing with a sandwich in her hand, staring hard at me. Then she put down the plate and came straight toward me. 'Now I know where I saw you before,' she said coldly. 'What exactly are you doing here?'

Fourteen

'What do you mean?' I asked.

'You're not one of us,' she said. 'So what are you doing here? Spying for the bosses, perchance?'

'Of course not,' I said angrily. 'What on earth makes you say something like that? I'm from Lowenstein's, with Rose. Ask her.'

Then suddenly I remembered where I had seen her before. She had worn her hair differently, and the light had been dim, but I had once sat across a table from her in a Greenwich Village café, at a meeting of anarchists that had almost cost me my life.

'And I could ask you the same question,' I said to her. 'The last time I saw you, you were plotting to bring down the government at an anarchists' meeting with Miss Emma Goldman.'

'Not I. I am a socialist, not an anarchist, Miss Murphy. I was there to support Emma Goldman because she represents change – empowerment of the masses, birth control. Anything that can improve the condition of women – that is my personal quest.'

'Then you and I have no quarrel,' I said. 'You know my name, but I don't know yours.'

'It's Nell,' she said. 'Nell Blankenship.'

I held out my hand. 'We are on the same side, Miss Blankenship, both working to right injustices.'

She took my hand reluctantly, but still looked at me quizzically. 'And is your name really Molly Murphy, fresh off the boat from Ireland?'

I decided to take a gamble.

'If I could have a private word, then some things would become clear.'

'Very well.' She moved away from the crowd around the food table to the far corner of the room.

'You are right that I am not really a garment worker,' I said in a low voice, even though the other occupants of the room paid no attention to us. 'I am actually a private investigator.'

'An investigator – is that not the same as a spy?' she asked, still frowning at me. 'Were you not spying at Emma's meeting? You clearly were not in sympathy with our cause.'

'I came to your meeting with Ryan O'Hare,' I said. 'He insisted that I meet Emma Goldman.'

'And that was your only reason for being there?'

'No, not my only reason,' I said. 'When you met me before I was on the trail of the man who killed my employer. I caught up with him, only too late.'

She looked at me quizzically again. 'A lady detective,' she said. 'I didn't realize that such things existed. The only question is for whom are you working this time? The sweatshop owners, so that all this will be reported back to them?'

'Of course not,' I said angrily.

'Then why throw yourself into a cause that is clearly not your own?'

'I could ask you the same thing,' I said, staring her down. 'You are not a garment worker either. Why waste your time on the lower classes when you could be dining at Delmonico's?'

'Precisely because I have the luxury of time,' she said. 'These girls are ill equipped to speak for themselves. If I can make their lot better, I shall have accomplished something worthwhile. This and getting the vote for my sisters – these have become my life's work.'

'Then I commend you, Miss Blankenship,' I said.

'And I hope I can equally commend you, Miss Murphy.' She still didn't smile.

At that moment a shadow fell between us. Jacob Singer, the young man in the wire-rimmed spectacles, approached with a plate of cookies. 'Are you bullying our newest recruit, Nell?' he said, giving me a friendly smile. 'I am Jacob Singer and we have not been introduced yet.'

'How do you do, I'm Molly Murphy,' I said.

'I am pleased to make your acquaintance, Miss Murphy.' He clicked his heels and gave a little bow in a charmingly foreign fashion. 'I hope Nell was not putting you through a grilling? She can become a little too passionate about her causes, I'm afraid.' He chuckled. Nell didn't return his smile.

'Just sounding her out, Jacob,' Nell said. 'Just trying to find out whose side she is on, because she is not a garment worker fresh from Ireland. She is a lady detective – so beware what you say.'

'A detective?' He looked at me with concern. 'Not a garment worker then?'

I looked around to see who was within hearing distance. 'I took on a job that necessitated my posing as a sweatshop girl. While working under such conditions, I decided I could not sit idly by. That's one of the reasons I'm here tonight. I want to help.'

'Excellent,' Jacob said. 'Just the sort of recruit we need, wouldn't you say, Nell?'

Nell looked at him, then at me. 'Perhaps I owe you an apology, Miss Murphy.'

'But I'm also here for another reason.' I looked around again, then moved closer to them. 'The English girl called Kathy you heard me asking about earlier. I have been asked to trace such a girl by her family in Ireland. This Kathy sounds very much like the Katherine I was asked to find.'

'I don't think anyone knows where she is now,' Nell said. 'She came to meetings for several weeks and seemed fired up with enthusiasm. We were hopeful that she would be a real force for change because she was so articulate and unafraid to speak her mind. Then one week she didn't come.'

'I'm afraid I might know where she is now,' I said. 'A body, resembling her description, was pulled from the East River.'

'Oh no. A victim of foul play?' she asked.

'The police are of the opinion that this girl took her own life.'

Nell shook her head. 'Then it is not the same person. Kathy would not have given in to despair any more than you or I would have done.'

'My feelings exactly,' I said. 'I never met her, but the face in the photograph I have is not of a weak character.'

'You have a photograph? Then I can verify that it is the same person.'

'I don't have it with me,' I said. 'And I don't know if there is any point in taking this matter any further. If she is dead, then I can't bring her back to life again.'

'But if she is dead, then someone is responsible and should be brought to justice,' Nell said.

It was strange to hear my own sentiments echoed back to me. 'I agree. But I am not the police. I have so little to go on and no way of investigating further.'

'You could be of help, Nell,' Jacob said. He turned to me.

'Nell is a reporter by profession. She writes articles for the major newspapers to expose the corruption and abuse in this city. She has made some useful contacts in many strata of this city. And this is just the sort of challenge you enjoy, is it not, Nell?'

I sensed that Nell was not really inclined to put herself out on my behalf, that she still had not warmed to me, but that she didn't want to turn me down in front of Jacob. 'I suppose I might be of some help, it is true,' she said.

'Splendid.' Jacob smiled at me again. 'Then why don't we continue this conversation at another time? Where do you live, Miss Murphy?'

'Patchin Place.'

Finally Nell looked interested. 'Patchin Place. How extraordinary. I have friends there. Do you know two delight-ful women called—'

'Sid and Gus?' I asked. 'I lived with them until a week ago. Now I have taken up residence across the street.'

'What an amazing coincidence. I should most like to renew their acquaintance,' she said. 'Tomorrow then?'

I shook my head. 'You forget. I am employed in a sweat-shop from dawn until night and have little energy for good conversation afterward. How about Saturday night? I don't have to rise early on Sunday morning.'

'Saturday it is then.'

'Am I to be included in the invitation?' Jacob asked. 'Perhaps I may also be of use in your inquiry.'

'Of course you are most welcome, Mr Singer.'

He bowed again. 'I shall look forward to it then.'

'Miss Blankenship? Could you come over here for moment? Bella has a question for you.' One of the girls approached Nell hesitantly.

'Of course,' Nell said. 'Excuse me.'

I was left alone with Jacob Singer. 'Have you had a cup of tea, Miss Murphy? Or one of these cookies?' He held out the tray to me. I took one.

'I've never been known to turn down a cookie,' I said. 'Or a biscuit as we say in Ireland, where they were luxuries reserved for special occasions.'

'One of the best things about America, wouldn't you say? We didn't even have such luxuries at home in Russia. Sugar was kept hidden away in a little wooden box for special occasions.'

His eyes, ringed by those wire spectacles, lit up with amusement. Such a pleasant face. Quite a handsome face too.

'I am very glad that you'll be joining us,' he said. 'As you can see, we need all the help we can get.'

'Are you involved in the garment industry yourself, Mr Singer?' I asked.

'He is involved in no particular industry,' Nell said, coming back to join us and slipping an arm through his. 'He is a professional rabble-rouser.'

Jacob Singer laughed. 'I am employed by the United Hebrew Trades to help fledgling unions get off the ground. I was active in the Bund before I left Russia, so I have experience in civil disobedience to share. But you must excuse me, you probably have not even heard of the Bund.'

'Oh but I have,' I said. 'Rose's brother was a member. He was executed.'

Jacob nodded. 'An all too common fate, I'm afraid. That or Siberia, which was often a death sentence in itself. I had to flee for my life when they came for us. I escaped by swimming across an ice-filled river. Not a pleasant experience, I can assure you.'

'How terrible. I've heard so many tragic stories.'

'But your country is no stranger to tragedy either,' Jacob

said. 'How many of your countrymen died in the Great Famine?'

'That's true enough. Everyone in our village had a story of lost relatives, including my own family. Apart from my father and my brothers I don't think I've a living relative in the world.'

'Then we are united in a struggle to make things better, are we not?' He smiled at me. His eyes held mine. I flushed and looked away.

'Jacob is a photographer, as well as being a rabble-rouser,' Nell said. 'He and I work together. I fish out the facts, he takes the pictures. Together we have been into the most disreputable parts of the city.'

'Then I am indeed fortunate to have met both of you,' I said. 'I can't tell you how much it riles me to have to abandon my search for Katherine.'

'Let us hope you will not have to abandon it,' Jacob said. 'If Nell recognizes your photograph, then we can start to trace what happened to this unfortunate Katherine. All will be made clear on Saturday.'

'And in the meantime,' I said in a low voice, 'please don't give away that I am not just an ordinary sweatshop girl. I am with them heart and soul in this struggle and I fear they would not trust me if they knew I was not really one of them.'

'You can count on us to say nothing,' Jacob said and glanced across at Nell for agreement. Her face remained impassive.

'At what time do you expect us on Saturday?' she asked.

'Shall we say eight? We are supposed to leave work at six on Saturday, as a special gesture of beneficence.'

Jacob laughed. 'She has the Irish gift of the gab, does she not? I am so glad that your investigation brought our paths to cross, Miss Murphy.'

'Eight o'clock on Saturday then,' Nell said. 'That will work out splendidly. We'll have time to go to the opening of that art exhibition first, Jacob. Are we done here, do you think? I am suddenly tired and would like you to walk me home.' She had her arm through his and she steered him away from me, toward the door.

They must be sweethearts, I thought, and was surprised at the rush of disappointment that I felt.

'I wondered where you'd got to, Molly. Have you tried these little cakes yet?' Rose took my arm and dragged me back to the group at the table.

Fifteen

On Saturday Sid and Gus insisted on preparing a feast at their house.

'But it's so long since we've seen Nell,' Gus said, when I tried to protest, 'and we've been dying to meet this Jacob Singer, so you can't be selfish and keep them to yourself.'

'All right, if you insist,' I said, 'but you have already done so much for me. Let me at least provide the food.'

'Nonsense. You know how we love trying new recipes,' Sid said. 'And we have just been reading a book about a woman who traveled alone through North Africa, disguised as a male Bedouin. Doesn't that sound like a simply marvelous thing to do? We were all set to try it when we finished the book, but then we decided we really couldn't abandon dear old New York and Patchin Place. So we've settled for the food. We shall cook couscous and kebabs – although I don't think we can procure camel's hump.'

I laughed. 'Camel's hump. Now I've heard everything.'

'It is considered a great delicacy among the Bedouin,' Sid said, attempting not to smile. 'But you may bring the wine and the grapes, if you insist.'

So when I was finally released from work at six thirty-five on Saturday I wandered among the Italian food shops south of Washington Square and chose a jug of robust red wine, enclosed in a neat raffia basket. I felt very worldly carrying it home. If they could see me now in Ballykillin, I thought with a smile of satisfaction. When I arrived at 9 Patchin Place I found that Sid and Gus had been up to their old tricks – they had transformed their parlor into an Eastern boudoir, with the walls draped in velvet and gauze and the floor strewn with Oriental carpets and large pillows. They had even produced an Oriental water pipe, which they insisted we should smoke later.

Nell and Jacob arrived at eight and we had a messy meal, eating with our hands, while perched on cushions.

'Now I know why they always have dogs around in such scenes,' Nell exclaimed, wiping a sticky chin with her napkin. 'It is to clean up the food that falls around them. I feel revolt-ingly primitive.'

'But remarkably free, wouldn't you say?' Sid asked.

I glanced at Jacob and found that he was watching me. We exchanged a smile.

I looked at the plates, still piled high with food. I ate another grape and felt instantly guilty.

'Doesn't it worry you sometimes that we can go home to eat like this while those girls at the sweatshops probably go to bed hungry each night?' I looked across at Nell and Jacob.

'I can't let it worry me,' Nell said. 'I do what I can to improve the lot of women. If I didn't get enough to eat, I wouldn't have the energy to accomplish what I do. And I see no sense in pretending to be poor.'

'And I only eat such meals as this when decadent friends invite me, Miss Murphy,' Jacob said. 'Then I return to starve in my garret.'

'Only because you choose not to make money from your photographs,' Nell said, slapping his hand and laughing. 'You know very well that you could be rich and famous and dine

147

at all the best houses in town if you chose. You are a brilliant photographer. You just choose to photograph slums and strikes.'

'You're right. We Russians don't know how to live without suffering,' Jacob said, also smiling, and again his gaze strayed across to me. 'Miss Murphy understands. She comes from Ireland where suffering is also the way of life.'

'Not exactly,' I said. 'We are under the yolk of the English and live in squalor, but we still like to enjoy life. As long as we've music and a good swig of liquor, then we're happy.'

'Is that all it takes to make you happy?' he asked. 'Music and a good swig of liquor.'

'I didn't say me,' I said, blushing at his teasing gaze now. 'But we like good friends and good company too, and I'll say amen to that.'

'When are you going to show us your photographs, Jacob?' Gus asked. 'I've been dying to see inside a photographer's studio.'

'You must come tomorrow then,' he said. 'All of you. I shall be honored.'

'What fun. We accept,' Sid said. 'Now, shall we try the hubble-bubble?' She indicated the water pipe.

'We have to work while our brains are still clear,' Nell said. 'It was the reason we came, after all.'

I opened my purse and took out the photos.

'This is the Katherine I was looking for,' I said.

Nell studied it. Jacob came to look over her shoulder. They looked at each other and nodded. 'It is the same girl,' Nell said.

I produced the picture of Katherine with Michael at her stirrup. 'And this is the man she ran off with. His name is Michael Kelly. I have learned that he was involved with the Eastmans gang. But he too disappeared and the police think he might have been one of the unnamed men who have been killed in recent gang wars.'

'All too probable,' Nell said. 'They lead violent lives. What else do you know?'

'Very little. I traced them to a boarding-house on Division Street. They left that address without paying their rent about the same time that they disappeared.'

Sid came to join us. 'If this Katherine is dead, as Molly has told us, then why are you still searching? Shouldn't she just write to the parents and tell them the sad truth then forget the matter?'

'Nell and I believe, as Molly does, that Katherine would not have taken her own life,' Jacob said, glancing across at Nell for confirmation.

She nodded. 'I only met her on a few occasions but I came to admire her. She had zest and fire. She was not going to let her current circumstances browbeat her.'

'Then I think we owe it to her to find out how she met her end,' Jacob said, 'and who better to find out the truth than you, Nell? You know every back alley of this city.'

Gus put a hand on my shoulder. 'Oh dear, Molly. You should never have met these people. Now you've found some- one to encourage your wild schemes.'

'I don't know that I agree with this one,' I said. 'I can't see how we can find out more than we know right now. The young woman pulled from the river is already buried in a pauper's grave. And it would be impossible to find out if she went into the river willingly or was pushed.'

'Not impossible,' Jacob said, leaning closer. 'If we know where the body was fished from the river and about how long it had been in the water, then we should be able to guess where she was thrown in. And if she was thrown in, then someone might have seen it happen.'

I looked at him with admiration. 'And I thought I was

supposed to be the investigator. You are far more suited to it than I, Mr Singer.'

'Why so formal?' Gus said. 'This is Greenwich Village. In this house we are on a first-name basis – no need for the restrictions of polite society. So it is Molly and Jacob and Nell. Is that clear?'

Jacob glanced across at me and smiled again. 'If you permit then, Molly?'

'I shall be charmed, Jacob. And you too, Nell?' I included her hastily, just in case she thought I had any designs on her young man.

'Absolutely. I have never been one for the conventions of polite society, which is why I have been such a trial to my parents. Twenty-eight years old and still unmarried. What is more, I told them that I see marriage as a legal method of condemning women to a life of subservence. But don't let me start on that topic – let us get back to our foul play, which is more interesting than my lack of nuptial bliss. How do you propose we tackle this, Molly?'

'I can ask the police if any records were taken of where the body was fished from the water and what kind of state it was in. I suppose they recorded what she was wearing, although if she wore any jewelry which might identify her, it will be in some policeman's pocket by now.'

Nell laughed. 'I can tell you have had experience with our delightful police force since your arrival here.'

'Including three different occasions in jail,' I said. 'But I do have a—' I was about to say friend. I corrected myself – 'a person I can contact who is a police captain.'

'Splendid,' Nell said. 'So you will find what details the police have on this woman. I will attempt to find out everything I can on Katherine's life here – where she worked, whether she had a confrontation with her boss there . . .'

I caught her gaze. 'You don't think—' I began – 'she might have made a nuisance of herself at the sweatshop?'

'Some of the sweatshop owners are in cahoots with the gangs,' Jacob said. 'In the past when there have been walkout attempts, the shop owners have hired starkes – strong-arm men – to intimidate the strikers. If they had an employee who was likely to create too much trouble, the simplest thing would be to pay a gang to get rid of her.'

'Holy Mother of God.' I put my hand to my throat. 'That had never even crossed my mind. Are they that ruthless, do you think?'

'Definitely,' Jacob said. 'Profit means everything. Anyone who stands in the way of profit must be eliminated.'

'In that case, finding out what happened to Katherine is all part of the same fight,' I said. I didn't add that I was now taking over Katherine's role. I might soon be seen as a nuisance who should be eliminated.

Jacob looked from Nell to me. 'Now that I think about it and have heard the circumstances of her disappearance, my advice to you is to let this lie,' he said quietly. 'I have seen much tragedy in my life. You can't bring this Katherine back to life. Do not risk your own lives for something that can't be undone.'

'Who's talking about risking lives?' Nell demanded. 'A few carefully phrased questions in the right quarter, that's all we're talking about. My first task will be to find out where she worked, and then to ask some discreet questions about that particular shop owner and his foremen.'

'You will never be able to prove anything,' Jacob said. 'And the deeper you delve, the greater the risk you take.'

Nell patted his arm. 'You are such a fussbudget, Jacob. Molly and I are intelligent, sensible women.'

'I worry because I have met too many people who do not play by the rules,' he said.

151

'Enough of such gloomy talk. Not allowed in this house,' Sid said firmly. 'I shall now produce the hubble-bubble and we will transport ourselves into a Bedouin black tent. And since you are the only male here, Jacob, you may be the sheik!'

We concentrated our energy on the water pipe with hilarious results, and the next morning, after our Sunday ritual of coffee and pastries at Fleischmann's Vienna Bakery on Broadway, we headed for the Lower East Side. I realized that I had become accustomed to it, as Sid and Gus pointed out sights that they found strange and exotic. 'Flavors of the Levantine, Gus dear. Does this not make you want to travel there after all? We could take in the Holy Land and Egypt and then on to Morocco and the Bedouins.'

'Think of the dirt, though,' Gus said, picking up her skirts to avoid the rotting fruit, horse manure, and other debris that cluttered the street. 'The smell of this is bad enough. I do not think I have the stomach for Oriental alleyways.'

Jacob's atelier was in a loft on Rivington Street, which was in the more prosperous side of the Jewish quarter. Here the houses were built of solid red brick, trimmed with white brick around the windows, and there was a lively trade going on in the many stores that lined the street. I was about to ask how they could be allowed to open on Sundays when I realized that Saturday was the Jewish Sabbath and Sunday only another ordinary day. I found myself wondering if Jacob observed Jewish rituals and went to worship at a temple.

He came down to greet us and escorted us up the stairs, past doors from which came the smells of fat frying and the sounds of a violin being played and up to the top floor. His studio was stark but neat, with a kitchen sink and scrubbed pine table at one side, a bed behind a screen, and the rest of the space taken over with photographic equipment and photographs he had taken.

'I am so glad you could come too, Miss Murphy,' he said after he had greeted Gus and Sid. He was dressed in a Russian worker's garb, a high-buttoned black tunic that suited him well. His black curly hair was freshly washed and slicked down in an attempt to tame the curls.

'We must be outside Greenwich Village, since I have reverted to being Miss Murphy, or have I in some way offended you?' I said, and was rewarded by his blush.

'You must forgive me. I was raised to a strict code of behavior. My parents lived by every rule society ever invented.'

'Your parents are still in Russia?' I asked, expecting to hear that they were dead.

'No, they are here. I managed to bring them to the New World soon after I arrived here. They live a street away on Delancey and think me a bad son and a terrible sinner because I do not choose to live with them. That an unmarried son should branch out on his own is unthinkable. Why, he might even entertain unchaperoned young women and then who would want their daughters to marry him?'

We laughed together at this absurdity. Living with Sid and Gus had made me forget that the rest of the world still adhered to strict rules of conduct.

'So will you allow the matchmaker to select your wife, like a good Jewish son?' Sid asked.

'I could throw the same question back at you, Miss Goldfarb.'

'Touché. But one only has to look at me to know the answer. You still choose to live in a traditional area and wear a beard.'

'Then to answer your question – I still adhere to the basics of my religion, but only when it does not conflict with reason and the twentieth century. I attend the occasional seder with my family, but see no reason to observe dietary restrictions, which were created for a desert lifestyle. My parents think I am lost beyond hope. And you, Miss Murphy – are you still a good Catholic girl?'

'I never was. When I was a small child I used to slip out during the middle of mass to raid the priest's blackberry bushes. There was always too much emphasis on the fires of hell for my liking. I think my God would be more forgiving and have a better sense of humor.'

'Then we worship the same deity,' Jacob said. 'Forgiving and humorous. The world would be a better place if such was the tenet of life.'

Gus had already started to wander around the room. 'These photographs are magnificent, Jacob. Nell was right. You do have a great talent.'

'I'm merely a novice, Miss Walcott. Still learning my trade.'

'But you've captured the life of the city perfectly,' Gus said. 'Come and look at this, Sid and Molly.' She held up a large print of some scruffy children, playing among lines of drying laundry on a rooftop. There were scenes in crowded streets, and ominous back alleys.

'Why,' I exclaimed, 'this is the alley that the Eastmans frequent – and, if I'm not mistaken, those are members of the gang, lurking in that doorway. How did you manage to take their pictures, Jacob?'

'I am amazed that you are so familiar with gang members,' Jacob said. 'You do lead a dangerous life, Miss Murphy.'

'My visit there was accidental, but you must have lingered long enough to set up your exposure.'

'I was there with Nell. She was writing one of her exposure articles on the worst slums in the city. This was one of the sites she chose.'

'She is remarkably fearless,' I said.

'I would rather say foolhardy,' Jacob answered. 'Sometimes her lack of regard for her own safety worries me.'

'And so you go on assignments with her to take pictures, but also to act as her protector,' I said.

He gave me a long hard look. 'You are remarkably perceptive, Miss Murphy.'

'Molly.'

He inclined his head. 'Molly.'

We drank more coffee then Sid got to her feet. 'I'm afraid we have taken up too much of your time, Jacob. I am delighted to have made your acquaintance and look forward to inviting you to our future soirees.'

'And I will be delighted to accept, Miss Goldfarb.' Jacob gave that curiously foreign bow. He escorted us to the door and down the stairs.

'We should hail a cab as soon as you see one, Gus dear,' Sid said. 'Or we may be late for lunch with the Wassermans.'

Jacob touched my sleeve lightly. 'Are you also expected at the Wassermans, Miss Murphy?'

'No, I'm not, and when will you get it into your head that my name is Molly?'

'In that case, maybe you would allow me to escort you home.'

'Oh, that's not necessary. I'm quite comfortable on these streets and it's broad daylight,' I said and watched his face fall. 'But if you've a mind for a walk on such a fine breezy day, then I wouldn't say no to the company,' I added hastily.

'In that case, I'll grab my hat,' he said and bounded up the stairs again.

'I think you've made a conquest there, Molly dear,' Gus said quietly.

'Oh, no. It is Miss Blankenship who has his heart. He is merely being gentlemanly,' I said, and felt myself blushing furiously.

Jacob and I set off, along Rivington until we struck the

155

Bowery. This broad thoroughfare was full of life on a sunny Sunday. Theaters were just opening, many of them offering plays in Yiddish. Cafés were doing a brisk trade. Jacob paused in front of one small theater that advertised moving pictures. COME AND EXPERIENCE THE WONDER OF THE TWENTIETH CENTURY, the billboard proclaimed. YOU WILL NOT BELIEVE YOUR EYES!

'Now that is something that truly interests me,' Jacob said. 'Photographs capture a moment, but moving pictures – that is the way of the future, Molly.' He looked at me expectantly. 'Would you like to go to a performance with me?'

'Now?' I asked. 'Why, thank you, Jacob, I'd love to. If you've nothing you should be doing at this moment, that is.'

'Nothing better than this. I've been twice already, but the scenes never fail to fascinate me.'

'I've heard about moving pictures, but I've never seen them yet.'

'Then what are we waiting for?' He took my arm and escorted me to the ticket booth.

We joined the crowd inside the darkened theater where an organist was playing in front of red velvet curtains. I was conscious of Jacob sitting close beside me in the dark, and it disturbed me how aware I was of his presence. Then even this closeness was forgotten. The curtains parted to reveal a screen.

Words appeared on the screen. 'Ladies and gentlemen. Prepare yourselves for an outrageous journey of entertainment and delight. Hold onto your seats, folks, and ladies, do not be alarmed. What you see is only an image on the screen. It cannot harm you.'

The organ music increased and suddenly an image appeared on the screen. It was an ocean with waves breaking. My, but it was so real, you could almost smell the salt in the air and hear the cry of seagulls. The waves came closer and closer. Suddenly a giant wave came crashing at the screen. I heard screams and several people leaped to their feet. I touched my own face, half expecting to be wet. I could see Jacob grinning in the darkness. 'A good illusion, wouldn't you say?' he whispered.

The next scene was of a group of inept policemen chasing a car. This was most amusing and the theater resounded to laughter. Then the car changed direction and drove directly at the camera. Again people leaped to their feet, then laughed in embarrassment when they realized it could not reach them. Then the scene changed again. The title appeared on the screen. *The Kiss.* We were in a lady's boudoir. A young man stole in through the open French doors. The young damsel, seated at her vanity, seemed amazed and delighted to see him. He took her into his arms. They gazed into each other's eyes and then there was a gasp from the audience as his lips fastened upon hers. The scene only lasted for a few seconds and then it faded. The show was over. The audience rose, still muttering in horror at what they had just seen.

'What did you think?' Jacob asked as we were jostled toward the exit.

'It was so real. Almost as if we were there.'

'If I ever make any money, I plan to build myself such a camera,' Jacob said.

'And make a moving picture called *The Kiss*?' I teased.

He shook his head. 'I have other plans. I could take my camera back to Russia and bring back living proof to the world of the cruelties and injustices going on there. I could take it to the Boer War in South Africa and show the world what war is really like. If ordinary people knew what was going on, we could change the world.'

'That's a wonderful notion, Jacob, but an awful risk for yourself.'

'Someone has to take risks or nothing changes,' he said.

We stood blinking in the bright sunlight.

'I almost forgot that it was daylight outside,' I said.

'Should we take the trolley or do you feel up to walking?' Jacob asked.

'Do I look like a frail young thing who might faint at any moment?' I demanded.

'No, I'd say that you looked most robust and healthy.' His frank gaze made me blush again.

He had barely uttered those words when Nell Blankenship appeared, like magic, from a café.

'Jacob. Molly. What a surprise,' she said. Her eyes were fixed on me and her expression indicated that she wasn't overjoyed to see me.

'Hello, Nell,' Jacob said. 'A lovely day, isn't it?'

'Sid, Gus, and I have been viewing Jacob's photographs. He is very talented,' I said hastily.

'He is indeed,' she said. 'So where are Sid and Gus? I should like to thank them for last night.'

'They had a lunch appointment and had to make a hasty departure,' Jacob said. 'I am escorting Molly home.'

'Ah,' Nell said. Her gaze passed from Jacob to me and back again. 'Well, much as I would like to stay and pass the time of day with you, I also must hurry. I'm due at my parents' home for lunch – my weekly penance and lecture session. Please excuse me.' She rushed to jump on an already moving electric trolley. 'I'll try to send you news about where your heiress worked as soon as possible,' she called as she swung herself aboard with agility. 'I'll start on it tomorrow!'

'Do not take any foolish risks, remember!' Jacob shouted as the trolley bore her away.

'Fiddle faddle,' she shouted back, laughing.

I looked at Jacob. 'Now I feel guilty. I hope she won't think badly of me.'

'Why should she think badly of you?'

'Because I was dallying with her young man.'

'Her young man? Nell and I are friends, nothing more.'

'But I thought – I saw the way she treated you with such familiarity.'

'She may well want a more intimate relationship,' Jacob said, 'but not I. I admire Nell. I think she is the most courageous woman I have ever met. But I would not choose such a woman for my wife. Sometimes she frightens me with the intensity of her dedication and fire.'

Why did I feel absurdly happy at this statement?

'I see you are smiling,' Jacob said. 'Could it be that you've just heard some good news?'

'I can't think what you are talking about, Mr Singer.' I tossed back my hair and set off at a lively trot.

'Jacob,' he said, keeping pace with me.

Sixteen

Knowing that a young man was interested in me certainly added spice to my life. And such a fascinating young man too. We had talked all the way home, touching on every subject under the sun. Daniel and I had been comfortable with each other, but we had never really discussed deep matters. Jacob and I thrashed out religion and royalty and socialism and communism and even birth control. I was amazed that I could talk about such things with a man. I had pretty much taken life for granted until I left Ireland. I knew that conditions were unfair and that the Irish were treated poorly in their own country, but I had considered those who fought for change to be rabble-rousers and hotheads, spoiling for a fight. In Jacob I saw someone who cared passionately and believed he could make a difference in the world. When he told me some of the things he had done as a member of the Bund in Russia, I was amazed. He couldn't have been more than seventeen at the time, but he had risked his life almost daily.

After we parted, I went to my room and stood at the window, watching him walk away. 'Now that is truly a fine fellow,' I said out loud. He wouldn't forget to mention that he was engaged to another girl or lack the courage to break off an engagement to a girl he didn't love. Thinking of Daniel reminded me that I had to write a note to him, purely professional, of course. I took out pen, ink, and blotter and started to write. I asked him for any details of Katherine's death that he could find – the point at which she was taken from the river, estimate of how long she had been in the water, where she might have entered, description of what she was wearing, any dressmaker's labels on the clothes to indicate where they were made, any jewelry, any sign of foul play – bruises, wounds, etc. I almost signed it, 'Yours, Molly,' until I remembered that I was not his and most probably would never be his. But the thought was no longer as painful. In fact I felt a great lifting of the spirit, as if I had awakened after a long hibernation.

I sent the message to the Mulberry Street police station with Shamey and waited for a reply, knowing it might not be until Monday, if Daniel had his weekend free. The moment I thought about Daniel's weekends, scenes flashed through my mind – Daniel and me strolling by the lake in Central Park, eating ice cream at a soda fountain, Daniel kissing me under the leafy boughs of the Ramble in the park. I knew then that I wouldn't get over him so easily, however diverting the fascinating Mr Singer might be.

As it happened, Daniel didn't have the weekend off. That evening a note was delivered by a uniformed constable.

I'm writing this at work, so forgive the terse tone of this message.

The young woman you think may be Katherine was pulled from the river below the Brooklyn Bridge. She was spotted from the deck of a docked cargo ship. Since she was in midstream, it is unclear where she fell in. She may have jumped from the bridge, which has become a popular suicide site. Her clothing is recorded

as a print muslin dress. No mention of dressmaker's
labels, laundry marks, etc. No mention of any jewelry
(and that would include wedding ring – hence the
motive for suicide?). Also no suggestion of foul play.

I'm sorry I can't help you more. I trust that your
reason for wanting these facts is to satisfy the curiosity
of her family, and that you do not entertain any absurd
notion of investigating her death. I need hardly warn
you that you have had several lucky escapes recently.
Do not test the fates again.
   Daniel

His lack of information gave me nothing to investigate, I
thought angrily as I reread the note. To be truthful, I hadn't
expected any jewelry, but she was married, or pretending
to be, so the lack of ring was strange – unless someone had
removed it along with any other means of identification. Of
course, it could have slipped off a cold, dead finger in the
icy East River, and I didn't think that the New York police
would be above even pocketing a wedding ring. But I had
been hopeful that an observant policeman might have noticed
an unusual label on her clothing or something that didn't fit
the picture. Even if she chose to dress simply, her underwear
would still be top-quality English, maybe even from Paris.
Ah well, it was too late to do anything about that now. The
poor girl was dead and buried. I just wished there had been
some proof that this was Katherine Faversham. How awful it
would be for her parents, never quite knowing what had happened to her. In spite of Daniel's warning, I hoped that Nell
would come up with some small fact that could start us on the
road to filling in the pieces of this puzzle.

Monday was another rainy day that found us garment workers
huddled together, wet and steaming in the warmth of Samuel's

Deli at lunchtime. Rose took the opportunity of speaking to the girls about the union and the plans for a walkout.

'So who's going to feed my kids while I'm on a picket line?' one of the older women demanded. 'And who is going to tell my Leon when I get the boot?'

'But nobody should be treated the way we are,' I said, joining Rose. 'You can't like working in such conditions.'

'Of course we don't like it, but we have no choice if we want to feed our families,' the woman snapped.

'We have to make them sit up and notice that we have power,' Rose said.

'Power, schmower,' the woman muttered. 'My mother's canary has more power than we do, and it lives in a cage.'

'But don't you see,' Rose insisted, 'if our timing is right, then we do have power. You know how Mr Lowenstein likes to get his clothes into the store before his rivals. If we walked out on the very day that he wanted us to get busy on the new line, I believe he'd listen to us.'

'She may have a point, Fanny,' another girl said. 'If he's not first in the stores, who would want his shoddy clothing? You know how he skimps on the fabric and it's the cheapest quality too.'

'It might be worth a try, Rose. Tell us what we have to do.'

Suddenly the girls were all around her. 'You tell us when, Rose. You give the word. We'll show him we're not made soft like butter.'

It was very exciting. I found myself swept up in their enthusiasm.

'Not a word until he hands us the new designs, eh? We don't want him getting a whiff of what we've planned for him,' I cautioned.

On the way back across the street Rose joined me. 'What do you think, Molly? Isn't it wonderful? They're all with us.

We might even get them to cough up the money for union dues.'

'I just hope one of them isn't a traitor,' I whispered.

'There's not much we can do about it, is there?' Rose glanced around at the girls hurrying back through the rain, their shawls over their heads. 'We can't sit back and do nothing, in case we might be betrayed.'

As we crossed the street, a fancy carriage clattered away, drawn by a fine matched pair of black horses.

'That looks like old Lowenstein,' Rose said. 'Trust him to pay a visit when none of us are there. He probably feels too guilty when he sees what we have to go through for him. But we'll show him, won't we, Molly!'

We came into the workroom, shaking the raindrops from our shawls.

'Careful of getting drops on that fabric!' Mr Katz yelled.

'Yeah, it might melt if it gets wet,' Rose commented and got a laugh.

'That will cost you, Rose Levy,' Katz said. 'You would do well to remember where you are and who is in charge.'

'As if I could ever forget where I am,' Rose said. 'I'm certainly not in our nice big living room back home in Poland with the porcelain stove in the corner and the grand piano.'

'Then go back, if you don't like it here,' Katz said. 'In fact, maybe you'll like to be one of my first volunteers.'

'Volunteers to do what?'

'Mr Lowenstein was just here,' Katz said. 'He's got some bad news.'

'They didn't have the right brand of caviar for his lunch today,' Rose whispered to me.

'The new designs won't be ready as soon as he expected and you girls have worked so well that the orders are up to date. So there's nothing much to do until we start work on the new line – maybe next week, who knows. Until then it's half time for everybody. Come in at seven, home at noon. He'll pay you two dollars a week, which is very generous when there's not enough work.'

'Very generous!' one of the girl blurted out. 'Does he pay us extra when there's too much work and you keep rushing us to get it finished?'

'You can't put everyone on half time,' Rose said. 'These girls have families who rely on their wages.'

'Like I said, Rose Levy, you could volunteer,' Katz said, giving her his sneering grin. 'Half the girls could volunteer to stay home until the new work comes, and then the other half would get full wages. It's up to you how you handle it.'

'I tell you how we handle it,' Rose said, sticking out her chin and putting her hands on her hips as she faced him. 'We don't accept his measly offer. We walk out. We shut down this crummy sweatshop and we keep it shut until Mr Lowenstein listens to us and treats us like human beings. Come on, everyone. Get your things. We're leaving now.'

It was fantastic. Every girl followed Rose to the door.

'If you go, don't think you'll be coming back,' Katz screamed. 'We'll get new girls to replace you.'

Rose turned and looked back at him. 'Even if you can get them to cross our picket line, do you think you can train them in time for the new line and the rush job? We're going to show you who has power around here. In the end you're going to wish you were nicer to us.'

Then she turned again and ran up the flight of steps, out to the street. We all followed her.

'Come on, everyone, let's go to Samuel's to plan,' she said.

We crossed the street to the deli.

'I thought we weren't going to walk out until he got the

new designs,' Golda said. 'Are you sure we're doing the right thing?'

'I know it's taking a big gamble,' Rose said, 'but he was going to put us all on half time anyway. Lowenstein won't want to pay any scabs to work this week because there is no work and our picket line is going to keep new girls away. We must all show up tomorrow prepared to stand our ground around the shop and not let anyone inside.'

'How can we do that?' a small, frail-looking girl asked. 'Look at us. If Katz tried to knock us out of his way, he could.'

'Then we need reinforcements,' Rose said. 'Let's go to the United Hebrew Trades and see if they can get us some male volunteers to help our cause.'

'Good idea,' I said. 'I'm sure that Jacob will want to help.'

'Jacob?' she asked. 'You mean Mr Singer?'

I blushed. 'Yes, Mr Singer,' I said.

She looked at me curiously. 'And how come you're on first-name terms with Mr Singer when you only met him last week?'

'He's a friend of my friends,' I said and hoped she wouldn't push me further.

Someone was sent to Jacob's house, and soon the word got around so that the Hebrew Trades headquarters on Essex Street was jam-packed when we met there later that day.

'They did it. The girls walked out of Lowenstein's.' The word went around quickly. Jacob arrived, so did some of the other men I had met the previous Wednesday night.

'Where is Miss Blankenship? She'd want to be here,' some-one suggested.

'Should someone take a cab to fetch her?' I asked.

Heads turned in my direction.

'Take a cab? Listen to Miss Rockerfeller here,' the girl beside me said, rolling her eyes. 'And where should you find the money for a cab? Not in this week's pay packet.'

'I only meant because it's so important and she'd want to be here,' I said quickly. 'And she has money to pay for cabs, doesn't she?'

'She has a telephone at her house,' Jacob said. 'The University Settlement a couple of blocks away has a telephone that they let us use. Do you know how to use a phone, Molly?'

'No, but I expect they'll show me.'

He took out a matchbook and scribbled on the back. 'Here is her number. You turn the handle and when the operator comes on the line, you ask for the number. Got it?'

'I think so.' I shoved the matchbook into my pocket.

'And I usually give them a dime for the privilege,' Jacob said, fishing in his pocket and handing me a coin.

I ran up the stairs from the basement, my heart beating fast. I was so annoyed at myself for making that slip. Of course these girls would never have taken a cab in their lives. Paddy Riley would never have slipped out of character so easily.

I reached the austere building of the University Settlement and went inside. It reminded me of the time I had lived in the hostel run by a Bible Society. Strict and cold. Not the kind of place you'd want to stay longer than necessary. A distinguished-looking woman took me into a cluttered little office and pointed at the telephone on the wall. 'Do you know how to use this contraption?'

'I'll manage, thank you.'

She stood behind me, her hands on her hips, watching. It was with some trepidation that I cranked the handle and then heard a voice in my ear. 'Number please?' I gave it to her and almost immediately a voice answered. 'Miss Blankenship's residence.'

'Is Miss Blankenship at home, please?'

'I'm afraid she's not. This is her maid speaking.' A slow voice with an unfamiliar drawl to it.

'When are you expecting her back?'

'We was expectin' her back by now. Would you care to leave a message for her?'

I dictated my message, suggesting that she might want to join us as soon as possible. When I returned to the headquarters, fifty picketers had been assigned to the morning shift, with the rest ready and waiting to take the places of those who felt faint from standing too long. The meeting concluded in great high spirits but Nell Blankenship didn't put in an appearance.

Seventeen

It was dark when we finally came out into the evening rain. I hurried home and not even the downpour was able to dampen my spirits. I was bursting with excitement that things were about to happen and that change was in the air. I was so caught up in the momentous things about to happen that I truly believed I was one of them, not just a girl from comfortable surroundings, playing at being a garment worker. This hit me, of course, when I crossed Washington Square and saw the lights from the elegant homes on the north side reflected in the wet pavement, and then Patchin Place with its own quiet serenity.

I came into my living room to find Shamey and Bridie sitting with their cousin Malachy.

'What are you doing here?' I asked coldly. 'I thought I made it very clear to your mother that you were not to come to this house.'

'Got a message for ya, don't I,' he answered, wiping his nose with the back of his hand before holding out an envelope to me. 'The lady asked if anyone could take a message to a Miss Molly Murphy at Patchin Place and I said I knew ya on account of my cousins lived at your house. So I got the job. And she said she'd pay me ten cents and I told her the

Eastmans always paid us twenty-five. Then she said, "Likely enough, but I don't have illicit funds at my disposal." Regular old tartar, she was. Real snooty like. She looks down her nose at me and says, "So do you want the job, or shall I ask one of these other boys instead?" so of course I took it.'

He handed me the envelope, now somewhat grimy and creased. I tore it open.

The letter had been written in obvious haste and uneven penmanship, which must have meant that she had scribbled the note while still out and about. It also meant, I realized with a slight pang of jealousy, that she must have one of those new fountain pens that didn't leave blots all over the place.

Molly – I have had a successful day. Kathy was
employed by Mostel's on Canal Street and I've just been
given some startling information that I have to check
out. Can you meet me at Ormond's Café at Canal and
Broadway? I'll wait for you.
– N.

I looked up to see three little faces watching me.

'How long ago did she give you this note, Malachy?'

'Not that long ago. Maybe an hour.'

'Then I must go out again at once. Come on, you and I can walk together.'

He glanced longingly and pointedly at the kitchen. I laughed. 'All right. I'll make us both some bread and dripping to keep us going. And you two—' I turned to Bridie and Shamey '– had better have some too. Who knows how late I'll be home.'

Thus fortified, I grabbed an umbrella and we set off down Broadway. This time we rode the trolley. Malachy was entranced. I don't think he had ever ridden an electric trolley

170

before. When we got off at the Canal Street stop, I glanced around and spotted the lighted windows of Ormond's Café.

'Where was the lady when she gave you this letter? Was it around here?'

'No. Down there a ways.' He nodded in the direction of the East River. 'Down on Canal, not far from Orchard Street and the Walla Walla.'

'Thank you,' I said. 'Now you hurry off home before it gets too late and your family starts to worry about you.'

'They don't worry about me. I can take care of myself,' he said with a swagger. Then he grabbed at the dime I offered him and took off down Canal at a lively trot. I crossed the street, successfully dodging hansom cabs, trolley cars, and even the occasional automobile, to reach the café. It was a large, opulent type of place, like a smaller Delmonico's, with lots of red plush and potted palms and chandeliers. A piano was playing a lively waltz. I went in and stood in the foyer, looking around. Several tables were occupied, but I didn't spot any familiar faces.

'Can I help you, miss?' A waiter appeared at my side.

'I was to meet someone here. A young lady. Tall, slim, dark haired. Well dressed.'

'There has been no unescorted lady here this evening,' he said. 'Do you have a table reserved?'

'If we did, it would be in the name of Miss Nell Blankenship.'

He shook his head. 'Then perhaps you would care to sit there and wait.' He indicated a red velvet sofa between two potted palms.

'Thank you.' I took the seat he indicated. The clock on the wall said seven thirty. Nell would have expected me to be working until seven, so she hadn't hurried. Maybe she was on the trail of more interesting facts. I wondered what she might have unearthed that was important enough to have summoned me here and couldn't wait. It was amazing enough that Katherine had worked for Mostel's. Amazing, but annoying too. All the time I had worked there, not realizing! If only I had asked the right questions, I might have found out what happened to her myself. This thought made me stop and reconsider. Nell had leaped to the conclusion that Kathy's workplace might have had something to do with her disappearance. Could Mr Mostel or Seedy Sam have possibly been responsible for what happened to her? I shook my head in disbelief. They were not the most pleasant of men – hard-hearted, greedy, but it was a big leap from treating girls badly to disposing of one of them in the East River.

I heard the clock on a nearby church chime eight and still Nell didn't come.

'Do you think your friend mistook the date?' the waiter asked. 'Is there something I can bring to you?'

I ordered a cup of coffee and sat sipping it as long minutes ticked by. I was beginning to feel distinctly uneasy. Why was she so late? And what had she been doing in the vicinity of the Walhalla Hall? It might not have been dark when she found Malachy to deliver the letter, but it was certainly dark enough now – and raining hard again. Not the sort of weather you would choose to dawdle outside, especially not in that neighborhood.

At last I could wait there no longer. I was as tense as a wound watch spring. Something had detained Nell Blankenship and something had prevented her from sending me a second message, letting me know that she had been detained. I wasn't sure what to do. It was now raining cats and dogs out there, the fat, heavy drops bouncing off the sidewalk and forming pools in the gutters. Miserable horses plodded past and cabbies sat, equally miserable with their derby hats jammed down on their heads and collars turned up against the rain.

I stood outside the café and stared down Canal Street. I was not foolhardy enough to go snooping down there alone at this time of night. Once bitten, twice shy as they say. Should I just go home and wait for Nell to contact me in the morning? It was, of course, possible that she had had enough of the rain and had gone home herself. If I could find a telephone, I could call her. I still had her number on the matchbook in my pocket.

After some trial and error I located a theater on lower Broadway with a telephone. It was a Yiddish theater and I hoped that the owner would speak English. He did and insisted on making the call for me, not out of kindness, I fear, but rather not trusting me with his contraption. Nell's maid answered again.

'Has your mistress not come home yet?' I asked.

'No, miss, and I'm real worried about her. She never comes home this late without getting word to me. She's always real considerate that way.'

'I'm sure she's just been detained somewhere,' I said, trying to sound more reassuring than I felt. 'Please let her know that I waited at the café for an hour, then I felt I couldn't wait any longer. She knows where she can reach me.'

'Very good, miss. I'll tell her, just as soon as she comes home.' The poor girl's voice shook. I knew how she felt. I should go home and wait for Nell to contact me, but I couldn't. Suddenly I made a decision. I would go to Jacob. He would know what to do. I made my way up rainswept Broadway and turned onto Rivington Street. I just prayed he'd be home by now and was not still involved in strike planning at the Hebrew Trades headquarters. The door to the building opened easily. I climbed the dark stairway and tapped hesitantly on his door. I had a sudden, absurd hope that Jacob would answer and Nell would be inside with him.

173

He opened the door. 'Molly!' He looked pleased but wary. 'To what do I owe this honor so late at night? I thought you'd gone home hours ago. I'm not sure I should invite you in without damaging your reputation.' He grinned to let me know that this was a joke.

'It's Nell. I was supposed to meet her and she hasn't turned up. I'm worried about her, Jacob.' The words came out in a rush. Quickly I told him what had happened and showed him Nell's note. 'I waited in the café for over an hour,' I said, 'and the boy who delivered the note told me that Nell had been near the Walhalla Hall when she gave it to him. The Walhalla Hall is frequented by the Eastmans gang, Jacob.'

Jacob gave a deep sigh. 'I've been afraid something like this would happen. She takes the most appalling risks without a second thought. Do you know what she was doing in that part of town?'

'She had discovered that Kathy worked for Mostel's. They are on Canal Street, not too far away, so it could be that she was pursuing some connection there.'

'I must go and find her,' Jacob said. 'You have already done enough for one night. You should go home and rest.'

'Nonsense,' I said. 'I'll come with you. There's safety in numbers.'

He smiled. 'Although two isn't a very big number.' He put his hand on my shoulder. 'But it's very companionable.' His hand remained there until we started down the stairs.

As we came out into the night the rain had stopped and a damp mist clung around the lampposts and area railings. The mist seemed to muffle all sound so that it felt as if we were alone in a dark world. Only the mournful tooting of ships out in the mist on the river told us that the city was still alive and awake. We cut down Chrystie Street. I kept an eye open all the way for any sign of a building that might be the

Eastmans headquarters, but of course they'd hardly be likely to advertise the fact. The street was quiet, respectable, and in darkness. We came out onto Canal, not far from Orchard Street and the Walhalla. The area was dimly lit by the occasional gas lamp and the mist swirled in from the East River so that we moved like two ghosts.

'Here is the Walhalla Hall,' Jacob said. 'We should ask if anyone has seen her.'

The hall itself appeared to be in darkness. Jacob stopped several men coming out of saloons and got only rude comments for his pains. 'Whataya want another girl for when you've already got one? Greedy, ain't ya?' It was most frustrating and after a while we gave up. There was nobody else on the street.

'We should maybe check the café again to see if she came there after I'd left,' I suggested.

'Good idea.'

We walked back along Canal Street.

'That's Mostel's,' I said, pointing at the looming dark shape. 'There is a furniture maker on the ground floors and Mostel's occupies the top three.'

Jacob tried the door but it was firmly locked and no lights shone in the building. We walked on to Broadway but the café was closed. So were most of the other businesses around it. Only the theaters were still ablaze with lights.

'Should we try calling her house?' he asked.

'I've tried twice. Her maid sounds very worried.'

'Then we must go back along Canal and systematically check each backstreet and alley,' Jacob said.

'But what would she be doing there, at this time of night?' I asked, not wanting to listen to the answer that echoed in my own head.

He shrugged.

'There is one possibility.' I could hardly make my mouth say the words. 'I was almost taken by the Eastmans once, until luckily the police intervened. If she was snooping too close to their activities, then maybe they've got her.'

Jacob stared at me with a look of sheer dread.

'But that's something we can't tackle alone,' I said hastily as I saw Jacob steeling himself to confront a gang. 'We'll have to alert the police. I have a friend who is a police captain. We should let him know right away.'

'But we should search the area first,' Jacob said. 'Just to make sure. If we pass a policeman on the beat here, we can tell him and have him spread the word that we are looking for her.' We turned back along Canal in the direction we had come. 'Of course, we could be worrying for nothing,' Jacob said, trying to sound bright and confident. 'Nell could have arrived at your house by now, at my place, at anyplace as the whim took her. It is impossible to know how her mind works. I have been out on assignments with her before and she has been off in all directions, like a dog chasing a rabbit.' He attempted a smile and I could tell it was himself he was trying to convince, more than me.

I wasn't sure what we were going to achieve by searching the area. Clearly Nell wouldn't still be walking around the area alone in the dark and damp. And it wasn't like Hester and Essex Streets and those livelier areas north of here, where shop fronts would still be open and street life still going on. If anyone lived around here, they had their front doors locked and their blinds drawn. I had to run to keep up with Jacob. He was striding out like a man on a mission. We turned up the first side street and then back to Canal. Singing floated to us from corner saloons. Drunken men staggered past us. Dogs barked. Cats slunk into alleyways. We tried the next side street and the next.

'This is a futile project, Jacob. How can we hope to find her this way? She could be anywhere in New York by now. And if someone had kidnapped her, we could be walking right past and not even know.'

'Don't say that.' He shivered. 'I need to feel that I have done everything I can do. We may just meet a street urchin or a woman of the night who has seen something.'

'All right. Press on, then,' I said gallantly, although my feet by now were throbbing. Ladies' shoes are not made for tramping over cobbles for hours. Pointed toes may be all the rage, but they are not designed for comfort. I glanced down enviously at Jacob's big workman's boots.

We passed Mostel's again and searched the area around it, but saw nothing out of the ordinary. We crossed the Bowery and kept going. Two ladies of the night lurked in a doorway. We asked them.

'We ain't interested in missing girls, honey,' one of them said. 'We only notice if a gentleman like yourself goes past. What's she done, run away from her old man?' They broke into peals of laughter. We trudged on, discouraged.

We were coming to the place where Canal Street changed direction, after it crossed Division. Surely Jacob didn't intend to scout it out all the way to the East River? Then suddenly we heard the clatter of boots and two small boys ran past us. I grabbed at one, hoping that it might be one of Nuala's boys.

'Here, let go of me, I ain't done nothing,' he yelled in fright.

'We aren't going to hurt you,' Jacob said. 'We're looking for a lady. We thought you might have seen her around here. A tall lady in black, nicely dressed?'

'Ain't seen no one like that,' the other boy mumbled.

I glanced down at the object he was attempting to hide behind his back. 'What have you got there?' I asked and made

177

a grab for it. He tried to jerk it away and the ostrich plume came off in my hand.

'Where did you find this?' I demanded. 'I thought you said you hadn't seen the lady. This is her hat.'

'We ain't seen no lady,' the first boy said. 'We found the hat on the ground. Finders keepers. We was taking it home to our mom.'

'Can you take us to where you found the hat?' Jacob said. 'Then I'll give you fifty cents as a trade for the hat. Is that fair?'

'Okay, mister. It was down here.' They led us back along Canal then down an alleyway where the houses from two streets backed onto each other. There were coal bunkers and all manner of sheds and shacks and outhouses and it smelled bad. We picked our way cautiously in almost total darkness.

'Right about here, mister,' the bigger boy said. 'It was just lying here, just like that. Tom kicked it and we thought it was a dead bird or something and didn't think much of it. But then we saw the ribbon and he picked it up.'

'You've been very helpful,' Jacob said. 'It belongs to our friend. Here's the fifty cents. And if you happen to see the lady we're looking for, tell her where we are, will you?'

'Sure thing, mister.' The boys grinned and ran off with their bounty.

Jacob and I stood looking at the hat.

'She wouldn't have taken her hat off in this weather,' he said.

'If she was being led away against her will, she might have let the hat fall to the ground as a clue,' I said.

Jacob nodded. 'She might indeed.' The words came out as a whisper. We were both whispering. It was that sort of place. 'On the other hand,' he went on, 'she might be around here – hurt or . . .'

He didn't need to say any more. We started looking. I wished we had a lantern with us. The darkness was almost complete. We peeked behind coal bunkers and sheds and called her name softly.

'She could have been thrown inside any of these,' Jacob said, his voice rising in annoyance. 'Nell! It's us. It's Jacob,' he said, more loudly now.

Then there was a sudden breeze. The mist swirled, the clouds parted, and for a moment the moon shone down, throwing grotesque shadows down the alley. And for a second something sparkled. I ran to it just as the clouds came together again and we were plunged into darkness once more. I bent over behind a large coal bin. Then my hand recoiled as I realized what I was touching. The sparkling object had been a buckle on a shoe and the shoe was still on a foot.

Eighteen

'Jacob, over here, quickly!'

He rushed to my side and dropped to his knees among the debris. 'Oh, *Gott*. Oh, *Gott*. Oh, *Gott*!' he repeated over and over. 'Help me, Molly. Move her carefully, she may still be alive.'

I said nothing, but the ankle I was touching was cold. She had been stuffed into a narrow area between the bin and a brick wall and it was hard to get her out. When at last we extracted her, her head lolled like a doll's, her mouth open in a silent yell of surprise. I shuddered and looked away. Jacob put his arms around me. 'Don't look. It is too horrible,' he said. 'Who could have done this terrible thing?'

I stood, twisting her bonnet nervously in my hands, then I recoiled as my hand touched something sticky. The outside of the bonnet was wet from the rain. It was the inside that was sticky. I bent to examine her head. Suddenly a bright light shone on us.

'What's going on here?' a deep voice demanded.

'Thank God you have come, Officer.' Jacob got to his feet. 'A young woman has been brutally murdered.'

'So it seems, sir.' The constable came closer, shining the light in our faces. The light was blinding and all I could see of the policeman was the silhouette of his distinctively shaped helmet. 'You'd better both step away and put your hands up.'

'We didn't kill her,' I snapped. 'We've just found her. She was our friend. We've been looking for her.'

'Put your hands up, I said.' The flashlight waved up and down, its beam bouncing from the high brick walls around us. Then the flashlight focused on my hand. The policeman came closer. 'What's that on your hand?'

I looked at it. 'It must be blood. We found her bonnet first, you see, and the inside is sticky.'

More feet came down the alleyway.

'Down here, Charlie,' the constable shouted. 'I caught the pair of them, bending down over the corpse, they were. Get out your handcuffs.'

'Don't be ridiculous,' I said as the second officer approached me, handcuffs at the ready. 'I have just told you. This is our friend. We have been looking for her all evening because she didn't meet me when she was supposed to. We feared that something bad might have happened to her.'

'Oh, and why was that, miss?'

'This is Miss Nell Blankenship, from a prominent family,' Jacob said quietly. 'You must have heard of her. She writes – wrote articles for the newspapers. I am Jacob Singer. I worked as her photographer.'

'Oh, yes. The lady reporter. I've seen her name in the papers. Charlie, run and send a message to headquarters that we've got a murder on our hands. And in the meantime you two stay right where you are.'

'We wouldn't dream of abandoning her,' I said. 'We want to find out who killed her as much as you do. And if you think we had anything to do with her murder, you only have to touch her. She has been dead for some time.'

The other constable departed. I was suddenly very cold and

hugged my arms to me, shivering. I was very conscious of my fingers sticking together and longed to wash that hand. I still found it hard to handle death and I was overcome with feelings of guilt. If I hadn't asked Nell to help me, she'd never have been in this part of town. She would never have uncovered a fact that cost her her life. It was too much to hope for that she had left any hint as to what that fact might have been. I tried to make myself think like an investigator. I got up and started to search the area.

'Hey, where are you going?' the constable asked.

'I was looking for her purse. I don't see it.'

'She was probably bashed over the head for her purse. If she was foolish enough to be out alone in this part of town, what can you expect?' the constable said, with the ease of small talk. I decided to remain silent and not let him know that robbery may not have been the motive and she may not have been a random victim.

'What in God's name was she doing in this part of town anyway?' the constable went on. 'She must have known it wasn't safe for a lady.'

'Nell didn't stop to think about things like that,' Jacob said. 'When she was onto a story, she took appalling risks. She never . . . she wouldn't . . .' His voice faltered. I reached out and touched his arm.

I was praying, for once, that the police detective who was summoned to this scene would not be Daniel. I really didn't feel up to facing him or the tongue lashing he would obviously give me. However, the detective sergeant who arrived shortly afterward, with two more constables, was a fresh-faced young man called Macnamara. He listened politely as we told him how we had found her after finding the boys with her bonnet. When we tried to describe the boys, I realized that the description fit every street urchin on the Lower East

Side. I was angry at myself for not getting their names, nor for searching them further to see if they had other items belonging to Nell in their pockets. Had they found her purse and stuffed their pockets with anything worth stealing?

'A curious fact, that has been worrying me,' I said. 'The boys had Miss Blankenship's bonnet, and yet the inside of the bonnet is sticky with blood. Doesn't that indicate it was on her head when she was struck?'

The young officer looked at me with interest. 'I wouldn't expect a young lady to think of things like that.'

'This is no ordinary young lady,' Jacob said. 'Miss Murphy is a private investigator.'

I was flattered that he had leaped to defend me, but I rather wished he hadn't mentioned it. Macnamara stared at me even harder. 'Then maybe she can tell me why a well-dressed lady came to be found alone, in this part of the city. Was this some kind of investigation she was carrying out?'

'I rather fear that it was,' I said. 'Although I have no idea what brought her to this alleyway.'

'As for that,' Macnamara said, 'she may well have been grabbed on the street in full view of anyone who happened to be passing. The types that frequent this area wouldn't think twice about grabbing her and dragging her into the alleyway – knowing that most folk would pretend they hadn't seen anything and pass by on the other side. So if her purse is missing, then we have to conclude that robbery was the motive.'

'Which doesn't make sense,' I said. 'She is still wearing gloves and I think I can see the shape of a ring under the leather. Why not take her jewelry too?'

'Someone was coming and they had to beat it in a hurry,' Sergeant Macnamara suggested. 'They clubbed her from behind. Her hat came off when they turned her over and they left the hat lying there when they stuffed her into that hiding place.'

'Rather careless, wouldn't you say?' I asked. 'If the boys hadn't picked up her hat, we'd never have found her.'

Sergeant Macnamara shook his head. 'Like I said, they were in a hurry to beat it. Maybe she had a nice fat wallet in her purse and that was enough for them.'

Another constable arrived to tell him that a morgue wagon was ready to transport the body. 'I'll need you to come to police headquarters on Mulberry Street to make statements,' Macnamara said. He didn't offer us a ride in the morgue wagon, for which I was glad. 'Constable Daly will show you the way.'

The original constable escorted us to the end of the alley and then motioned for us to go with him along Canal. As we came to the first cross street I glanced up and noticed that it was Chrystie. Somewhere along that street was the Eastmans headquarters in a building that must have backed onto that very alleyway. I might suggest that line of inquiry when we made our statement.

It was a long weary trudge back along Canal to the police headquarters. We gave them our names and addresses and dictated our statements to a uniformed sergeant. Then we were told to wait. Someone brought us cups of tea, which were most welcome. We sat in a small, windowless room, on hard, straight-backed chairs, and waited. Jacob looked around him. 'I have been in rooms like this before,' he said. 'They would always keep you waiting. There would be screams from other rooms. Sometimes I still have nightmares.'

I wanted to take his hand, but it still seemed too forward. 'I'm so sorry,' I said. 'I dragged you into this. I can't tell you how badly I feel at this moment.'

'It is I who feels guilty,' he said angrily. 'How could I have let her go alone to a place like that? I should have protected her better.'

'You were not her bodyguard, Jacob. And from what I saw she would not have listened to you. She led her own life.'

He nodded. 'But it doesn't ease the guilt,' he said.

'I know. Nothing eases the guilt at the moment. I feel terrible myself. It was I who sent her there.'

He reached out and took my hand. I was glad it was the other hand, not the one sticky with dried blood. His hand was as cold as mine. We sat there, clutching each other for support.

'At least they don't suspect us anymore,' I said. 'For a while I was scared that—'

I broke off as the door was flung open and a disheveled, wild-eyed Daniel came bursting in. He looked as if he hadn't slept in several days. His shirt collar was unbuttoned and he wore no tie. 'I hope you are finally satisfied,' he shouted. 'What have I been telling you all along, and you don't listen. Did you drag her into one of your crazy schemes?'

Jacob rose to his feet. 'I don't think that's any way to address this young lady,' he said quietly. 'She has done nothing wrong.'

'Done nothing wrong? She insists on poking her nose into things better left alone,' Daniel said. 'And who are you?'

'Jacob Singer. A friend of Miss Murphy.'

I saw Daniel's eyebrow go up. 'Is that so?'

'Miss Murphy came to me when she was concerned that Miss Blankenship had not shown up at the appointed time for their meeting.'

'And just what was Miss Blankenship doing in an alleyway behind Canal Street at night?' Daniel spat out the words.

'I have no idea,' I said, staring him straight in the eye. 'The only matter in which she was giving me help was finding out details about that missing couple. The couple you were helping me to trace. Katherine and Michael Kelly.'

'Michael Kelly?' he said, still glaring angrily. 'The man who met an unpleasant end after getting himself mixed up with the Eastmans? You sent her to investigate that?'

'No, I didn't. I wanted to find out where Katherine had worked.' I was yelling too, now. 'I had discovered that she worked in the garment industry. Nell knew all about sweat-shops. She offered to find out for me. And she did find the name of the company Katherine worked for. It was Mostel's on Canal Street – which explains what she was doing in the area to start with. Why she stayed around after dark I cannot tell you. She scribbled a note to me to say that she had learned something interesting and was going to follow up on it. That's all I can tell you.'

Daniel's bluster had subsided. 'And she paid for the interesting fact with her life. Is any piece of knowledge worth the life of a human being?'

'Of course not. And I would not have wished her to take any kind of risk,' I said. 'I had no idea—'

'That's just it, Molly. You have no idea. If you were a cat, you'd have already used up eight of your nine lives. Maybe this will teach you a lesson you won't forget in a hurry. If ever you get another harebrained scheme in your head, think of Miss Blankenship lying there with her head bashed in.'

'I really think Miss Murphy has been through enough for one night,' Jacob said coldly. 'If you don't mind, I'd like to take her home now.'

Daniel looked at him, long and hard, then nodded. 'Well, I know where to find you if I have more questions,' he said. 'But I don't think we have a hope in Hades of finding out who killed her.'

'You have your informants among the gangs, don't you?' I asked. 'You could find out if one of the Eastmans killed her.'

Daniel nodded. 'I could probably glean that fact after a while, but they'd never tell me what she discovered or who was paying them, so it would be a lost cause. There would be no point in making an arrest or trying to bring anyone to trial. Believe me, I've tried it often enough.' He stared hard at me again. 'It could have nothing to do with the Eastmans. It could have been as simple as snatching her purse or wanting her shoes. Life is cheap in the Lower East Side, as you have just discovered. As Katherine and Michael discovered too. They are dead, Molly. A lost cause. Your friend lost her life for nothing.' He went to say something else, then tossed his head abruptly in the direction of the door. 'Go on, then. You can go.'

'Thank you,' I said as I rose to my feet. As I stood up the room swung around. I teetered and swayed. Daniel and Jacob steadied me at the same moment. 'I'm fine, honestly,' I said quickly. 'I haven't really eaten since midday, and then the shock.'

'I'll give you the money for a cab,' Daniel said.

'That's not necessary. I have money,' Jacob answered. 'I'll make sure she gets home safely.'

'Then please go and secure a cab for Miss Murphy. I'll bring her out momentarily,' Daniel said.

As soon as Jacob had left the room Daniel spun around to me, his eyes dark and angry. 'And who, pray, is that gentleman?'

'A good friend, Daniel.'

'He didn't think he was just a good friend. I saw him looking at you.'

'Maybe more someday, then.'

'He is not of your race or religion, Molly. Don't you see that this can lead nowhere?'

187

'Maybe I am becoming an expert at relationships that lead nowhere,' I said. 'And I didn't think that you and Miss Norton shared the same religion. Maybe it's not a stumbling block when money and power are involved.'

He winced as if I'd slapped him across the face, which, I must confess, I had wanted to do – actually longed to do now.

'This is stupid, Molly,' he said. 'You don't love him. You can't love him.'

'I'll go and see if Jacob has found me a cab, if you'll excuse me.'

'Molly—' He reached out his hand to me.

'Good-bye, Daniel,' I said, then spun on my heels and fled.

Nineteen

'That man's behavior toward you was quite insufferable,' Jacob said as the cab carried us away at a fast clip clop. 'Give these fellows a badge and a uniform and the small amount of power goes to their heads.'

I didn't think this was the moment to point out that Daniel, as a detective, wore neither badge nor uniform, and as one of the youngest captains on the force, he wielded a considerable amount of power.

'He has saved me from a couple of awkward situations in the past and was annoyed that I was still trying to pursue the notion of being an investigator,' I said, not wanting to go into further explanations. I was starting to shiver as delayed shock set in.

'That doesn't give him permission to shout at you,' Jacob said, 'especially after what you have been through tonight.'

'What we have both been through tonight. I still can't believe it,' I said. 'Poor Nell. It doesn't seem possible, does it?'

'I find it hard to believe too,' Jacob said. 'I saw so many terrible things as a young man in Russia, but one does not expect to see them repeated, here in America. She was a fine woman. She could have accomplished much. I should have . . .' He turned away from me.

189

'You tried to warn her. You tried to warn both of us,' I said. 'You are blameless in this, Jacob. Don't put yourself through this torment.'

Without thinking I reached across and stroked his cheek. He seized my hand and brought it to his lips. 'When I first saw you, I thought a bright ray of sunshine had come into my life, Molly. I thought – that could be a girl who would make me laugh and dance and forget all that I have been and seen.'

'I think it will be a while before either of us can laugh and dance again, Jacob,' I said, 'but we will help each other get through this.'

His arms came around me and he held me fiercely to him. I let him hold me close, not sure what I felt, still too conscious of Daniel's angry, worried face in that police headquarters room.

Then Jacob released me suddenly, putting his hands on my shoulders. 'I want you to promise me that you will not attempt anything more to do with Nell's death,' he said. 'Whoever did this is heartless and ruthless. Swear you won't try to track down her killer.'

'I promise you I won't do anything stupid, Jacob,' I said, 'and you must promise me the same.'

'I couldn't bear to lose you, so soon after I have found you,' he whispered and cradled my head to him again. I lay against his shoulder until the cab stopped at the entrance to Patchin Place.

'Are you sure you'll be all right?' Jacob asked. 'Would you like me to come in and make you a hot drink maybe?'

'It's late,' I said. 'You should get some rest yourself. You look terrible.'

'Thank you for the kind words.' He managed a smile.

I reached up and touched his cheek, my hand savoring the strangeness of his beard. 'We're both exhausted and upset, Jacob. I think sleep is what we need most.'

He nodded. 'Very well, then. I'll take the cab home and see you tomorrow.' He brought my fingertips to his lips, then he was gone.

As I went to open my front door, the one across the street opened and Gus was standing there in a flowing Oriental robe, her hair hidden behind a purple turban.

'Molly, it *is* you. I was painting in my studio and I thought I saw you getting out of a cab with the attractive Mr Singer. Have you been somewhere exciting? Do come inside and tell all!'

My first instinct was to invent some harmless event that Jacob and I had attended together, but I couldn't lie to such a dear friend.

'Actually, it's been a horrible, beastly evening,' I said, and heard my voice shake. 'We found a friend murdered.' I realized as I said it that Nell had been their friend rather than mine. 'Nell Blankenship,' I added.

'Nell? Nell has been killed?'

'What's this?' Sid's head appeared behind Gus's turban.

I had no option but to go in and tell them everything. The reliving of the evening was almost as painful as the experience itself.

'How awful for you, Molly,' Sid said.

'Me? What do I matter? I'm alive,' I burst out. 'It's poor Nell! If I hadn't asked her to help me, she'd be alive. I feel so terrible.' I sank my head into my hands. 'She didn't even like me very much, you know. She saw me as a threat. She was really only carrying out this assignment to please Jacob because she was smitten with him. So I've betrayed her all around.'

'Brandy, I think, don't you, Gus?' Sid rose and went for the decanter.

'Brandy in hot milk. She'll need to sleep and it won't be easy.' Gus brought out a saucepan and lit the gas.

191

'Stop blaming yourself, Molly,' Sid said as she poured a generous amount of brandy into a glass beaker. 'You didn't set out to lure Jacob away from her with your feminine wiles, did you?'

I had to smile at this thought. 'No. Of course not.'

'And you didn't ask Nell to take on anything you knew to be dangerous?'

'No.'

'Then stop blaming yourself.' She took the hot milk off the stove and poured it into the brandy. 'I know – I knew Nell Blankenship quite well. She would never have been forced or tricked into doing anything she didn't want to do. She went looking for this person Katherine because she was intrigued, because she saw it as a challenge. It appealed to her reporter's instinct. Her choice, Molly, not yours.'

'Now drink up and then get a good night's sleep,' Gus said. 'And if you will take advice from two friends who care for you, you will take this terrible event as a warning. Somebody out there killed Nell Blankenship because of what she discovered. That person is still out there and even more desperate now. So no heroics, Molly. Leave the detective work to the police.'

'That's what Jacob just said.'

'I knew I liked him,' Gus said, turning to Sid for a confirming nod.

'Has anyone notified her family, I wonder?' The ever efficient Sid rose to her feet.

'Her poor maid should be told, at least,' I said. 'Last time I spoke to her, she was sick with worry. Do you think I should call her at this late hour?'

'I'll do it,' Sid said, putting a firm hand on my shoulder. 'You go to bed. Do you want us to come with you?'

'No, you've been more than kind, as usual.' I got to my feet. 'One day I must find a way to repay you.'

'Repay us by staying out of trouble and not ending up like Nell in an alleyway,' Gus said. Then she gave me a little push. 'Go on with you. To bed before the brandy wears off.'

In spite of the brandy that warmed my whole body, I lay awake long into the night, listening to bare branches scratching against the window, my mind in a turmoil. It didn't matter that everyone had insisted that Nell was headstrong and impulsive and made her own choices, I was overcome with guilt and remorse. This was the second time that I had let someone else do my dirty work. I had put young Shamey's life at risk and now I had cost Nell Blankenship her life. If I, instead of she, had found out some vital fact about Katherine's life or death, then maybe I would have been lying behind a coal bin tonight. I swore to myself that I would never again involve another person in my investigations and that, by hook or by crook, I would find out who killed Nell. I couldn't bear the thought that her death would just be ignored by the New York police.

I sat up in bed and reached for my notebook and pencil. I could hear Paddy's voice in my head – start with what you know. I knew that Nell had discovered that Katherine worked for Mostel and Klein. She had also uncovered another useful piece of information, one important enough that she wanted to share it with me immediately – a piece of information so important to somebody that it had cost Nell her life.

What else did I know? Her body was found close to Mostel's factory. I tried to picture Mr Mostel or Seedy Sam throwing Katherine into the river, or stalking Nell and luring her down an alleyway. Somehow it was hard to believe. I could imagine the despicable Mr Katz at Lowenstein's doing a thing like that, but not Seedy Sam, for all his bluster. Then I thought how important money was to Mr Mostel. If he thought his business was being threatened, he might have paid someone to do away with Katherine. That I could imagine. And who better to get rid of her quietly than one of the Eastmans?

If that was so, there was no way I would ever be able to prove it. I was not foolish enough to go poking around the Walhalla Hall and Chrystie Street again – and I had just promised Jacob that I wouldn't act stupidly. But I could go back to Mostel's, I decided. It occurred to me that this strike at Lowenstein's would give me a perfect excuse to return to Mostel's, especially if Lowenstein did fire some of us for striking. On the other hand, I reminded myself, I would probably not be able to complete my other commission and find out who was handing over Mostel's designs to his competitor. Which would mean I wouldn't get paid.

Item to remember for future reference, I said to myself. Never try to take on two cases at once. Item number two – never get romantically involved with anybody connected with the case. I thought of Jacob's arms around me, his lips against my fingers and the strange, not unpleasant, tickle of his beard. Had Nell guessed that Jacob was falling for me? Had Jacob, ever honest and open, actually told her his true feelings for me? In which case we had both driven her to her death.

I fell at last into troubled sleep, only to be woken by the alarm clock what seemed like minutes later. It was still dark. The wind was still blowing, making the bare branches dance crazily in the light of the street lamp. I stood on the cold lino-leum, wondering what I was doing awake at this hour, until I remembered that I had to join my fellow workers on a picket line before Mr Katz arrived at Lowenstein's.

I dressed in my warmest clothing, looked longingly at my wool cape, then took a shawl like the other girls. I made myself a cup of tea, a thick slice of bread and cheese for later sustenance, and some toast for breakfast. I was just eating it hurriedly when I looked up to see Seamus standing there.

'So you're really going to walk a picket line, are you?' he said.

I had given him sketchy details when I came home the night before.

'I'm afraid so. Those girls need all the support they can get.'

'Be careful, Molly,' he said. 'Those bosses don't play fair. Don't try to do anything too heroic, will you?'

'No, of course I won't.' I was touched by his concern.

'You're a good woman, Molly,' he said. 'I've been feeling so guilty that you've taken us in like this and I'm doing nothing to support my own family. I'm going out this very day to find something. I may not be strong enough to go back down the tunnel yet, but there are other jobs that don't require strength.'

'You recover your health first, Seamus,' I said. 'I can take care of things until you do.'

'No, you've made it too easy for me,' he said. 'Life is not supposed to be easy. We're born to a struggle and we die in a struggle, and it's a struggle in between too.'

Trust an Irishman to be poetic at five in the morning!

'I'm going to visit Tammany Hall,' he said. 'I'm a loyal voter. They owe me something. Surely they'll find a loyal Irishman a job.'

'Good luck, then,' I said. 'Tell the children good-bye for me and make sure they wash their faces before they go to school.'

He smiled. 'You're a good little mother to them. I was thinking, Molly – when the end does come, for Kathleen, I mean . . .'

'Don't even let that thought cross your mind,' I said severely. 'She's not dead yet and maybe she's not going to die. And even if she did, I'm not the wife for you, Seamus.'

Then I beat a hurried retreat. I had enough on my plate at

the moment without having to worry about proposals from Seamus O'Connor.

The streets were still wet from last night's downpour and I picked my way carefully between puddles. I had actually been looking forward to this moment, especially to seeing Katz's face when confronted by a cordon of angry girls. But that was before the events of last night. I couldn't get the image of Nell's dead face out of my mind. I had to do something, at least follow up on Mostel's connection, but I couldn't approach him until I had gone through the motions of this strike. Besides, these girls needed my support. I couldn't back out on them now.

When I reached Lowenstein's, a knot of excited girls had already gathered, whispering together in the shadows. Rose was among them. She looked up and saw me.

'Molly – over here, quick, we need you,' she said. 'We're making signs, but we don't write English so good.'

They had some squares of cardboard, a pot of black paint, and a large brush.

'What do you want me to say?'

'You'd know the right thing,' Rose said. 'We can write it in Yiddish and Italian and even Polish, but not in English.'

'How about "Lowenstein unfair to workers! We want better conditions"?' one of the girls suggested.

'We demand better conditions,' I suggested.

'That's good. And tell the world we are not slaves, we are free human beings with rights,' another girl chimed in.

'And we need a workplace that is warm enough and light enough.'

'And a proper water closet that doesn't freeze.'

'And a foreman who keeps his hands to himself.'

'And why should we work on the Sabbath? My papa wants to throw me out because we work that day.'

'He doesn't even let us get home in time for Shabbat on Friday nights!'

The suggestions were coming thick and fast. 'Hold on,' I yelled. 'I only have a few signs here. We just need to state why we are striking and that's because they are unfair.'

They nodded and watched as I wrote the messages, then Rose handed them out to several girls. While this was going on the three men who were the cutters and pressers came to work. They needed a little persuading to join us, but when they saw that they weren't going to be allowed inside and that fifty angry girls might set upon them, they changed their minds. Two of them went home and one decided to join our line.

'I watched the police hack strikers to death with their swords in Poland,' he said. 'That is why I come to America. Now I see if democracy works or not.'

Jacob arrived, carrying his camera, and with him the young Russian from the cloak-makers' union arrived and a couple of men I hadn't met before. While the Russian was instructing the girls about passive resistance and not losing their tempers whatever was said to them, Jacob drew me aside. 'I've been worrying about you all night,' he said.

'And I about you,' I replied. 'I don't suppose you slept any better than I did.'

'Hardly a wink. I could not shake off the awful feeling of guilt.'

'Jacob, you shouldn't feel guilty. You admitted yourself that Nell was headstrong. She did what she pleased.'

'It's not just that,' he said. 'I feel guilty that she wanted more than friendship from me and I was unable to give it to her. I can't help thinking that some of her bravado and daring were attempts to make me admire her.'

'Love doesn't work that way,' I said. 'You can't choose when you fall in love. It just happens.'

'This is so true,' Jacob said, and his gaze held mine.

I smiled uneasily. 'We have sterner things to occupy us this morning, I fear.'

'Yes. And I wish you weren't involved in this matter, Molly. I don't want you to be involved in more danger.'

'How can there be danger?' I demanded. 'Look how many of us there are. You have your camera. You can take pictures and get public opinion on our side.'

'I intend to, but just in case – could you not go home?'

'Of course not. I'm one of these girls at the moment. I suffered with them in Lowenstein's. Their conditions are intolerable, Jacob. They do deserve better, and they might need a spokeswoman who speaks English.'

'This Katherine you seek was a spokeswoman who spoke English,' he said, 'and look what happened to her. Look what happened to Nell last night.'

'All right everybody. To your places,' Rose shouted. 'And remember, we don't scare easy. We are not going to be bullied, whatever they say. This is America. We have a right to strike here.'

'God bless America,' a voice from the crowd said and was echoed down the line.

I stepped into the line beside Rose. Jacob and the other men moved off to one side, where they could observe from a stoop. At around six thirty Mr Katz arrived. He came striding down the street, his black derby at a jaunty angle on his head, and didn't notice the line of girls until the last minute.

'What's this?' he demanded.

Rose dug me in the side. 'It should be fairly obvious, Mr Katz,' I said. 'We don't like the way Lowenstein's treats us. We're on strike until our demands are met.'

He glared at me. 'I should have known you were trouble. A rabble-rouser like all the damned Irish.'

'It was not I who instigated this strike,' I said. 'All the girls feel the same. The place isn't fit for a pig, it's freezing cold, you cheat us out of our money by fining us, by charging us to use the washroom, and by turning back the hands on the clock too. Don't think we haven't seen you! And now you want to cut our wages in half because we worked too fast and finished the order. That was the final straw. It made the girls angry enough to walk out.'

Katz looked up and down the line. 'Those of you who are stupid enough to listen to these troublemakers will find yourself out of a job and right before the holidays too. Just when you'll be needing money for heat. And don't think another firm will take you on, because they won't. So it's up to you. Get inside now and nothing more will be said. Stay out and you're all fired.'

'And who's going to make the new season's dresses for you then, Mr Katz?' Rose asked sweetly. 'Won't the designs be ready in a few days?'

'Don't think we'll have any trouble replacing you, Rose Levy. I'll put out the word today and by tomorrow girls will be lining up from here to the Battery.'

'They can line up as long as they want,' Rose said, 'but they are not going into this building. Neither are you.'

'You think you can stop me? A few little girls?' He laughed.

'Not just a few little girls,' Jacob said as he and his friends stepped from the shadows. 'We are representatives of the United Hebrew Trades and the cloak-makers' union. If necessary we will call out more of our members in support. We will provide a ring of steel around this place. So try your best, Mr Foreman. You are wasting your time.'

Katz shot us a look of pure venom, then stalked away again.

'We've won! He's going away!' one of the girls shouted.

'Don't be silly,' Rose said. 'This is just the beginning. He

199

will be back with Mr Lowenstein and they will do everything in their power to try to frighten us. But we will not give in. If we can hold out this time, then we'll have made it better for every working girl in New York City.'

'Let's hear it for Rose! Rose is our champion!' someone shouted and the line of girls broke into applause.

Daylight came and with it a watery sun, making the sidewalks steam as the puddles evaporated.

'I prayed last night that it wouldn't rain today,' Rose said, adjusting the shawl around her shoulders. 'Maybe I should have prayed that the sun wouldn't shine. Only in New York can November be as hot as summer if it pleases.'

We stood and stood. Passersby shouted out words of encouragement. Mr Samuel from the deli came across with hot tea for everyone. Clocks across the city chimed out the hours. We drew quite a crowd of bystanders, some curious, some supportive, some mocking. Then around noon the crowd parted to let a long, elegant automobile through. Its hood was down and it was driven by a chauffeur in brown livery. It came to a halt and Mr Lowenstein got out of the backseat. He came toward us cautiously.

'Girls, girls,' he said in a soft, gentle voice. 'What foolishness is this? You risk your jobs because some socialist tells you to strike? These Hebrew Trades fellows – they don't have your welfare at heart. They're anarchists, every one of them. They want to bring down the economy, bring down the government. They don't care about you.' He looked up and down the line. 'I tell you what – I'm going to make you a most generous offer. Any girl who goes back to her machine right now, I'm not even going to take a note of her name, and I keep her on at full pay. The rest of you – out. Finished. On the street. Is that what you want?'

Rose dug me in the side again. I stepped forward hesitantly.

'We want better conditions, Mr Lowenstein. Fair conditions – enough heat in the winter, enough fresh air so we don't get sick, enough light so we don't go blind, and a foreman who doesn't try to cheat us by winding back the clock. That is all we ask. We work as hard as we can for you. We want you to be fair.'

Lowenstein held up his hand. 'All right. All right. I get better lighting put in, just as soon as electricity comes to this street.' He held up his hand to silence the angry mutter that rose from the line. 'And any girl who goes back now – I give a dollar bonus.'

Several girls stirred on the line. Rose stepped out in front of them. 'Not good enough, Mr Lowenstein. We want six dollars a week, like the girls get at the other shops. And no more paying for the washroom towel and mirror, and no more being fined if we have to stand up to stretch our backs or we need to use the washroom.'

Lowenstein looked up and down the line. 'You want six dollars, go to one of those other shops who pay this magnificent amount. You are trying my patience. All right, girls. Back to work now if you want your jobs and the bonus I promised you.'

One tiny, frail-looking girl stepped out of the line. 'Please, Mr Lowenstein, does that mean that we'll all go back on full wages right now? No more half pay until the new line is ready? My sister and I are the only breadwinners and my mother is sick. We'll starve if I don't work.'

I saw that a new idea had occurred to Lowenstein. His brain was ticking: if he kept us out on strike for a few more days, he wouldn't have to pay us a cent. 'Full wages when there's work to be done. I don't pay girls to sit twiddling their thumbs,' he said. 'I guess none of you want to be sensible and loyal. Fine with me. I'll replace the lot of you.'

He spun around and stalked back to the car. The chauffeur leaped out to open the door. I noticed then the other occupants of the backseat. They sat together, very chummy, whispering and smiling. One of them was his daughter, Letitia, in her fur-trimmed bonnet. The other was a handsome young man. It took me a moment to place him. As the car drove away, spattering mud from the puddles on those who stood too close, I remembered who he was: he was Mr Mostel's son.

Twenty

Mostel's son and Lowenstein's daughter – did Papa Mostel know about this relationship, given his distrust of Lowenstein? I rather thought not. But Mr Lowenstein obviously approved. I took this one stage further – here was an obvious connection between the two garment shops, an easy way to pass information. Mostel had told me that he took the designs home at night. How easy it would be for his son to copy them and hand them over to Lowenstein? So it was possible, but it didn't make any sense. If Papa Mostel didn't prosper, who would pay the fees to keep the son at his fancy university? And what son would be such a traitor to his father?

All the same, it was an interesting thought and my first real lead in the case. With all the momentous things that had just happened, I had all but forgotten that this had started with a simple case of stealing fashion designs. It might still be the one case I had the ability to bring to a conclusion.

I let my thoughts wander as I stood on that sidewalk, stamping my feet to keep them warm. It had become cold and windy again, with the threat of more rain. After Lowenstein had left, a tremor of fear had gone through the line of girls.

'He's going to fire us all. We'll be out in the street,' I heard one girl sobbing.

Rose strode up and down the line. 'You're not using your brain, Gina,' she said. 'If he doesn't get this place back in full operation in a week, he's not going to win the race to get his new line of clothing into the stores, is he? And there is no way that he can hire and train a whole new set of girls in one week. All we have to do is be strong and wait this one out, and stick together. Right?'

'That's right, Rose. You tell her!' voices shouted encouragement.

We broke for the night when darkness fell. We didn't think that Mr Lowenstein could do much overnight and the girls were cold, hungry, and exhausted. Jacob put his hand on my shoulder as the strikers dispersed.

'Come and have a bowl of soup and a glass of wine with me. You must be ready to drop.'

I smiled at him. 'My feet are about ready to fall off. Other than that I'm fine.'

He took me to a small café and we had borscht, which Jacob told me was a Russian beet and cabbage soup, served with coarse brown bread and a glass of red wine. I felt my strength returning immediately, although that may have been because Jacob was sitting opposite me. He had the sweetest smile and the way he gazed at me from behind those owlish specs was quite heartwarming. We sat chatting until the café owner started sweeping around our feet. Jacob wanted to walk me home, but I could see that he was as tired as I.

'Don't worry. I'll be fine,' I said.

'But I do worry,' he said. 'I couldn't sleep last night. I kept thinking what if they find out the connection between you and Nell? What if they think she told you more than she did, and they come looking for you?'

This was something that hadn't crossed my mind before and I rather wished he hadn't mentioned it.

'Nonsense. They could have no way of knowing that Nell was asking questions on my behalf. I'm perfectly safe,' I said, 'and I intend to stay that way. I'm heading straight home to a hot bath and bed.'

I waved, smiled, and set off with more bravado than I actually felt. He stood on the sidewalk watching me until I reached the corner of the block and turned out of sight. Jacob – an added complication in my life. He was obviously smitten with me. What did I really think about him? He was kind and wise and had a good sense of humor. If I could only shake off my last remaining dreams of Daniel Sullivan, then I could allow myself to fall for a man like Jacob Singer.

Next morning it was back on the picket way at first light. A cold day with frost in the air. The girls stomped their feet and clapped their hands together to stay warm. I wondered how long this standoff would continue. Until Mr Lowenstein had his own designs completed or he had managed to acquire designs from Mostel's, obviously. In which case I should do something to speed things up.

I've never been known for my great patience. Another of my major faults, or cardinal sins, according to my mother. I would always be the one who dipped her finger in the cake batter or who opened the oven to see if the Yorkshire pudding was rising and thus made it go flat. So by the third day of standing outside Lowenstein's, I was suffering more from boredom than from cold, hunger, or fear.

I knew that I had promised Jacob that I wouldn't pursue Nell's killer, but I was itching to get back to Mostel's again. I told myself that it was only because I wanted to get the business of the designs sorted out and with Lowenstein's out on strike, that could never happen. But at the back of my mind loomed the question of Nell and what she had found out.

And Mostel's was the one concrete link I had in the chain of Katherine's disappearance and Nell's death.

I slipped away from the line, on the pretext of finding a washroom, found a nearby stationer, bought paper and envelope, looked longingly at the new fountain pens displayed in the glass counter, then persuaded the clerk to let me use his pen and ink. As soon as I had money, I would buy myself one of those new fountain pens so that I could write notes anywhere – along with the watch that was so necessary to my profession, of course. Having left the store, my head swimming with such grand ideas, I was soon reminded that, if I didn't conclude a case soon, I was not likely to have the money for food, let alone luxuries.

The message I had penned was to Mr Mostel, asking if he could meet me at Steiner's Coffee House on Lower Broadway, sufficiently far away from prying eyes. Half an hour after I delivered it, he appeared at the door of the coffeehouse.

'Miss Murphy?' he said, sitting down at the table beside me. 'You have news for me?'

'How can I have news for you when the Lowenstein girls are out on strike?' I asked. 'Nor am I likely to find out anything unless they return to work.'

His broad forehead crinkled into a frown. 'I heard about that. A sorry matter, Miss Murphy. Not that I would shed a tear for Lowenstein, but it's the rest of us that I worry about. Once our girls hear about it, they'll all be getting ideas. We have to nip this in the bud before it spreads to the other garment shops.'

'That's precisely why I wanted to see you, Mr Mostel. How can I complete my assignment and ferret out your spy if Lowenstein's is closed?'

'Of course this could be a blessing in disguise,' he said. 'My new designs could be finished and in the stores while that criminal Lowenstein wrings his hands in despair and his factory remains closed.'

I was not happy with this way of thinking. It was an all too probable line of development and would mean that I was not paid. I shook my head. 'He told the girls he intends to fire them all and hire new workers if necessary. He'll get those garments into the stores, by hook or by crook. And having all new girls wouldn't stop your spy from slipping the designs to him.'

'True.' He nodded, his large, melancholy jowls quivering. 'So what is the answer, Miss Murphy?'

'I've been thinking, Mr Mostel, and I've come up with a solution.' He leaned closer to me, across the marble-topped table. 'You must announce to everyone at your factory that your new designs will be completed, let's say, next Tuesday. Make sure everyone knows this. I have another idea as well – why not make a false set of designs, dresses you never intend to make and sell, and see if your spy takes the bait. Add something outlandish to the design – a big frilly collar, a velvet hood, a gentleman's bow tie – and see if Lowenstein is tricked into making it.'

Mr Mostel rubbed his hands together in delight. 'I like it, Miss Murphy. Oh, the joy of getting the better of Lowenstein.'

'You must make sure that these drawings are easily accessible on your desk and you are away from your office enough so that the spy is able to sneak in and take them.'

'Naturally. Naturally.' He was still rubbing his hands and beaming. 'And if that fool Lowenstein is stupid enough to make a dress with a frilly collar or a bow tie, you'll make me the happiest man in New York City!'

'Let's hope he takes the bait,' I said, 'and that we catch your thief. I have to admit that I've found no hint of suspicion so far, but time will tell.' That wasn't exactly the truth. An image of Ben Mostel in the back of Lowenstein's car came into my head, but I didn't think it was the right moment to tell Mr Mostel that I had my suspicions about his son. 'You are not personally worried that your employees might follow suit and go out on strike then?'

'My employees? I'm like a father to them, Miss Murphy. Why should they think of striking?'

I bit my tongue and moved to the next topic. 'So you've no particular troublemakers at the moment?'

'You saw for yourself. They are happy and content and if anyone wants to make trouble, then I show her the door. I don't tolerate troublemakers.'

I took a big swig of coffee and grasped the bull by the horns. 'I heard you had an English girl working for you who was a bit of a rabble-rouser? One of the girls at Lowenstein's told me, because she thought I was English too.'

His face didn't register any change in expression. 'I don't recall any English girl. She can't have lasted long. I leave the hiring and firing to my foreman and concentrate myself on making the profits.'

'So your business is flourishing, is it, Mr Mostel?' I asked sweetly.

'I can't complain, Miss Murphy. It's a living.'

'And your son – that was your son who came into the shop once, wasn't it – he plans to follow you into the business one day?'

'My son?' He rolled deep soulful eyes. 'You speak of my oldest son, Ben? He plans to break his father's heart, that's what he plans to do, Miss Murphy. We made a mistake with that boy – we brought him up to have everything he wanted, all the things we never had ourselves. And has he thanked us for it?' He shook his head. 'My wife cries herself to sleep worrying over him. We scrimp and save to send him to Harvard

208

University, the finest in the land, and what do I hear but that he's failed his latest examinations. All he's interested in is having a good time and going through his father's money. He'll be the ruin of me, Miss Murphy.'

'Does he have a sweetheart who might be a sobering influence, Mr Mostel?'

'Does he have a sweetheart? It's a different sweetheart every week, Miss Murphy. And it's my money that is buying them expensive presents and jewelry and taking them to dine at Delmonico's. He won't hear of a matchmaker. He tells us that he's an American and he lives in the twentieth century and he'll choose himself a bride when he's good and ready.'

'It must be a great worry for you,' I commiserated, 'but I'm sure he'll come to his senses soon enough.'

'He'd better. This time I've laid down the law. Any more failed exams and you're not getting another penny from me, I told him. You'll be out earning your living by the sweat of your brow like your father had to. That shook him up, Miss Murphy.'

'I'm sure it must have.'

He pulled his watch out of his vest pocket and glanced at it. 'I must get back to work, Miss Murphy. I've enjoyed our little chat and I like your thinking. I'll come up with some outlandish sketches over the weekend and by this time next week we may have found out the traitor in our midst.'

He escorted me from the coffeehouse, bowed, and we went our separate ways. As I walked away I tried to digest all that I had learned. He truly didn't seem to remember Katherine and somehow I couldn't picture him ordering her murder – which meant that if anyone ordered her death it was the foreman, Seedy Sam.

And concerning the other matter of the purloined designs, Mostel's son now stood clearly at the head of my list of suspects. He had opportunity and he had a motive, if he was angry with his father for cracking the whip and stopping his pleasurable lifestyle. It was clear that he needed more money than his father was giving him and I presumed Mr Lowenstein would come up with a handsome finder's fee. I wondered if he was sweet on Lowenstein's daughter, or if he was also only courting her in an effort to slight his father. However, if he were the traitor in the camp, the designs could move smoothly from one garment shop to the other without either party in the transaction going near the workplace. Which meant I would have no way of catching the suspects, and thus no way of being paid. I'd also have to tread very carefully if I wanted to make an accusation against Mostel's son. Parents do not take kindly to suggestions that their offspring are not all they should be, however plain this might be to the rest of the world. It occurred to me that I should check up on the infamous Ben Mostel and see if I could uncover any other unfavorable facts against him.

I rejoined the picket line outside Lowenstein's. Nothing much had happened during my absence, except that frail little Fanny had fainted and was currently sitting in Samuel's being revived with a bowl of their best chicken soup. We stood, stamping our feet to keep warm until darkness fell and the icy blast from the East River made us decide to call it a day.

Jacob had a meeting of the United Hebrew Trades and I went home, grateful for a chance to warm up and get some sleep. I came in on a peaceful domestic scene, Bridie in her nightgown sitting on her papa's knee and Shamey curled up at his feet as Seamus told them a story. As I listened, I caught the words and realized that the story was about their mother, Kathleen, and their life back in Ireland. I climbed the stairs thinking of my own half-forgotten life back in Ireland. Was it really less than a year ago that I had lived in a cottage and gone to our plot to dig potatoes in the rain and walked on the cliff tops in the wind and gazed out at the ocean, wondering what would become of me? Never, in my wildest dreams, could I have pictured this.

Major Faversham's letter, along with the pictures of Katherine and Michael, were lying on my bedside table. I really should be writing that letter to him, telling him the sad news of his daughter's demise. I couldn't put it off much longer. I took out paper, pen, and ink, then sat, studying the photograph of Katherine again. The haughty face stared back at me, head held proudly, dressed in all her finery. Such a waste. Just like Nell – two lives that held so much promise, both cut short. Tears of compassion welled up in my eyes.

Then I blinked away the tears and stared harder at the photograph. I had asked Daniel if the body pulled from the East River had been wearing any jewelry and the answer had been in the negative. I took the photo under the gas and peered at it harder, wishing I had a magnifying glass. The locket Katherine was wearing around her neck was very distinctive – it was heart-shaped, and had a flower design on it in what looked like precious stones. My heart started racing. Now I knew what had disturbed me when I first saw Letitia Lowenstein. She had been wearing an identical locket around her neck.

Twenty-one

All thoughts of a hot bath and rest were put aside. I rushed down the stairs again, clutching the photograph, past the astonished O'Connor family and across the street to Sid and Gus.

'Dear God, don't tell us something else is wrong,' Sid said, looking at my face. 'I don't think we could take another tragedy.'

'No, nothing is wrong,' I said, 'but I wondered if you might own a magnifying glass.'

'But of course,' Sid said, as if people showed up on her doorstep at nine o'clock every night demanding magnifying glasses. 'Come in, do. We were just about to have coffee.'

Sid's Turkish coffee late at night was a guarantee of no sleep, but I missed the reassurance of their company, so I accepted and was taken through to the kitchen, where Gus was putting a pot of water onto the stove.

'Molly!' she exclaimed. 'Have they found Nell's killer yet? We tried to find out when her funeral will be, but the police have not released her body to her family. What a tragic business for them. We are extremely cut up about it too, are we not, Sid?'

'Positively melancholy,' Sid echoed. 'Poor Gus has been

quite out of sorts since you left and even worse since she heard of Nell Blankeship's death, Molly. You should see the painting she has started – all dark swirls, like deep gloomy pools.'

'Don't mind me,' Gus said, 'I always get this way with the approach of winter.'

'Then we must whisk you south to the sun,' Sid said. 'Florida, do you think?'

My heart lurched at the thought of Sid and Gus going away, then Gus shook her head. 'We couldn't abandon Molly, and Ryan will expect us to hold his hand while his play opens in the city. Let's just go out and fill the place with flowers and oranges tomorrow. That should suffice.'

'Here is the requested object.' Sid handed me the magnifying glass she had found in a drawer. 'Are you planning to become Mr Sherlock Holmes?'

I laughed. 'No, I just wanted to examine this photograph more closely.' I placed it on the table.

'That is the English girl who you were trying to trace – the one they said had drowned in the East River.' Sid peered over my shoulder. 'Molly, you are not still pursuing this inquiry, are you? Wasn't Nell also looking into this girl's disappearance when she was killed?'

'Molly – I thought we gave you enough stern warnings,' Gus added.

'I promised to do nothing foolish, and I plan to keep that promise,' I said. 'This is another matter altogether. I wanted to examine the necklace she is wearing. I think I might have seen it in New York.'

'She pawned it, perhaps.'

I hadn't thought of that possibility. Katherine could well have pawned her jewelry to keep herself and Michael going and Letitia Lowenstein could have bought the locket quite legitimately at a pawn shop. Nothing underhand involved after all.

I put the magnifying glass to my eye and examined the locket. In closer detail I could see that the stones were arranged in a design that looked like forget-me-nots. How very appropriate, I thought. I am not going to forget you, Katherine! And I am going to find out how Letitia Lowenstein came by a very similar locket. I remembered Mr Mostel lamenting that his son showered his lady friends with jewelry. Had Ben acquired this particular jewel? It was too much of a coincidence that he had come across it in a pawn shop. Yes, Mr Ben Mostel, I must really check into you, I thought as I walked home across Patchin Place.

The next day was Friday, the fourth since our strike began. It was obvious to me that Mr Lowenstein was going to be content to have us standing out in the street until the moment he wanted work to commence again. Then it would be a case of accept my conditions or I find replacements. Only then would it start to get ugly. I hoped that my meeting with Mr Mostel yesterday might bring things to a swifter conclusion. If he had announced the unveiling of his new line, as planned, then Mr Lowenstein would want us back at work by sometime next week. It would be interesting to see when he made his move.

Around midmorning, Jacob came running up, waving a copy of the *New York Herald*. 'Look, they printed my photograph,' he exclaimed and we gathered around to see. Under the headline GARMENT WORKERS DEMAND BETTER CONDITIONS was a picture of our picket line. Jacob had chosen to focus on the frailest-looking girls. Little Fanny was positively sagging against her picket sign. The girls looked like frozen waifs. The whole scene was most appealing.

'It's wonderful, Jacob,' I said. 'If this doesn't stir up public sympathy, I don't know what will.'

By midday we had had a visit from various reporters, plus some society ladies who were part of the Ladies' League, working for justice and equality for women. They brought hot buns and cocoa with them and promised to approach the big department stores on our behalf, pressuring them into not buying Lowenstein's garments if he didn't settle the strike favorably. This was a big boost to morale and the girls sang as they stood in line – 'She's Only a Bird in a Gilded Cage', 'Mighty Like a Rose' – all the latest popular songs as well as plaintive Yiddish, soulful Russian ditties, and sprightly Italian ones. The rest of us clapped and stamped our feet. A crowd gathered and cheered us on.

Toward evening the mood of the crowd changed. A group of unsavory-looking men with battered derbys or caps pulled down over their eyes, oversize jackets, and big boots started jeering and hurling insults at us. They pushed past the onlookers and came right up to where they thought the line was weakest, towering over the smallest girls.

'Well, lookee here. Ain't they sweet? Poor little orphan girls out on the street – hey, honey, why are you wasting your time standing in this line for a few measly dollars when you could be making yourself big money if you come to work for me?'

'Work for you?' one of the girls asked. 'Do you run a garment shop?'

'Yeah, only my girls take their garments off,' the man guffawed. 'Ain't that right, Flossie?'

A hard, brazen-looking woman, wearing tight tawdry clothing that proclaimed her to be a streetwalker stepped out of the crowd and stood in front of the girls. 'You get paid for lying flat on your back, girls. Make money in your sleep. What could be easier?'

215

Another flashy woman had joined her, this one in a red velvet gown with an outrageous ostrich feather in a hat which was tilted rakishly down over her face. 'Not this one, Floss,' she said. 'She ain't got what the gentlemen likes. She's flat as a pancake.' She moved down the line, standing in front of Sophia, a plump little Italian. 'Now you could do very well for yourself, dearie. Nice round little derriere – something for the gentleman to get his hands around.'

'And a good pair of water wings in front too, right, Floss?' The other woman cackled.

'I'm a good girl. Don't say things like that.' Sophia pulled her shawl around her and looked as if she was about to cry.

'If you stand out here on the street, the police are going to think you're one of us,' the streetwalker continued, reaching out to tug at Sophia's long hair.

Jacob had started to move toward the confrontation. 'Leave these girls alone. They are respectable and don't want anything to do with the likes of you,' he said.

'With the likes of us?' the man demanded. 'Who are you insulting?'

'I'm telling you to hop it, or I'll call the police.'

'Call the police – that's a good one!' The man laughed and looked around. I noticed several policeman standing on the corner watching us.

'Officers, these people are upsetting our girls and trying to intimidate them,' I called to constables who stood, arms folded, and grinning.

I saw the louts move in my direction. There was something about one of them lurking at the back of the pack that caught my attention. I had seen him before – one of the Eastmans maybe. Then I had no time for idle contemplation as the biggest and most brutish looking of the bunch swaggered right up to me.

'It's the other way around, girlie,' he growled. 'Youse is blocking dis sidewalk so that honest folk like ourselves can't get by without stepping in the nasty dirty street. My poor Flossie doesn't want to get mud all over her nice clean shoes, do you, Floss?' He turned back to grin at the brazen hussy behind him. 'Now move out of the way, or else!'

I remembered now why the men and their actions seemed familiar to me. If I wasn't mistaken, these same bullyboys had been accosting passersby outside the polling booth on election day. They were gangland enforcers and, since the Eastmans ruled this part of the city, Eastmans they obviously were. The brute coming toward me was one I hadn't seen before. I faced him, confident that he wouldn't try anything with all these people looking on.

'We're not moving,' I said. 'We have every right to stand here. Cross over if you want to get past.'

'Step aside, or I'm just going to have to push past you.' The lout was leering down at me. I could smell his stinking breath, laced with alcohol.

I glared up at him. 'Get away from me, you great brute! You don't frighten me.'

'Don't say I didn't warn you.' He was still grinning inanely.

'Try to push past me and you'll be sorry!' I said.

'Molly!' Jacob shouted. 'Just ignore them.'

But he was too late. The brute came at me with his shoulder, like a rugby charge. I stuck my foot out and he went sprawling forward, grabbing onto a lamppost to prevent himself from falling.

'Did you see what she did? She attacked me!' he yelled, righting himself against a street lamp and turning on me. 'Youse going to get what's coming to you now, girlie!'

He swung at me. I dodged aside but too late. His fist glanced

217

off my face and I staggered backward. He was still grinning at me, looking like a great brutish ape.

'Holy Mother of God!' I exclaimed, putting my hand up to my stinging face. 'Now you're the one who's going to be sorry.'

I snatched Rose's picket sign and swung it at him. It was only made of cardboard and flimsy wood so that the contact sounded worse than it really was as it crashed against his head. It certainly felt satisfying.

'Get out of here now and leave us alone!' I yelled, raining blows against his head as the sign splintered and all I was left with was a stick of wood.

Then I looked up in relief as blue uniforms finally came into the fray.

'Arrest her, Officer. She is attacking innocent citizens,' one of the streetwalkers shouted.

Hands grabbed both my arms.

'Let go of me at once,' I shouted angrily. 'These louts started attacking us. We were just defending ourselves.'

'Not what I saw, miss,' one of the constables said. 'You're the one holding the weapon. Come on, into the paddy wagon with you.'

I was bundled into a waiting wagon, along with Jacob, Sophia, and a couple of other girls.

'This is outrageous,' I stormed as the wagon took off at a gallop. 'When we get to police headquarters, I'm going to make a big stink. Those policemen just stood and watched while we were harassed.'

'Of course they did, Molly,' Jacob said calmly. 'The whole thing was set up. It's been done a hundred times before. When shop owners want to break up a strike, they hire starkes – strongarm men – to do their dirty work. They want the girls intimidated so that they go back to work with no fuss.'

I grabbed hold of Jacob as we were thrown around by the lurching wagon.

'Then why didn't the police arrest them if they knew what was happening?'

'Because the police have been bribed, of course. They were waiting for the moment when you did exactly what they wanted you to do. You struck one of them.'

'Just because a few police are corrupt, doesn't mean we won't get fair treatment when we get to headquarters,' I said. 'Those starkes were propositioning Sophia, making lewd comments to her. You heard them threaten me.'

Jacob was shaking his head patiently. 'You are still very naive,' he said. 'To tell you the truth, I had been expecting something like this since the very first day of the strike. I had warned you that these bosses do not play fair, hadn't I?'

'But you did nothing,' I said. 'You didn't attack anyone. Why have they arrested you?'

'Because I am known to them. I am safer in custody and they hope to break the strike without people like myself around to let the girls know their rights.'

'Do you think they will succeed?' I peered through the small back window of the paddy wagon. 'I hope Rose is strong enough to keep the girls from giving in.'

'And someone has gone to the Hebrew Trades for reinforcements too,' Jacob said. 'With any luck they just wanted to scare us and think they have done so.'

'So Lowenstein hired bullies, did he? I thought I recognized one of them, lurking in the shadows at the back. Could they have been members of the Eastmans?'

'Very possible,' Jacob said. 'They often use gangs to do their dirty work.'

'The police stand by and watch while gang members beat

up young women?' I demanded. I was still hot enough to explode. 'What sort of society is this?'

Jacob shrugged. 'Much the same the world over. The poor have no voice. The rich have the money and power. Money buys anything.'

'Then it's a rotten world,' I snapped. I looked across at the three girls who had been arrested with us, frail little girls who had done nothing, now clinging to each other in a terrified huddle.

'Don't worry, it will be all right,' I said to them. 'I'll tell the policemen that you did nothing wrong.'

One of them had her hand up to her mouth, sobbing. 'My family will be ashamed when they hear I go to prison. My papa, he will throw me out.'

'Nobody's going to throw you out. Jacob and I will come and talk to your family and let them know the truth if you want. Once we get to headquarters and we can talk to some uncorrupt policemen, they'll let us go right away, and we'll be home in time for supper, I'm sure.'

The girls gazed at me, wanting to believe me. One managed a watery smile.

The wagon came to an abrupt halt, almost throwing us onto the floor. The door opened.

'Okay, you lot. Out you get and no funny business,' a voice ordered.

Jacob stepped down first then held out his hand to escort us women down the steps. His calm demeanor was reassuring and he handed each of us down like a society lady, arriving at a ball.

I glanced around as we stepped out into the dark street.

'This isn't police headquarters,' I said. 'Where have they taken us?'

'I rather fear it's the courthouse,' Jacob said.

'Courthouse? They're going to try us as common criminals – without a proper investigation?'

'It looks that way,' Jacob said. 'Now remember, Molly, stay calm. They'll say things to try and make you blow up. Act like these other girls will – confused, innocent, scared. That's what might work on the judge, not hotheaded and indignant.'

'I've never played the helpless female in my life,' I said, tossing back my hair.

'No, I don't suppose you have,' he admitted, smiling, 'but this would be a good time to learn.'

'Come on now. Move it. Up the steps.' A constable swung his baton to chivvy us along.

'We are not cattle, Officer,' I said, 'and we do not need driving.'

'What have I just been telling you?' Jacob whispered. 'This is serious, Molly. If you annoy the judge, you could find yourself in prison.'

'Nonsense. You can't send someone to jail without proof that they've done something wrong.'

'But that's just what I'm trying to tell you. They will manufacture proof. Now, please, keep quiet and act submissively, I beg you.'

'No talking. In you go,' the voice behind the cattle prod said.

We were marshaled into a long hallway and then into a small holding room. A clerk was sitting at a high, old-fashioned desk. He took down our names and addresses, then left us with just a police guard.

One by one the three girls were taken out and did not return. Jacob and I sat on the hard bench waiting. It must have been well past my suppertime and my insides were growling with hunger. I was also cold and tired, and just a little bit scared too, if the truth be known. I had always been a staunch believer in right and wrong, and the ultimate triumph of right. Now it seemed that right might not be about to triumph. Should I do what I had sworn never to do again and summon Daniel to my aid? A disturbing thought crossed my mind. He might not wish to go against the official police position.

I had heard, of course, that the New York police could be bribed, but I had never seen it in action until now. I went through that scene again in my mind, those constables standing on the opposite corner, arms folded, smirking, as the louts came at us. I could almost smell that foul breath again and I shuddered. I tried to picture their faces – were any of them gang members I had seen before? Could the police really be working with a gang? That one familiar face at the back of the crowd – where and when had I seen him before? Then it hit me like an ice-cold shower. He was in shadow, at the back of the group, and I hadn't had a chance to see him clearly before the brawl began. In fact I had never seen his face clearly. The only time I had seen it before was on a newspaper cutting from Ireland, standing at Katherine's side as she prepared for a day's hunting. If I was not completely mistaken, the man I had spotted today was Michael Kelly.

Twenty-two

If Michael Kelly was still alive, and working with the Eastmans, then that changed everything. He would probably know
who killed Katherine. Was he out to get revenge right now,
and did this mean that the Eastmans had no part in her death?
Somehow I would have to find him and talk to him. Then I
reminded myself that a lot of Irishmen have that sort of face –
the typical look of what they call Black Irish. Daniel himself
looked not unlike Michael Kelly. And I had only glimpsed
him for a moment in the shadows, hardly enough to make a
positive identification.

'Miss Murphy.' I jumped to my feet as my name was called.

Jacob reached across and touched my arm. 'Now remember,' he said. 'Helpless, innocent, frail. No outbursts.'

I nodded, hung my head, and looked coy, making him smile.

I was taken into a drafty, dimly lit courtroom. It was empty
apart from a judge, sitting at a high bench, and a couple of
policemen. My footsteps clattered on the marble floor as I
was led forward.

'Miss Molly Murphy, Your Honor,' the bailiff said. 'She is
charged with disturbing the peace.'

The judge peered down at me. He had a cold, beaklike face,
like a stone eagle, and I couldn't tell if he might be moved by

my youth and frailty. Did he know that I had been framed? Had he also been bribed?

'I understand that you were part of a street disturbance, earlier this evening.'

'I was part of a picket line. My coworkers and I are on strike against Lowenstein's garment factory, Your Honor.'

'I also understand that you struck passersby with a wooden sign.' His voice matched his face in coldness.

'Only after I was struck myself by a very large loutish bully. It was self-defense, Your Honor.'

He glanced down. 'The witness's statement only mentions your attack with the sign. The complaint says that you were blocking the sidewalk, preventing pedestrians from passing by. When one attempted to pass, you hit him with your sign. So I ask you now, Miss Murphy, did you or did you not attack a person with a sign?'

'Yes, but it was after . . .'

He held up his hand. 'I'm not asking what preceded it. This is America, Miss Murphy, not Ireland. You can't just go around brawling in the streets here. We have laws to protect innocent citizens.'

'Innocent citizens?' My voice rose. 'You call those louts innocent citizens? They were baiting us and you know very well that they were paid to bait us, just as the police were paid to watch them. If this is American law, then I don't think very much of it.'

'Nobody asked you to come here, Miss Murphy,' the judge said. For an awful moment I thought he was going to send me back to Ireland. 'I can be lenient with you and charge you with disturbing the peace. That carries with it a ten-dollar fine and a night in jail. I could also add to it a charge of inflicting grievous bodily harm, which would mean a month in women's prison and a hundred-dollar fine. It's up to you.'

He paused and frowned down at me, like a parent appealing to a naughty child. 'If you swear to me that you will not attempt to disturb the peace again, then I'll let you off lightly this time. However, if I catch you back on the street protesting and harassing innocent passersby, I won't be so generous next time. It will be a month in prison, and I think you'll find that prison isn't a very pleasant place to be, especially not at this time of year.'

He leaned forward. 'So what is it to be, Miss Murphy? Do I have your solemn word that you will not attempt to disturb the peace again?'

I was not going to have anyone to speak for me. I was not going to find justice in this court. I looked down at my feet, playing the repentant child. 'Yes, Your Honor,' I said.

'In that case I sentence you to one night in jail and a ten-dollar fine.' He brought down his gavel. 'Take her away. Bring in the next case.'

Hands led me away. I was still seething with anger. If this was America, did I really want to be part of it? The moment I got out of jail, I'd take the first boat anywhere – South America, Africa, Australia . . .

I was led down a flight of stone steps, then a door was opened with a big key. It felt cold and clammy down there, dimly lit and very unpleasant.

'Another one for you, Bert,' the man with me said cheerfully as he presented me at the half door of a small cubbyhole. An elderly, toothless man got to his feet. 'What's she done? Killed her old man?'

'Disturbing the peace. She's in for the night.'

'Okay. Just a moment while I get the featherbeds in the guest room ready.' He gave a wheezy laugh as he shuffled down the corridor ahead of me. An iron door squeaked open. 'In you go, honey. All modern conveniences. Bucket in the corner. Breakfast at seven.' I was propelled inside with a hefty shove and the door clanged shut behind me.

I looked around, afraid to see with whom I might be sharing this cell. But I was alone. A narrow wooden plank ran along one wall. There was a bucket in the corner. That was it. I sat on the bench and hugged my arms to me. It was miserably cold and I was sick with hunger. I was also sick with anger that I was so powerless. Were those three little girls also in similar cells, I wondered? Was Jacob also locked up here? I longed for the comforting calm of his presence, but I didn't wish him in this place. After what he had been through in Russia, a night in a cell like this must be like reliving a nightmare.

I sat on my plank, hugging my knees to me to try to keep warm. There was no way I was going to be able to sleep on this thing. As my anger dissipated I began to feel wretched and alone. My chosen profession was not turning out to be what I had wanted at all. I seemed to be going to prison with monotonous regularity. And it wasn't as if I was much closer to solving any cases either. When I got out, my next step would be to prove to my own satisfaction that Michael Kelly was alive, and I wasn't sure how I was going to do that safely. If he was still alive, then who killed Katherine and how did Letitia Lowenstein get her locket? Every step forward I took, things just became more muddled.

I started as something scurried across the floor. It was too dark to make out what it was – either a rat or a mouse or a very large cockroach. Either way I had no intention of letting it anywhere near me. I hugged my knees tighter to myself and kept watch.

It was a long cold night. Several times I nodded off, only to wake myself as my head banged against the cold damp stone of the wall. At times voices cried out in sleep, waking me from my doze. And in my half consciousness I saw phantom rats about to eat my toes. I wanted to spend a penny, but not into that bucket, not having to cross that floor.

'It's only one night,' I told myself. 'I can put up with anything for one night.' Then I shifted myself into the corner and touched a spider's web. If there's one thing in the world that I hate, it's spiders. Without warning I started to cry. It was all so shocking and unfair and I was being punished for something I didn't do when all I was trying to do was help people . . . I sat there sniveling and feeling pretty sorry for myself until I gave myself a stern talking-to. 'Just listen to you, behaving like a proper ninny,' I said out loud. 'Poor Jacob had to endure far worse than this. They tortured him, they tried to kill him when he was only a boy, and he's come through it all right. He's even brave enough to go on fighting, so the least you can do is stick this out for one night.'

Thus fortified I rested my head on top of my knees and fell asleep. At first light I woke to the rattle of something against bars and a mug and piece of bread were shoved through. I drank the hot coffee, and ate all of the bread. Then I spruced myself up in preparation for my release. I was not going to let them see that my night in jail had upset me or dampened my spirits.

An hour or so later old toothless-mouth shuffled up to my door and opened it. 'Out you go then, girlie. You're free.'

A guard escorted me up the flight of steps, through to the front of the building, and out into the gray morning air. I stood, breathing deeply and watching the pigeons flapping and pecking in the little park opposite. As I came down the flight of steps I saw a figure sitting on a bench in the little park. He got to his feet.

'Molly!' He called and ran to me.

'Jacob!' I was enveloped in his arms.

227

'Are you all right?' he asked.

'Never felt better. The food rivaled Delmonico's, the bed was softer than at the Waldorf Astoria.'

He gazed at me. 'I am in awe of you. What does it take to dampen your spirits?'

I neglected to mention my weeping session in the small hours of the morning. 'What's one lousy night in jail?' I said with a good attempt at a carefree smile. 'Uncomfortable maybe, but not unbearable. I'm ready to go right back on duty and let them see that they can't crush us so easily.'

'You are not going back on duty,' he said firmly. 'You are going straight home to bed and you are going to stay there.'

'But the girls will think I've deserted them.'

He put his hands on my shoulders and held me securely. 'Didn't you understand what the judge said? The first offence is minor. If you are arrested again for the same offence, it will be off to prison for a long while. People die in prison, Molly – typhoid and any number of foul diseases are rampant. And you'd be sharing a cell with the dregs of society – violent, conscienceless criminals. I am not going to let that happen to you. If necessary I'm going to lock you in your room and take away the key.'

'You can't stop me,' I said defiantly.

'Molly, you seem to have forgotten. This is not even your fight. It was brave of you to help in this way, but you are not one of them.' He was shouting at me now.

'Oh, and you're a lady garment worker yourself, are you?' I demanded. 'You could have fooled me.'

'I help them because I have the knowledge. It is the business of the United Hebrew Trades to help all unions. I paid your fine, by the way.'

'You didn't have to do that. I'm not a pauper.' I was still angry with him.

'It wasn't my money. We have a fund to assist strikers who run afoul of the law.'

'Then save your money for the real strikers, since I'm not really one of them.'

'So your present job makes you a millionaire, does it?'

I couldn't come up with a ready answer to that one.

'Molly,' he said quietly now. 'Don't be so stubborn. I admire the way you have taken these girls' cause as your own. As I said before, I am in awe at the way you toss off a night in jail as if it were no more inconvenience than a broken fingernail, but when it comes to your common sense—' He shook his head and I had to laugh.

'Come,' he said, taking my arm. 'First things first. You need a good breakfast, then I am taking you home.'

I gave him an embarrassed grin. 'If it's first things first, then I need to find a public convenience in a hurry. I wasn't about to use that bucket in my cell.'

Jacob laughed and escorted me across the public garden where a wrought-iron-decorated public lavatory was indeed a welcome sight. Then I allowed myself to be led up Broadway, away from city hall, away from Lowenstein's.

'But what about the other girls? Do you know what happened to them? And what about you? Did they release you last night?'

'The three girls were sent home with just a warning, so I understand. I was detained for the night just like you.'

'But that wasn't fair, Jacob. You did nothing. At least I hit that great lout.'

He shrugged. 'I am used to it by now.'

'Do you think that those strong-arm bullyboys – starkes, did you call them – managed to break up the strike without us there?'

'We'll find out soon enough, won't we?' he said. 'Although

229

I rather think that their behavior last night was merely a warning. They wanted to show us how rough they could get if we keep going.'

'All the more reason for me to go back and help.'

We stood at the curb, waiting for a milk wagon to pass with churns and harness jangling merrily. 'We will not go through this again.' He swung me to the right and marched me into a café, seating me at an oilcloth-covered table then ordering coffee and sweet rolls for us. We were both equally hungry and ate in silence until the plate was empty.

'More?' Jacob asked.

I shook my head. 'Sufficient unto the day, as my mother always said. Now I'm back to my old self and ready to tackle anything.'

'All right, I'll make a deal with you,' Jacob said. 'We will visit the strike scene and let the girls see that you have come through your ordeal with flying colors. That itself will boost their spirits. Then I will escort you straight home, where you will stay. Understood?'

'For a gentle soul, you can be quite forceful when you want to,' I said.

He smiled. 'When I care about something or somebody enough, I can be passionate.'

We walked close beside each other in companionable silence.

'Jacob?'

He looked up.

'Do you think there is any way to find out about Michael Kelly – without getting involved with the Eastmans, I mean?'

'Straight home,' he repeated, 'and stay there.'

Twenty-three

I fell into a dreamless sleep the moment my head hit the pillow and was not conscious of the hours passing. I came to, like a diver coming up from deep water, to a rhythmic hammering. I lay for a while, trying to remember where I was and what I was doing lying in bed with the setting sun glowing red onto my face. Then I realized that the hammering was someone pounding on my front door.

'All right, I'm coming,' I heard Seamus calling.

He opened the door. I heard men's voices and sat up, afraid that the police had come to arrest me again, or, worse still, that the Eastmans had found where I lived. Then men's boots coming up the stairs in a great hurry. I leaped out of bed and reached for my dressing gown. I was only half into it when my door burst open.

'How dare you come into a lady's boudoir,' I started to say, then my jaw dropped in astonishment. 'Jacob! What are you doing here? Don't tell me that the starkes have broken the strike?'

He was beaming. 'I had to come to tell you the good news straight away – we won, Molly. We won!' He took my hands and danced around with me. 'Mr Lowenstein came and told the girls that he would meet their demands – six dollars a

231

week, like the other shops, and finish on Friday and Saturday nights by six o'clock to be home in time for Shabbat, and better heat and light too. They go back to work on Monday morning. It's a miracle.'

'It certainly is,' I said. I was pleased too, of course, but more skeptical than Jacob. Of course he didn't know about my little scheme with Mr Mostel. If Lowenstein had found out that he could get his hands on Mostel's designs on Tuesday, then he'd need his shop up and running again on Monday, wouldn't he? And how easy it would be to pay the girls the promised six dollars a week, then manage to dock them that extra dollar in fines. And as for heat and light – he could keep promising those until the cows came home.

But for now the news was good all around. The girls could go back to work. Lowenstein could get his hands on Mostel's designs. I could catch Lowenstein's spy, collect my fee, and go back to sleeping late.

'Come on, get dressed,' Jacob said, panting a little after his crazy dance. 'We are celebrating tonight at the meeting room. This is not just a victory for the ladies garment workers, it is a victory for all unions. We have shown that we can strike and win in a small way. Next time we can make demands to a whole industry.'

'Then go and wait downstairs, if you want me to get dressed,' I said, pushing him away. 'I'm sure your match-maker will never be able to find a good match for you, if you've been discovered in a lady's boudoir.'

'I think I may have found a good match myself, without any help of the *schadchen*.' He gave me a quick glance then closed the door behind him.

I stood staring at the door, my heart beating rather fast. What did I feel about Jacob Singer? I wasn't sure. Oh, I liked him, I certainly admired him, and if I were honest, I liked the way he wanted to take care of me. But marry him? I had never considered marrying anyone but Daniel. Maybe this was the right time to put that foolish notion behind me, once and for all.

The Hebrew Trades meeting room was full to bursting by the time we got there. Music was spilling out onto the side-walk. A violinist and an accordion player sat on stools in one corner, playing a lively tune, while the rest of the floor was a milling, seething crowd of dancers, all of them girls. The young men stood around the wall, looking on and clapping. The tune ended and the girls, red-faced and glowing, made for the punch bowl.

'Molly!' Rose spotted me through the crowd and made her way to me. 'You've heard the wonderful news. Isn't it grand? And all thanks to you.'

'Thanks to me? Oh no, I was only one person among all of you.'

'But you stood up to those starkes. You made that bully look like a fool in front of all of us. It made them think twice, Molly.'

'Then I'm glad I could help.'

She slipped her arm through mine. 'Come and taste my mama's stuffed cabbage rolls. Best cabbage rolls outside Warsaw, she says. Was prison really terrible?'

'Could have been worse,' I said. 'I survived, as you see.'

'We're all so proud of you.' She grabbed a plate and started piling cabbage rolls on it.

'Enough.' I laughed. 'Save some for the others.'

'Look at all this good food. A holiday feast. Everyone brought something – Italian spaghetti and German potato dumplings and blintzes – a grand tour of the world.'

We ate and drank and danced some more.

'That young man in the worker's cap is looking at you,

Rose,' I whispered to her. 'Why don't you get him to dance with you?'

'Dance with me?' A look of pure horror, with just a tinge of delight. 'If my papa heard I had danced with a man, I'd be turned out of the house. He'd want nothing more to do with me.'

'But in America men and girls dance together all the time. What is the harm in it?'

She shook her head. 'Not Jewish girls,' she said. 'Not Jewish men.'

'Wait a minute.' I forced my way through the crowd to Jacob. 'I want you to dance with me,' I said.

He looked a little uncertain.

'What – you don't find me attractive enough? Or are you afraid it will get back to the matchmaker?'

He laughed and put one hand awkwardly around my waist. Then he nodded to the musicians who struck up another lively number.

'Can you do the polka?' he asked.

'No, but I'll pick it up soon enough.'

We started around the floor. Even over the music I thought I could detect a collective gasp from the Jewish girls – maybe from the Italians too. But after a while I noticed one of the young men leave the wall and ask one of the girls to dance. Soon there were three or four couples. But I also noticed most girls slinking away shyly or flat-out refusing.

Some of the eyes watching us were openly disapproving.

'Those older women are looking at us as if we're doing something highly improper,' I whispered.

'In their eyes we are,' he whispered back. 'A young man and woman are not supposed to touch each other, and a Jewish man and a Christian woman – *oy vay,* that is the worst!'

'I suppose it will take a while,' I said.

'It will take a generation, maybe more,' he said. 'Not every-one is as freethinking as we are. They call this the melting pot, but we haven't yet had time to melt. As of yet, we are still separate ingredients floating around in the broth.'

'So are we condemned as hopeless sinners?'

'I'm afraid so, but who cares?' His grip tightened around my waist as he spun me around the floor, faster and faster.

At last a collective tiredness came over the crowd. These girls had been on a picket line since early morning, and they had just run out of steam. The girls started to drift away. I noticed Jacob's eyelids sagging and realized that he hadn't had the luxury of being able to sleep the day away.

'You must go home to bed,' I said.

He kept hold of my hand. 'Molly, tomorrow is Sunday when I usually try to visit my parents.'

'That's all right. You and I don't have to see each other every day.'

He swallowed hard before saying, 'I was wondering whether you would come with me.'

Visiting his parents. This was indeed becoming serious. His eyes were pleading.

'Of course, Jacob. I would be delighted to come with you,' I said and watched his face light up.

So at noon the next day I walked down Delancey Street, my arm through Jacob's. Delancey on a Sunday was bustling with life – street peddlers, musicians, the shrieks of children play-ing tag, and at the far end of the street, the tower of the new East River Bridge reached steely arms out across the river to Brooklyn. Cables were strung across to the far side of the river, but as yet there was no roadway beneath them, so that they looked like the beginnings of a giant spider web in the morning sun.

'This street is busy enough now,' Jacob said. 'I don't know what will happen when traffic from Williamsburg comes streaming across. The city is already jam-packed with people. We should lock the gates and keep the rest out!'

I looked at him and saw that he was joking. I was glad that he was relaxed and enjoying himself. I was distinctly nervous. Being taken home to meet the family was something I was unsure about.

'They do know I'm coming, don't they?'

'Not exactly, but don't worry. They'll be delighted to meet you.'

'I'm not at all sure that they will be thrilled to meet an Irish Catholic girl who goes about unchaperoned in the company of a young man.'

'They like to meet new people. My mother doesn't get out much. She is still unsure of herself in a new country. It will be good for her, also good for them to see that their son is happy and meeting nice girls.'

'Meeting nice girls by himself,' I reminded him. 'Without a proper introduction through the matchmaker.'

'We're in America. They'll have to accept that,' he said. 'Come on. It will be fine. My mother is a good cook.'

He led me into a solid brick building and up four flights of stairs to the front door of the Singer household. The door was opened by a small, shrunken man who started in surprise or horror when he saw me standing beside Jacob.

'Hello, Papa. I've brought a friend with me,' he said. 'This is Miss Murphy. Molly, this is my father, Itzik Singer.'

Jacob's father clicked his heels together with the same little bow that I remembered when first meeting Jacob.

'How do you do? I'm pleased to meet you.' For once I stammered out the words.

'Come in, please.'

He ushered me inside graciously enough. The room was spartan with no curtains at the windows, a rug covering part of a bare wood floor, a simple table, and several chairs. But the table was laid with a white cloth and some good cutlery. Jacob's father called out something in Yiddish and a woman came scurrying through from the kitchen, wiping her hands on her apron as she came. She looked older than she probably was, with a wrinkled, worried face. I can't tell you what color her hair was because it was hidden under a scarf, tied tightly around her head. She stopped, gazing at me with mouth open. Again I couldn't tell if the look was surprise or horror.

'Hello, Mama.' Jacob crossed the room to give her a kiss on her cheek. 'I've brought a friend to join us for a meal.' A rapid conversation in Yiddish followed and I saw her give me a quick glance. Then she managed a smile.

'Please,' she said, pointing at the best chair. 'I sorry. Not speaking good English yet.'

'Can I give you any help in the kitchen?' I asked.

'No thanks, better not,' Jacob answered for her. 'Just sit and enjoy yourself. Is there any more of that wine I brought you, Papa?'

'Wine? Now? Before we eat? Okay. I get wine.'

He brought out a wine bottle and glasses on a silver tray.

'What a beautiful tray.'

'We bring – from old country. Many things – must leave behind.'

'My parents haven't been here long,' Jacob said.

'My son – he send us money for boat,' Mr Singer said proudly. 'My wife – she very shy. Not learn English yet. Please excuse.'

'Nothing to excuse,' I said. 'I'll just have to try and learn Yiddish.'

Another look of astonishment then he burst out laughing. 'Learn Yiddish, she say! That's good.'

Jacob's mother appeared again at the sound of the laughter and my statement was obviously repeated to her. She didn't laugh. Any girl wanting to learn Yiddish must obviously have designs on her son – that's what the expression said.

'Sit down, Mama. Drink wine with us,' Jacob said.

His mother hesitated then perched on the edge of the nearest chair. She took the glass he offered her.

'Cheers,' I said, raising my glass. 'How do you say "cheers"?'

'*L'chaim*,' Jacob said, then nodded in approval over my pronunciation of the word. I took a sip. The wine was red and very sweet, but not unpleasant. 'It's good,' I said.

Jacob's mother fired another question at him.

'She wants to know where you are from,' he said. 'I told her Ireland.'

Her look indicated that Ireland was only one step away from the moon.

She said something else, making Jacob smile. 'She asks if there are Jews in Ireland.'

'There are, but I'm not one of them,' I answered, and this was relayed to Jacob's mother. I thought as much, the look said.

Then she jumped up and disappeared into the kitchen again. A few minutes later we were summoned to table and Mrs Singer carried in a platter of fish and a bowl of potatoes. I helped myself cautiously, not wanting to appear greedy and waited in case anyone was going to say a blessing. Luckily, I was right. Jacob's father said some words in Hebrew and then picked up his fork.

'My mother makes the best potatoes with sour cream. It's good, isn't it?' Jacob said.

'Very. And the fish are herring, aren't they? We used to eat a lot of herring at home.'

Jacob translated this and for the first time I saw a small nod of approval.

After the main course we had a sweet macaroni pudding, followed by tea and honey cake, then Mrs Singer headed for the kitchen again. I, wanting to be the good guest and suitable friend for their son, jumped up and followed her.

'Let me help you with the washing up,' I said. 'I'm well house-trained.'

She held up her hands to say no.

'But I'd be happy to,' I said as I picked up the dishes and put them in the nearest sink. She gave a cry of horror as Jacob appeared behind me.

'What did I do? I'm not going to break anything,' I said.

Jacob said something reassuring to his mother, then gave me an embarrassed grin. 'You put the dairy dishes in the meat sink.'

It was then that I noticed for the first time that there were two sinks, and two stacks of dishes on the shelf.

'There are different dishes for meat and for dairy?'

He nodded. 'And we can't eat them together and there different cloths for washing and drying the dishes. One of our crazy food rules, of which there are many.'

'I'm sorry. I had no idea.'

'How could you?' he said. 'It really doesn't matter.'

'I'm sure it does matter,' I said noting his mother's distressed face.

Jacob shrugged. 'They will have to get the kitchen made kosher again. It's not the worst thing in the world. There are too many religious customs from the old country that are not practical in our new life over here and will probably be lost someday.' He brushed it aside with a gesture, but I looked at the stricken face at the sink. Jacob might take his religious background lightly, but I had the distinct feeling that his parents weren't about to toss aside their religious customs in a new country.

'I'm really sorry,' I said to Jacob's mother this time. 'I wanted to help. I didn't know.'

She managed a weak smile. '*Ist nichts.*'

'Forget it.' Jacob took my arm and escorted me out of the kitchen, before I could break another rule, I suspect.

The atmosphere was decidedly awkward after that and we left soon after.

'They must think I'm a proper heathen.' I gave an embarrassed laugh.

'Not at all. They will think you are kind and sweet and very pretty, just like I do. They will learn to love you in time and think that I have made a good choice for myself.'

'Whoa – hold on a minute, aren't we rushing ahead a little?' I asked, laughing nervously. 'We've only just met, Jacob.'

'Some things you know straightaway.'

'But we know nothing about each other yet. You have only seen my good side. You haven't had a chance to witness my terrible temper or my stubbornness. And I, in turn, know little about you. For all I know you might snore at night and be prone to fits of black despair.'

He was smiling at me the way a father smiles indulgently at his beloved child. 'Whatever my faults, I promise to correct them instantly for you.'

'But Jacob—'

'Molly, is the idea of marriage so repugnant to you?' He stopped and turned to face me.

'Of course not. Sometime, in the future, I hope to marry.'

'Then the idea of marrying *me* does not thrill you with anticipation?'

'I didn't say that either. It's just – too soon, Jacob.'

'I'm not trying to rush you, Molly. It's just that I knew the moment I saw you, and it would have been wonderful if you had known too.'

'I do enjoy your company, Jacob, and I think you're a fine person too. So let's take it slowly from there, shall we?'

'Of course. Why not? It's a lovely Sunday and we have the day to ourselves. Let us not even think about tomorrow.'

He slipped his arm through mine and we walked arm in arm down the street. It was hard to enjoy a free day, strolling in the sunshine when I had so many things I should be doing. I really should be trying to find out whether Michael Kelly was still alive. I should also be looking into Ben Mostel and his extravagant lifestyle. Then I gave in to temptation and put those thoughts aside. Just for once, everything could wait until tomorrow.

Twenty-four

On Monday morning I joined the line of girls waiting outside Lowenstein's. There was an air of anticipation in the crowd. I think some of the girls truly believed that they would go down those steps and find the place miraculously transformed into a place of heat, light, and beauty. It was a freezing cold morning, with ice in the gutters and a wind that cut right through me coming off the East River. Thank God we had not had to face temperatures as bad as this last week or we'd never have held out for four days!

Mr Katz made a grand entrance just before seven and walked down the steps ahead of us, brandishing the key.

'You should be very grateful you have such a generous boss,' he said. 'You should be very grateful you're still working here. Me – I would have thrown the lot of you out.'

Then he stood in the doorway, scrutinizing each girl as she went in. When it was my turn, he put out a hand and stopped me.

'Not you,' he said. 'The boss don't want you back. You're a troublemaker.'

There was a clamor around me. 'But you have to have Molly back! That's not fair.'

I was gratified to hear this, but those girls didn't realize how relieved I was never to have to work in that place again.

'It's all right.' I turned to face the girls. 'Don't worry about me. I'll be just fine. No sense in making a fuss about me. I'll get myself a better job somewhere else.'

Rose pushed her way to stand beside me. 'No, Molly, it's not all right.' She stood on tiptoe and glared at Katz. 'If you don't let her come back then we'll all go on strike again.'

'Rose – it's all right.' I put my hand on her shoulder to restrain her. 'The girls have got you and you'll do just famously, so don't worry about me.' I gave her an encouraging smile as she looked at me dubiously. 'No, honestly. I have a hundred plans of things I want to do. Just make sure you don't let that bully Katz get away with anything. Remember what Lowenstein promised you and make sure he puts in electric light straightaway. And better heating too.'

I leaned across and gave her a little kiss on her cheek. 'I'll stay in touch,' I said. 'I'll come to Samuel's Deli at lunchtime to get all the latest news.'

I gave Mr Katz a haughty stare, then I pushed past the rest of the girls waiting on the steps. I was free of Lowenstein's. It felt wonderful. And it was also playing into my plans – I could now quite legitimately go back to Mostel's, tell Mr Mostel what had happened, and start working there again. That way I could keep an eye on his son, as well as on anyone else who might want to sneak up to his office and come down with his designs. And I could ask questions about Katherine too. Just perfect, in fact. I skipped down Essex Street with a sprightly step.

Later that morning I was reinstated at Mostel's. The conditions inside were not much better than at Lowenstein's – cold and drafty and the only heat coming from a couple of oil stoves, one at either door.

'I don't know why the boss was softhearted enough to take you back,' Seedy Sam said, looking at me with great distaste.

'First you walk out and then you want to come back. You should recognize a good thing when you see it.'

'I'll let you know when I see it,' I said, eyeing him with the same distaste. Then I breezed past him to take my old place next to Sadie. She looked surprised and delighted to see me.

'How come they took you back?' she whispered.

'My uncle did the boss a favor once. I'm not letting him forget it,' I said.

A little later Mr Mostel himself showed up. 'I've been working on the new designs all weekend, girls,' he said, waving a briefcase at us, 'and I think we've got the goods this time. My new styles will be all the rave. They'll go off the racks like hotcakes. I just need to put some finishing touches and get the sample hands to work on them, and then it's full speed ahead.'

At lunchtime the girls crowded around me as we went down the stairs.

'How come you're back again? Mostel never takes anyone back!' Golda said.

'Where did you go, anyway?' Sadie asked.

'I had things I had to do,' I said vaguely. 'Now I've done them and I need to start earning money again.'

'I know where she went.' Little Sarah gave me a knowing look. 'She went to work for Lowenstein. And I know what she was really doing there too.'

'You do?' The alarm must have shown on my face.

'Sure. You're not really one of us, are you?' She stood on the sidewalk, smiling at me, blushing at being the center of attention for once.

For once I didn't know what to say. 'What do you mean?' I asked.

'I heard about the strike,' she said triumphantly. 'Everyone is talking about it. I heard you were sent there to help organize the workers. You really work for the union ladies, don't you?'

'Not exactly,' I said, relief rushing to my face. 'But I did help organize the strike there, it's true.'

'See, I knew it.' Sarah looked smug.

The rest of the girls pressed closer. 'You helped organize a strike? And did the girls win?'

'Yes, they did. They went back to work today with better pay and better conditions.'

'And is that why you're here – to do the same thing for us?' Sadie asked, her fact alight with excitement.

'I'm here to earn money,' I said.

'Oh sure. Of course you are.' Sadie touched the side of her nose and winked at me.

'You tell us how we can go on strike too.' One of the girls tugged at my sleeve. She was a beautiful stately Italian called Gina and had been very upset when Paula was fired.

'Strike? Us? Why should we want to go on strike?' an older woman asked. 'We have it good here. Six dollars a week and no funny business.'

'Good? You call that good?' Gina demanded. 'All garment workers are treated like dreck and you know it. It's about time we show Seedy Sam and old Mostel that they don't rule the world.'

'This isn't a good time to go on strike, you know,' I said hastily. 'Mr Mostel wants to start work on his new designs this week, remember.'

'Then what better time?' Gina said. 'He wants to get those garments in the stores for the holidays. He'd probably agree to anything we wanted just to keep us working.'

'He could also fire the lot of you and hire new girls to replace you,' I said. 'That's what Lowenstein threatened to do. I don't know why he gave in so quickly.'

Disappointed faces looked at me. 'Are you saying we shouldn't go on strike like the Lowenstein girls?' one of them asked. 'You think we have it so good here that we should all be happy?'

'Of course not,' I said, 'and I didn't say you shouldn't go on strike. But you have to know what you're doing. It's not as easy as it sounds. You need the backing of the Hebrew Trades and the other garment workers, or they'll make mincemeat of you.'

'Mincemeat? They kill us?' one of the Italian girls asked, staring at me with huge eyes.

I laughed. 'No, but they'll threaten you. They sent the starkes to attack us and when we tried to defend ourselves, some of us got carted off to jail for causing trouble.'

'You got sent to jail? *Oy vay!*'

I looked around the group of expectant faces. 'Look, if you really want to organize, you need to join the union. You need to choose your union representatives to go to meetings for you and get advice on how to go about your strike.'

'We already had one girl start doing that stuff, didn't we?' Golda asked. 'Remember Kathy?'

'Oh sure. Kathy.' The name went around the circle of girls.

'Kathy? Was she American?' I asked.

'No, she was English. She talked funny, like you,' one of the girls said.

'She was the greatest. She stand up to Sam and she don't take no nonsense from him.'

'What happened to her?' I asked.

Blank faces stared at me. 'We don't know,' Golda said. 'She was at work one day and then she got called out of the room and she never came back.'

'We asked Sam where she had gone and he didn't know neither,' another girl added.

'Did somebody come for her? Who called her out of the room?' I asked.

Several shrugs.

'We're not supposed to look up when we're working,' Sadie said. 'You know how Seedy Sam likes to take our money from us.'

'I work near the door,' a bouncy little redhead called Ida said. 'I saw her go past and I heard her say, "What are you doing here?"'

'But you didn't see who it was?'

'No, but soon after that Mr Mostel's son came in.'

'Enough of this,' Sadie said loudly. 'Kathy's gone. All the talking in the world isn't going to bring her back. Let's go eat. You know Sam is just dying to dock our pay for being late again.'

Nobody could disagree with this and we surged down the street to the little café where some girls bought hot drinks to go with their sandwich and others splurged five cents on the daily special. I joined the latter and had a bowl of stew that must have been made from a tough old buffalo. As I chewed on pieces of gristle, I also tried to digest what I had just heard. So Katherine had actually disappeared in the middle of the day from Mostel's, lured from the room by someone who came for her – someone she knew. And another interesting fact had come out – Ben Mostel had come into the room right after Kathy disappeared.

If Michael Kelly was still alive, maybe he would be able to take up the story from that point. Surely he would have found out what had happened to her, especially if he was a member of the Eastmans. Gang members always have an ear to the ground, don't they? So my number-one priority was to find Michael Kelly. Not an easy assignment. I had no desire to follow Nell Blankenship to my doom. Maybe it was now time to shake off all notions of foolish pride and ask Daniel to help me.

That evening when I returned home, I took up pen and paper.

Dear Daniel,

*I witnessed an ugly incident at a garment workers'
strike on Friday last. I think that some of the starkes
were members of the Eastmans gang, and one of them
looked very much like the photograph of Michael
Kelly. Since I am forbidden to do any more foolish
investigating in that part of town, I wondered if you
could find out for me if Michael Kelly is indeed still
alive.*

Yours sincerely,

M. Murphy

On Tuesday morning I hurried to work with great anticipation. Today was the day that Mr Mostel was going to bring in
the finished designs for the sample hands to work on. Today
someone might try to borrow, steal, or copy them. Of course,
if that someone was his son Ben, then why would he need to
do it at the office? He could more easily take a peek at them
at home in his father's study – unless the old man kept them
under lock and key.

I sat at my machine and worked with an eye on the door
until Mr Mostel came in.

'Here they are – my new designs,' he said, tapping his briefcase. 'All finished and ready to go like I promised. And they
are spectacular, if I say so myself. So different – so chic. You
girls are going to be proud just to be working on them.' He
looked around the room and was met by a lot of blank stares.
Of course many of the girls just didn't understand him, but
those who did were not showing enthusiasm. Mostel smiled at
us. 'If you girls work hard and we get the first lot shipped by
December first, there will a bonus all around. Then we'll all
have a good holiday with something to celebrate, won't we?'

'A good holiday? He doesn't even give us one day off

over the eight days of Chanukah,' Sadie muttered to me. 'He gives us Christmas Day off and what good is that to Jewish families?'

Mr Mostel went up to his office and then returned. 'Sam – I got to pop out for a while,' he called down the length of the room. 'If the sample hands come in before I get back, tell them the designs are in the top drawer on the right. Got it? They can start work straightaway.'

He's certainly laying it on thick, I thought. If I were the spy, I might begin to smell a rat.

'New designs. As if we care,' Sadie muttered to me. 'A collar is a collar is a collar.'

We hadn't been working long when the door opened again and Ben Mostel came in. With his top hat and silver-tipped cane he looked like a peacock in a henhouse.

'Morning, girls. You're all looking very lovely today,' he said, picking out some of the younger, prettier girls to grace with his smile. A general titter followed him down the room.

'Your dad's not here, Mr Ben,' Sam called as Ben passed us in the direction of Mostel's office.

'No matter. I just wanted to leave something for him,' Ben said.

I was on my feet instantly. 'I need to go to the washroom, Sam,' I said. 'It's really urgent. Can I go?'

'Okay, I'll give you permission this once,' he said. 'Only don't make a habit of it.'

'How come she gets permission when I don't?' Sadie asked.

'Because she ain't running in and out all day like some I could mention, including you,' Sam said. He jerked his head to me. 'Go on then, if you're going.'

I sprinted through the door like a girl who has to go in a hurry. I even opened the washroom door, went in, and closed it behind me, just in case Sam was still watching me. Then

I opened it a crack, checked around it, and was up the stairs like a shot. The door to Mostel's office was open and Ben was so busy looking in one of the drawers in his father's desk that he didn't hear me coming.

'Did you find what you are looking for?' I asked.

He spun around with a guilty look on his face.

'Your father has worked hard to give you all the benefits he never had,' I went on, 'and this is how you repay him?'

'Who the hell are you, and how did you know?'

'I've been watching you, Ben Mostel,' I said. I was enjoying this moment, confident that I could run down the flight of steps ahead of him and was within shouting distance of a roomful of girls. 'What do you think your father would say if he knew you were betraying him to Lowenstein?'

Without warning he came around the desk and, while I was still thinking I might have to defend myself after all, he closed the door.

'What do you want?' he hissed at me. 'Is it money? Is that it? All right then, how much?' He reached for his wallet.

I was no longer feeling quite as brave as I had been, but I decided I was still within shouting distance.

'Since all the money you have comes from your father and he is paying me in this Lowenstein business, I don't require to be paid twice over,' I said.

Ben looked puzzled and horrified. 'My father is paying you to follow me? He must have heard about me and Letitia then. You can tell him he doesn't have to worry – it's nothing serious. Just a bit of fun, you know.'

He was talking very fast, his eyes darting nervously like a schoolboy caught at the cookie jar.

'What do you mean, it's not serious – betraying your father to his rival?'

'Betraying?' He laughed uneasily. 'Oh, come on, that's a

bit strong, wouldn't you say? I only took the girl to supper a few times. I take hundreds of women to supper.'

'Only this girl's name was Lowenstein. But taking Letitia Lowenstein to supper wasn't what I was talking about, and you know it. I'm talking about the other matter – your father's designs. You were looking in the wrong drawer, by the way.'

'Designs – what designs? I don't follow you.'

'Isn't that what you came here for, the moment your father left his office? Had he kept them locked away at home?'

He laughed again, a little more easily now. 'I'm afraid I don't see what my father's designs have to do with me and Letitia.'

'Oh, so you weren't just about to copy them and slip them to Mr Lowenstein?'

'Why on earth would I want to do that? My old man might be dashed annoying, but I'm not out to ruin him.' He stared at me and I saw the worry grow on his face. 'Is that what he believes – that I'm out to betray him? I know he thinks poorly of me, because I'm rather a duffer where money is concerned, but surely he must know – I mean, you must set him straight, miss – uh.' He was looking at me like a scared schoolboy again.

'So you're telling me that you didn't come here to sneak a look at your father's new designs then?'

'I had no idea he had come up with new designs. I'm not at all interested in the fashion industry, much to his disappointment.'

'Then what were you doing in his desk?' I couldn't help asking.

He blushed scarlet. 'If you really must know, he keeps his checkbook in that drawer. I thought I might – uh – borrow one of his checks.'

If Ben Mostel was acting then he had better apply for the

lead role in Ryan O'Hare's next play. 'You're not going to tell him, are you?' He tried a winning smile.

'Not if you replace it immediately.'

'Oh, very well, although there will be a certain restaurateur who may not be happy if I don't pay the bill after dinner tonight.'

He gave a sheepish smile, half opened the drawer, then looked up at me thoughtfully.

'You say you are working for my father, but I've seen you before, among the girls on the shop floor.' Not quite as inane a young man as his father had thought. 'So it seems to me that you might not want the fact that you are working secretly for my father to be revealed.'

'Most astute of you. So you are suggesting that we have a bargain – I say nothing about your helping yourself to your father's checks if you say nothing about my not really being a seamstress?'

'Exactly.'

We looked at each other for a long while in silence. 'Very well,' I said. 'However, if your father ever comments on anything missing from his desk, I shall feel obliged to tell him what I witnessed.'

'And if any of the girls comment that you are behaving strangely, I shall be obliged to set them straight.'

'I never behave strangely,' I said with the ghost of a smile.

'So sneaking up to the boss's office isn't strange behavior?'

'I am supposed to be in the washroom, which is where I am going when you are ready to leave.'

'Don't trust me in here alone, huh?'

'Your father tells me you give him a lot of grief.'

'My father is a stingy old man who keeps me permanently short of cash. How is a fellow to enjoy life if he has no money?'

'It must be hard to have to go without champagne every

now and then, or not to be able to see every new show that opens,' I said sweetly, but he caught my sarcasm and blushed again. 'So tell me – how did Letitia Lowenstein come by that very attractive, unique locket I saw around her neck?' I knew this was really taking a chance. If Ben had acquired Katherine's locket, it might have been taken from her dead body. This inane, overgrown schoolboy act might conceal a clever killer for all I knew.

This time he flushed almost beetroot red. 'So that's what you were getting at all the time! I guess you already know, don't you?'

'I might do, but I'd like to hear your version.'

He winced. 'Did my father find out and send you to get an admission of my guilt?'

'He may have. So how did you meet Katherine?'

'Who?'

'The girl who owned that locket.' I inched toward the door, feeling more secure when my hand wrapped around the door-knob behind me. 'But surely you knew that, didn't you? Did you meet her here, at the factory?'

'I've no idea who you are talking about. You know where I found the locket – at the bottom of my father's drawer in his desk here. I wanted some cash to buy Letitia a present and I thought to myself, what does he need a pretty little thing like this for, so I pocketed it – as I think you knew all along, didn't you?'

'Oh yes,' I stammered. 'I knew that all along.'

Twenty-five

I don't remember how I came down that flight of stairs again. I sat on the W.C. letting the cold bring me back to my senses. Mr Mostel after all – that genial man playing the worried father and betrayed employer so well. Had he paid someone to remove Katherine or had she been lured up to his office and dispatched right here? Until now I had dismissed the notion that I was dealing with a highly dangerous man.

'You took long enough, didn't you,' Seedy Sam commented as I returned to my seat.

'Sorry, but I'm not feeling too well today,' I said, giving the phrase enough meaning to make him refrain from further questions.

At lunchtime I decided that my ill health was a good excuse for staying put and keeping an eye on the place.

'Aren't you coming to eat?' Sadie asked me.

'No, thanks. I've got a piece of bread and cheese in my bag if I feel like eating anything at all,' I said.

'Do you want me to bring you something back from the café?' Sadie asked.

'I think it was their food that did it in the first place,' I said. 'That stew yesterday.'

'It was bad. I couldn't finish mine,' she said. 'I didn't even

254

want to look at it. But I could bring you some noodle soup and a roll. It's very nourishing.'

'Thanks, Sadie. You're a pal, but I think I'll survive,' I said. 'You better get going or you'll be at the back of the queue.'

She left. It was completely quiet in the sewing room. Even Seedy Sam had gone to have his lunch with the cutters and pressers downstairs. I nibbled nervously on my bread and cheese. I hadn't had to lie about that one – I really did feel sick. Katherine's locket in Mostel's drawer. One day she disappeared and never came back. And if Mostel got wind that I was snooping, or was involved in starting a strike, then the same thing could happen to me. 'Get out while you still can,' a voice whispered in my head.

I looked up as I heard footsteps coming up the stairs. The half hour for lunch wouldn't be over for fifteen more minutes and girls were not usually in a hurry to return. Sadie came into the room. She had flushed cheeks from the cold wind.

'Horrible food again. Be happy you didn't order anything. I came back early – couldn't stand the smell,' she said. 'Now I need to go to the washroom myself.'

She went through the inner door without even pausing to take her shawl off. I heard the washroom door close, then another sound that had me up on my feet – it was the creak of floorboards. Sadie was going up the stairs to Mostel's office. I gave her a head start and then I crept up the stairs after her. Mr Mostel's office door was closed. Cautiously I inched it open. The office was empty. I crept through into the back room beyond, which the sample hands occupied when they were at work. Empty apart from bolts of cloth and a couple of forlorn dummies.

Could those creaking floorboards have been the product of my overactive imagination? I could have sworn I heard feet going up the stairs. But she couldn't just have vanished.

She must have heard me following her and be hiding, waiting for me to go downstairs again before she looked for the designs. I checked the drawer to see if she had maybe taken them already and was sitting somewhere, copying them furiously. But the folder still lay unopened in Mostel's drawer.

I felt the back of my neck prickle. Where was she? I spent futile minutes turning over bolts of cloth to see if she was behind or under any of them. I was about to go downstairs again when I noticed a door I had overlooked. Mostel's door had always been open as I had come up the stairs, concealing another door to the left of the little landing. This door was not properly shut. I pushed it open and found another short flight of stairs. I crept up it. It was dark and seemed to be leading to some kind of attic storage space. Bolts of cloth were stacked high on either side. It smelled musty. What on earth could Sadie want up here, unless she was doing what Mostel had dreaded and quietly helping herself to a few yards of trim?

Then I heard a girl's voice whisper, 'Wait. I think I hear something.'

And the whispered answer, 'It's okay. They're all at lunch still.'

I went up the final steps, around the bolts of cloth, and stood staring at two frightened faces.

'Molly,' Sadie stammered. 'What are you doing up here?'

'More to the point, what are you doing?' I asked. 'And who is this?'

I stared at the other girl. She looked somehow familiar. She was staring back at me, frightened, poised for flight, and yet at the same time defiant.

'Don't tell on us, please, Molly,' Sadie begged. 'She had nowhere else to go. If they find her they'll kill her.'

I came closer, trying to make out her features in the poor light.

'It's all right, Sadie. I should go anyway. It's not right for you to take risks for me,' said a very haughty English voice.

'Katherine?' I said.

She started in horror. 'Who are you? I never saw you in my life before. How do you know me?'

'It's a long story,' I said, 'but for now let me just assure you that I am a friend. I'm on your side.'

'Did you tell her, Sadie?' Katherine asked.

'Of course she didn't tell me, but don't worry, you can trust me. What on earth possessed you to hide out here, of all places?'

'We couldn't think of anywhere else. This room is hardly ever used, so we thought I'd be safe enough.'

'But so close to Mostel. What if he'd discovered you up here?'

'He'd have been annoyed, of course.'

'Annoyed. Wasn't he the one trying to have you killed?'

They looked at me as if I was speaking Chinese.

'Mr Mostel? He's really an old sweetie,' Katherine said.

'Then who?'

'Why, her husband and his horrible friends, of course,' Sadie said. 'She came to me one night in a terrible state and I couldn't think of anywhere else to hide her but here. I smuggled her in early next morning and I've been bringing her food.'

'So that's why you've been leaving the café early, and going to the washroom so frequently.'

She nodded.

'You've been taking a terrible risk.'

'I know,' Katherine said, 'that's why I should go now, while I have the chance.'

'Where will you go?' Sadie asked.

'I've no idea.'

'I've an idea,' I said. 'My name is Molly and, believe it or not, I've been trying to find out what happened to you. I've just thought of a perfect place for you to hide out. Go to Nine Patchin Place, behind Jefferson Market in Greenwich Village. Two women live there. Their names are Sid and Gus – don't ask. Tell them you are Katherine and Molly says they should hide you until she gets home. I'll explain everything later.'

'Are you sure?' She was still regarding me suspiciously. 'Why should you put yourself out for me?'

'I said I'll explain everything later, but for now you have to trust me, Katherine. And nobody would think of looking for you as far away as Greenwich Village, would they?'

'I suppose not.'

'Then wrap yourself up in a shawl and get out of here while you can.'

We were just about to bundle her down the stairs when the sound of voices rose from below. The girls were back from lunch.

'We'll have to wait until after work,' I said. 'Sadie and I will work out how we can distract Sam while we get you out of here somehow.'

'Don't put yourself at risk for me,' Katherine said.

'I wouldn't dream of it,' I replied breezily. 'Come on, Sadie. Let's get back down there before Sam docks us half our pay.'

We rushed down the stairs.

'So where have you two been?' he demanded.

'Washroom again,' I said. 'We're both sick from the stinking stew we ate yesterday. We're not eating at that café ever again.'

Sam just grunted.

'It's like an icehouse in here,' one of the girls commented as a group of them came back into the room. 'Can't you turn up those stoves any higher?'

'If I do, they'll burst,' Sam said. 'If only you try working hard enough you'll create your own heat.'

'Very funny,' the girl muttered.

Machines started clattering again. The afternoon dragged on. Girls clapped their hands together and stamped their feet to bring back the circulation. Sam walked up and down the lines of girls.

'What kind of work are you doing here?' he demanded, stopping beside a machine in the far row. 'Those are supposed to be straight lines, not zigzags. Only a blind person would want to buy that garment.'

'Maybe I could keep my lines straighter if my hands weren't so cold,' the girl he was speaking to said. 'The wind comes in through the cracks around this crummy window. I'm so cold I'm one big shiver. I can't take it no more.'

'Fine by me,' Sam said. 'You don't have to take it. Get your things and go. You're out.'

'Wait a second.' Gina, the tall Italian girl, rose to her feet. She was almost the same size as Sam and she glared at him, eye to eye. 'You can't fire her because you don't heat this lousy place well enough for us to do our work.'

'I just did,' Sam said. 'You want to join her – fine by me too.'

'This place is too cold for anyone to work properly,' Gina said. 'It's a disgrace. Look at it. Nobody ever sweeps the floors. Nobody cleans the W.C. No light, no heat. We're treated no better than animals.'

Sam was still lounging against the window ledge with a lazy grin on his face. 'Like I said, anyone who don't like it can hit the road, anytime.'

'Fine,' Gina said. 'We take you up on your kind offer.' She looked around the room. 'You said it wasn't a good time to strike now. How much worse does it have to get? Look at our hands. We all got chilblains from the cold. Come on, girls. What are we waiting for? Let's show them.' Several girls had risen to their feet. 'You can tell Mr Mostel he better treat us nice if he wants his new designs in the stores anytime soon,' Gina said loudly, 'We're walking out. Let's go, everyone.'

Some girls jumped up, cheering, others lagged, looking at each other with scared faces, but in the end they were all on their feet, nobody wanting to be the last out of the door. I had no alternative but to rise to my feet with the rest of the girls. As they all surged forward to grab their bags and scarves from the hooks along the back wall, Sam pushed past and stood in the doorway.

'Nobody's going anywhere,' he bellowed in a threatening voice.

'You can't stop us, Sam,' someone shouted back.

'You wanna bet?' He leaped through the doorway and slammed the door shut. We heard the sound of bolts being shot. 'You ain't going nowhere till I get the boss,' he called through the door. 'You're going to sit there and stew.'

Then we heard the sound of his heavy boots running down stairs.

Girls began to whimper.

'Oh, *Mein Gott*, we're in trouble now.'

'He's gonna get the boss.'

'He's gonna bring the police.'

'We'll all be fired.'

'My papa will throw me out if I lose my job!'

The wail rose in different languages, most of which I couldn't understand, but understood anyway.

'They can't keep us in here against our will,' Sadie said, pushing through the crush of girls at the door. 'It's against the law. Let's see if we can break down that door.'

'You heard the bolts. We can't break through bolts,' some-one said.

A great mass of girls pressed around the door.

'I want to get out. I hate being locked in,' one little girl screamed from the middle of the crowd. She forced her way to the door and pounded on it. 'Let me out! Let me out!'

'They locked her in jail when she was a kid in Russia, then they shot her parents,' someone explained. 'No wonder she's scared.'

'Henny, calm down.' Gina grabbed at her, but Henny fought her off like a wild thing.

'Leave me be. I have to get out—'

There was a crash and the oil stove toppled to the floor. With a whoosh flame raced along the spilled oil, eating up the lint and scraps of fabric in its path. Panicked girls tried to get away, screaming as the flames reached them. A skirt blazed up and screams rose with it. Other girls batted out the flames with their shawls.

'Somebody get water,' someone was shouting and girls were already racing for the washroom. I was one of them, but there was nothing in there in which to carry water, except for an old tin mug.

Someone filled it and raced away in a futile attempt to put out the flames with four ounces of water.

'Soak some cloth,' I shouted. 'We can lay that on the flames to beat them down.'

We grabbed at the nearest bolt and tried to tear it, then slopped water over the whole thing, staggering out with it between us, like a battering ram.

But it was too late. Fueled by the debris on the floor the flames had caught at the first tables and the machine oil made them leap higher and fiercer. The whole area around the door was now on fire. Black smoke billowed out and the acrid smell drove us back, coughing and retching. The girls were huddled together like a flock of sheep, herded together and moving this way and that as the flames drove them.

'Maybe it will burn down the door and someone can rush through the flames to get help,' a voice suggested, but I couldn't imagine anyone volunteering to rush through those flames that now licked ceiling-high. Wooden rafters were blazing and crackling like a bonfire.

'They'll come up from downstairs to rescue us,' I heard someone saying.

'Perhaps they won't even know until it's too late,' I said. 'Fires don't spread downward. Let's see how we can get out of here.'

We ran across to the windows and tried to get them open, but the frames were buckled and they wouldn't budge. Besides, they only led to a daunting five-story drop.

'Come on, up to Mostel's office,' I shouted. The girls nearest me surged forward, fighting to be first up the stairs.

'Don't panic. Don't push!' I yelled over the screams and shouts. 'We don't want anyone getting trampled.'

Stinging, blinding smoke accompanied us up the stairs. With eyes streaming and smarting we burst into the office. There was one small window to one side. We opened it, but again it was useless – a sheer drop into the well between buildings.

Girls screamed from the window. 'Somebody help us!' But they were shouting to nobody in a useless well of blank walls.

We could feel the heat of the flames and the acrid black smoke coming up the stairs behind us now. Girls packed tighter and tighter, not wanting to be the last on the stairs. I tried to herd them back again, out of the office, but nobody was willing to retreat toward those flames.

'It's no good. There's nothing this way. We'll have to try the attic,' I yelled, 'and if that doesn't work we'll just have to break the windows and see if we can find any cloth long enough to lower ourselves to the street.'

'Lower ourselves to the street, are you crazy?' someone close to me screamed.

'Move!' I shouted, trying to close Mostel's office door enough to open the door to the attic hidden behind it, but nobody wanted to risk being shut in the office.

'Help me, Sadie!' I screamed and we literally pummeled and clawed girls out of the way to open the other door. When the girls saw that there was indeed another door and maybe a way of escape, they didn't fight us as much. We opened it and staggered up the stairs to be met by a frightened Katherine.

'What's happening? I can smell smoke.'

'Place is on fire. We have to get out,' I gasped. We were all finding it hard to breathe by now. The girls weren't screaming anymore, but coughing and moaning and praying. Ave Marias and Hebrew prayers rose simultaneously to the smoke-filled rafters.

'This is not good,' one of the girls groaned. 'Look at all this fabric. Look at the gauze and muslin. It will burn like crazy. We better get back down again and try the windows.'

'Wait,' Katherine shouted. 'There is a window at the end that leads onto the roof. We may be able to get out that way.'

She ran to the skylight at the far end. It was cut into the slanted roof above our heads. 'Help me push this table under it,' Katherine shouted as I ran to join her. We shoved the heavy table between us. She climbed up beside me and we pushed at the window with all our might. Just when I thought we were going to have to smash it, it came flying open.

'Give me a push.' I hoisted up my skirts and dragged myself out. The pitched roof of the attic ended in a broad flat strip of tarred rooftop.

'Come on, it's all right. We can get out this way,' I shouted back as smoke licked around my ankles. 'Help them up, Katherine. Give us your hands.'

'I'm not getting on no roof,' someone said but a little girl scrambled onto the table.

'I ain't waiting to be cooked like a chicken,' she said and reached up to me. Katherine shoved from below and I hauled her through the narrow window.

'Sit on your bottom and slide down gently to the flat part,' I said, then reached for the next one.

One after another we handed the girls out onto the roof until the flat area was jam-packed with terrified, sobbing bodies. Now I just prayed that the roof didn't collapse under the weight of them.

There was an explosion as glass blew out from a window on the floor below us and flames licked upward. Smoke billowed up toward us, making it hard to see.

'Where do we go now?' someone shrieked.

That was a good point. I hadn't had a chance to see how we might get off the rooftop.

'Hold on a minute. Katherine, you get the last few out,' I said and slithered down the slates myself, working my way through the crush of bodies. When I reached the end of the roof and turned the corner they followed me, like rats after the Pied Piper. We kept on going down the other side. I had hoped that this roof would join the next building somewhere, but it didn't. There was a six-foot gap between them. Safety was a few tantalizing feet away.

At the other end of the building there was a crash and sparks shot high into the air as part of the ceiling fell in. A collective scream arose again.

'We're going to be burned alive.'

One girl threw her leg over the parapet. 'I'm not waiting to fall into that,' she said. 'I'm ending it now.'

Katherine grabbed at her. 'Don't be stupid,' she said. 'We're going to get out of this. Listen – I can hear the fire engines.'

And it was true. In the distance we could hear bells ringing as fire engines galloped toward us. I looked at the flames, now licking up from all sides and knew that there was little the firemen could do. Even if they had ladders long enough, how could they put them through the flames to reach us? I stood at the parapet and looked at the rooftop on the next building. It was maybe less than six feet away and stacks of lumber were piled on it. If only I could get across –

Without hesitating any longer I unlaced my boots, undid my skirt, and pulled it off, then off came my petticoat until I stood there in my drawers and stockings. This produced a gasp of horror almost as great as the original flames had done. I climbed up on the parapet and heard screams behind me.

'Molly, don't do it,' someone called.

'I'll be fine.' I didn't feel fine. I had done some stupid things in my life, including jumping little ravines on the cliff tops, usually on a dare, but that was long ago now and I was out of practice for such stunts. I glanced down. My eyes were streaming from the smoke and all I could see was a blurred mass of upturned faces five floors below me beneath the drifting smoke. If I missed, it would be a quick death and maybe the girl had been right. Maybe it would be better than being burned alive.

I'm not usually a religious person – in fact definitely heathen, according to my mother – but I crossed myself hastily, just to make sure. 'Jesus, Mary, and Joseph and all the saints, just help me this time, not for myself but for those girls,' I whispered, 'and I promise I'll start going to mass again.' Then I took a deep breath and leaped. Cold air rushed past me, then my fingers grabbed onto the brickwork, my legs scrabbled, and for a second I teetered on the brink. Another shriek behind me as I hauled myself over the parapet and stood, safe and secure on the other rooftop. I rushed to the lumber and came up with a plank that I thought was long enough.

'Catch the other end,' I shouted, standing it up and then letting it fall in their direction.

Hands caught it as it fell. It reached, but only just. I ran back and found a second one, a little longer. Then a third. We had a bridge of precarious planks. I stood up on the parapet at one end.

'Come on, I'll help you,' I said.

Nobody moved.

'Look, any moment that roof is going to collapse and you'll all fall into the fire. Is that what you want?' I yelled, my voice harsh and scratchy from the smoke. I rubbed at my eyes and tried to focus as I set my balance.

'Come on, hurry up,' Katherine shouted, stepping up to steady her end of the plank.

After what seemed an age one girl climbed up, looked down, shrieked, and hastily got down again.

'Come across on all fours then,' I suggested. 'Crawl like a baby, only hurry.'

The girl tried again, this time hitching up her skirts and clambering across on hands and knees. When she reached safety she burst into tears. Another girl followed and soon there was a stream of frightened animals coming toward me on all fours. I shouted across to make sure they only came one at a time, as once the first girls had succeeded they all wanted to be next.

It was going well until Henny, the one whose panic had set off the whole thing, got to the middle. She looked down, then cowered, frozen on the middle of the planks.

'Henny, come on. Give me your hand,' I shouted. 'You're almost there. Hurry. The other girls are waiting.'

'I can't,' she whimpered.

There was nothing for it. I leaned over the side until I could grab at her hands, then I yanked her like a sack of potatoes. On the other side a cheer went up and girls started coming across again. The fire bells came closer until I could see a flash of red beneath us, but I didn't see how they could ever get a ladder up here. Hoses started spraying the lower floors, plunging us into clouds of billowing smoke that made the crossing impossible.

'Idiots!' Katherine shouted down. She started handing girls across to me, shouting at them to get a move on. It seemed to take forever. Every now and then there would be another crash, another roar as more of the building collapsed. My heart was beating so loudly, I'd swear you could hear it over the other noises. We'd never get them all across in time. I became a machine – reach out, grab girl, drag her to safety, reach out again. When I looked around behind me, the square roof was packed with girls. Only the last few remained on the other side.

'Hurry up, the roof's going!' I shouted. 'Run if you dare. Hold the plank steady, Katherine.'

We knelt on either end. A girl screamed as she ran across, but it was the same half-exhilarated scream that a roller-coaster produces. Another followed, then another. One girl froze. It was little Sarah and she held her lunch bag in one hand.

'Drop the bag, you'll be unbalanced!' I shouted, but she didn't obey. She just stood there, like a statue.

Sadie got up behind her and gave her a mighty shove that sent her staggering across to me. As I caught her she went sprawling. The bag fell from her grasp. Sheets of paper flew out over the parapet to be lost in the smoke. I caught a glimpse of a dress with a high frilly collar, another with a gentleman's bow tie. I turned to look at Sarah but she had melted into the crowd and I had more important things to take care of.

Four more girls, then at last I held out my hand for Sadie and Katherine.

'Well done. You did a marvelous job,' the latter said as she stepped down gracefully.

'So did you.'

'Good old British sangfroid. We don't lose our nerve like the continentals do.' She gave me a triumphant smile as we joined the crush of girls.

Then behind our backs came a great cracking sound. Flames shot up, making us all jump back and brush off the sparks that landed on us. We turned around to see the roof fall in. There were a few moments of panic when it looked as if the fire might spread to our building, but before that could happen a door onto our rooftop opened and a fireman appeared.

'They're all up here, Barney,' he shouted. 'They're safe.'

Weeping and hugging we made our way down the stairs, into the arms of relatives, friends, and well-wishers. Families snapped up daughters and mothers and whisked them away, weeping with joy. I looked around for Sarah. She was hurrying toward the outstretched arms of a frail-looking woman and a girl I recognized – the sister who worked for Lowenstein's. Little Fanny who looked as if she wouldn't hurt a fly. As I started to push my way through the crowd to reach them then I saw them hugging and kissing and I lost my nerve.

One by one girls were whisked away from me. I stared out through a blur of tears feeling suddenly alone and helpless. Then through the crowd I thought I saw Daniel's face and started toward him.

Suddenly I heard someone shouting my name.

'Molly!' I spun around to see Jacob running toward me. 'Molly, I've been looking everywhere. Thank God.'

I had thought the tears in my eyes were just from the smoke. Now I knew they weren't. I fell into his arms, blubbing. His arms were warm and strong around me and I lay my head against his shoulder, feeling safe.

'This is enough,' he said, stroking my hair. 'I can't take any more of this. I want you to marry me right away, so that I can look after you.'

At any other moment I would have told him that I could look after myself very nicely thank you, but I had to admit it sounded most appealing.

'Your mother won't approve,' was all I could think of saying.

'She'll have to learn to accept it, won't she? And who could not learn to love you, Molly?'

I looked up into his face. He was smiling at me with infinite tenderness. To be cherished and protected – what more could any woman want? I felt a warm glow spreading all through me.

'Now we had better get me home before your mother learns that I was on the street in my underwear,' I said.

Jacob eyed me. 'At least I know that you have good legs before I sign the wedding document,' he said, still smiling. 'Most Jewish men are not so fortunate.'

'How did you know I'd be here?' I asked, as my brain started to clear.

'I've been keeping an eye on you. I had a feeling you'd be doing something else stupid.'

'I didn't intend this to be dangerous,' I said. 'They locked us in. A stove was knocked over and the place was a complete firetrap. It was an accident that could have happened anywhere.'

'It wasn't deliberate then?'

'No, of course not.'

269

'But I thought Mostel was responsible for Katherine's disappearance?'

Katherine – I had forgotten all about her. I looked around and saw her sitting on a doorstep, all alone, looking as shocked and bewildered as I had been. I took Jacob's hand.

'Over here,' I said. 'There's someone I want you to meet.'

She rose to her feet as we approached her.

'Jacob,' I said. 'This is Katherine.'

Twenty-six

'Katherine?' Jacob looked from her face to mine. 'You found her? You mean she didn't drown then?'

'Obviously not.'

'Why did you think I had drowned?' Katherine asked.

Spray from fire hoses and flying particles from the fire coated us in a sooty rain.

'The police told us that a woman resembling your picture had been pulled from the East River,' I said.

'My picture? How did you get my picture?' She looked completely bewildered.

'Your father sent it to me,' I said. 'I am an investigator. He hired me to track you down.'

The bewilderment was replaced by a look of utter horror. 'Then you weren't – I mean, we thought the woman who—'

'The young woman who discovered you?' I said, suddenly putting the pieces together. 'Her name was Nell Blankenship. She was trying to find out what happened to you after you disappeared from Mostel's. We suspected foul play, you see.' As I spoke it was my turn to go cold all over. I had just taken in the implication of her words. 'You thought she was the detective,' I said.

She nodded. 'We got word from Michael's cousin who also

worked for my father that a woman detective had been dispatched to find us. Naturally we thought . . .'

'So you killed her?' I demanded angrily.

'Not me. Of course not.'

'The Eastmans then.'

She shook her head, a look of bleak despair on her face. 'Not the Eastmans. The man I married, Michael Kelly.'

Jacob forced his way through the crowd, stepped out into the street, and flagged down a cab. The driver looked at us in horror. 'You're not thinking of putting them young ladies on my clean seat, are you?' he asked.

'They've just been rescued from the fire,' Jacob said. 'Surely you don't want them to have to walk home in their condition. What if they were your own daughters?' He reached into his pocket. 'There will be an extra dollar to aid with the cleanup,' he said.

The cabby's eyes widened as Jacob produced the dollar bill. 'You're right, sir. We couldn't expect them to walk in their condition, could we?' he said with a grin. Jacob opened the door and bundled us inside. As we drove away I glanced out of the window and again I thought I caught a glimpse of Daniel's face in the crowd.

The cab made its way slowly through the great crush of people. I looked back but Daniel's face had gone. I turned back to Katherine, who was sitting tight-lipped, staring straight ahead of her.

'You say that Michael was the one who killed Nell Blankenship? Couldn't you have stopped him?' I asked as the cab got up speed and turned into the Bowery.

'I had no idea.' She hugged her arms to herself, shivering. 'My God, don't you think I would have stopped him if I had known what he was going to do? She found out where we were hiding. Michael had done some work for the Eastmans,

272

so they let us hide out in a shed behind their headquarters. This woman came and she asked questions about me. Mike thought that—' She bit her lip, looking younger and more fragile than her photograph. 'He said he'd take care of her. I never dreamed . . . then he came back and told me he'd killed her by mistake and we'd have to stay hidden until we could make a run for it and go out West where they'd never find us.'

'What I don't understand,' Jacob said, 'is why it was so terrible that the detective found you? You are a married woman, after all. Your parents might be annoyed but legally there is not much they can do.'

Katherine sank her head into her hands. 'You don't know the half of it,' she said.

'Don't worry about that now,' I said. 'I'll hide you where you'll be safe.'

The cab driver reined in his horse and poked his head down to us. 'Patchin Place did you say, sir? I don't want to take the horse all the way down, on account of how it's hard to back him up again.'

'That's fine. We can walk a few yards,' I said.

Jacob jumped down first and handed us down from the cab. Katherine looked around her. 'This is nice,' she said. 'It reminds me of London. Quite different from the New York I have seen up to now.'

We walked the length of Patchin Place and stopped outside Number Nine. I knocked on the front door. Sid opened it, looked at me, then her jaw dropped open.

'Molly – what in God's name have you been doing to yourself?'

I had quite forgotten that I had no skirt or petticoat on, that I was dirty and covered in soot. Katherine didn't look much better.

273

'We were in a fire,' I said. 'We got trapped and we had to climb out over the rooftops.'

'Mercy me.' For once Sid sounded less sophisticated than usual. 'Come inside, do. I'll find the brandy and I'll get Gus to run you a hot bath. What an awful experience for you.'

Her eyes moved past me to Jacob and Katherine. 'You were in the fire too?'

'Katherine was. I was merely the comforting shoulder afterward,' Jacob said.

'Katherine?' Sid's eyes opened wide. '*The* Katherine?'

'*The* Katherine.'

'But I thought she had drowned.'

'Does everyone in New York know about me?' Katherine asked uncertainly.

'Only my very closest friends,' I said. I looked up at Sid. 'I want to ask you a favor.'

'Other than a hot bath and a good meal?'

'I want to ask you to hide Katherine for a few days. Her husband is trying to find her and that would not be a good idea.'

'Then for God's sake don't stand there on the doorstep. Get inside.' Sid grabbed at Katherine's shoulder and yanked her into the house. 'Gus, dearest,' she called, 'you'll never believe who has come to visit!'

Gus came running down the stairs, wearing a painter's smock, brandishing a paintbrush and with a smudge of orange on her nose.

'Molly, what on earth have you been doing to yourself? Are you making a protest against the wearing of skirts, a la bloomer?'

'I had to abandon it in a fire,' I said.

'When she jumped from rooftop to rooftop,' Katherine said. 'She was fearless.'

Gus's gaze turned to Katherine.

'This is Katherine,' I said.

'*The* Katherine,' Sid added.

'Resurrected from the dead?' Gus asked.

'Never died in the first place. Went underground. Wicked husband,' Sid said. 'Wants us to hide her.'

I smiled at Sid's succinct account. That pretty much summed it up.

'Well of course we'll hide her, but let's clean her up first,' Gus said.

'May I suggest brandy for shock first,' Jacob said.

'Oh, Mr Singer. I didn't notice you standing there,' Gus said. 'Were you part of this amazing exploit?'

'He was there at the fire, looking for me, worried sick,' I said.

'You can't imagine how powerless and wretched I felt, watching the building go up in flames and being kept away by the fire crews,' Jacob said. 'And then she was one of the last girls to come down from the next building. I don't ever want to go through that again.'

'He wants to marry me,' I said in response to Sid's raised eyebrow.

'And do you want to marry him?' Sid's voice sounded sharp. 'Not that I am against the principle of marriage for the rest of the world, but . . .'

'I think I might,' I said, smiling shyly at Jacob.

'Could do worse, I suppose.' Sid gave Jacob an appraising glance. 'At least he won't try to put you into a glass case like a stuffed bird.'

'I don't know about that.' Jacob laughed. 'It may well be the only way of keeping her out of trouble.'

'You do have a point there,' Gus agreed. 'She does seem to attract trouble, I'll agree. Molly dearest, you haven't told us how you came to be involved in a fire in the first place.'

We sat at the kitchen table, sipping brandy, while I told the whole story of the fire.

'I must be confused, but I don't quite see how Katherine comes into a fire at Mostel's. I thought she left there weeks ago,' Gus said.

'I ran away from Michael and Sadie hid me in Mostel's attic,' Katherine said.

'You ran away from your husband because he ill-treated you?'

'No, he didn't ill-treat me, but I couldn't stay with a cold-blooded murderer.' She filled in the gaps, including what she knew about Nell's murder. It can't have been easy for her and Sid and Gus nodded with sympathy.

'One thing I don't understand,' Sid said. 'If you were married, then there's nothing much your father could have done about it, is there? He couldn't have forced you to come home.'

'I asked that same question,' Jacob said.

Katherine sighed. 'I lied about my age. I lied about almost everything to get married. For all I know the marriage isn't valid at all. But it wasn't myself we were worried about, it was Michael. I knew he was with the freedom fighters in Ireland and that was one of the things that made him attractive to me. I thought it was wonderful to be passionate about a just cause. I mean, we English really have no right to rule Ireland, do we?'

She looked at me as if wanting my personal forgiveness.

'It's not your fault,' I said. 'You were born to it. You didn't choose it.'

'Go on about Michael,' Sid said. 'You say he was a freedom fighter.'

'I knew that he loved danger, but I thought that he was also noble and good. After I married him I found out that he loved violence. He had killed a police officer when the police tried to break up a demonstration. He was proud of it. And I found out something else too – he only married me as a way of getting his hands on some money and leaving Ireland in a hurry.' She put her hands over her mouth and sat fighting with emotion for a moment, then composed herself again. 'I have been such a fool,' she said.

'So Michael was scared that he could be sent back to Ireland to stand trial for killing a policeman,' I said.

'Of course. And then this second killing. I couldn't abide it any longer.'

'So you ran away from him.'

'Not at first,' she said. 'He told me that I'd be an accessory to the murder. He'd tell everyone that it was my idea and that I had egged him on, so I'd hang with him. I didn't know what to do. Then – then something else happened.'

'Another murder?' I asked.

'In a way,' she said. 'One of the reasons I agreed to marry Michael and flee to America with him was because I was expecting his child. I knew how ashamed my parents would be and I couldn't face them. After Michael killed that young woman, I miscarried. It was awful – and you know what Michael said when it was all over? He said, "Well at least that's one stroke of luck, isn't it? Now we won't be saddled with a brat."' She gave a big, shuddering sigh. 'I had just lost my baby.'

Without warning she began to cry, hiding her face in her hands before mastering herself again. 'I promised myself I wouldn't give in to self-pity,' she said.

I reached out and put my hand on her shoulder.

'Don't worry, Katherine, you'll be safe now,' I said.

'You're going to turn me over to my father.'

'You don't want to go home?'

'No, of course not,' she said. 'I hated that life – the boredom

277

was awful. Hunting and parties and then over to London for more parties and inane chatter. I don't ever want to go back to that.'

'Your parents are very worried about you. I understand your mother is an invalid.'

'When it suits her,' Katherine said. 'So will you tell my father?'

'Your father is my client,' I said. 'I shall have to write and tell him that I've found you, safe and sound. What you do after that is up to you, although I beg you to write to them yourself and ask for their forgiveness.'

'It sounds to me that the marriage wasn't legal,' Jacob said. 'And if you're underage, they could demand that you come back to them.'

'Then I shall go somewhere where they can't find me until I turn twenty-one. I shall be quite a rich woman then.'

'How will you manage until then?'

'I don't know,' she said. 'I can't think about that now. My concern at this moment is that Michael doesn't find me. I know he's been looking for me.'

'He still loves you then?' Gus asked.

'I doubt if he ever loved me. He wants me with him for his own protection. I am a bartering tool – not much more.'

'You should tell the police what you know about Michael,' Jacob said.

'Turn in my own husband, you mean?' She shook her head. 'I can't do that. However he has behaved toward me, I really loved him. I believed him when he said he loved me. I was carrying his child. I can't betray him now.'

'Even if he wants to hurt you?' I demanded.

She shook her head. 'I'm sure he doesn't mean me harm. He's just frightened at the moment. He doesn't know where to go. He doesn't know whether he can trust me or not.' She grabbed at my arm suddenly. 'You won't tell the police about him, promise me that. Not until I've decided what I must do next.'

'All right,' I said. 'We will say nothing until you've made up your own mind. But he killed somebody, Katherine. He killed a good woman. You can't expect us to sit by and do nothing. You know in your heart that you have to tell them.'

Katherine sighed. 'I know. I'm so confused and so frightened – I don't know what I feel anymore. But I did love him once.'

'But you are afraid for your life. You can't go on living this way,' Jacob said angrily. 'The man must be brought to justice.'

'The man is a brute. You were quite right to leave him,' Sid said.

'Don't worry, you'll be safe here. He'll never be able to find you. Our lips are sealed,' Gus added.

'Thank heavens for that. Now we can all relax,' Jacob said. It turned out he wasn't one hundred percent right.

An hour or so later we were bathed, changed, and restored. Sid and Gus insisted on feeding us. After a large filling meal of roast beef, cabbage, and potatoes (the Moroccan phase having begun to wane), Jacob took his leave reluctantly.

'You're sure you will be all right now?'

'You've said that a dozen times. How could I possibly not be all right? I am among friends and my own home is across the street, complete with large male bodyguard. Nobody would think of looking for Katherine here. We will sleep soundly tonight, believe me.'

He went then. I crossed the street to my own house and returned with pen and paper.

'I am writing to your father, Katherine,' I said. 'I will limit

279

my news to telling him that I have found you safe and sound if you will complete the letter yourself.'

She chewed on her lip. 'But he'll come after me as soon as he gets the letter.'

'Then tell him not to.'

'You don't know my father. He was used to ordering men around in the army for most of his life. He expects everyone else to salute and obey – wife and daughter included.'

'Tell him that you have left Michael Kelly and it appears that your marriage might not be legal – that will make him happy. Then tell him that you are not ready to come home yet, but will keep in touch from now on. He can't ask for more.'

Still she hesitated.

'Katherine, if it were your child and you were desperately worried about her, wouldn't you want to get a message from her, saying that she was safe?'

She nodded and sat at the table. She blotted and folded the letter before I could read it and thrust it into an envelope.

'That's done then,' she said.

She put her hand instinctively to her throat.

'You used to wear a locket,' I said.

She nodded. 'My grandmother's.'

'What happened to it? How did Mr Mostel get his hands on it?'

'We needed money. Michael told me to pawn it. I asked Mr Mostel if I could pawn it to him. He gave me twenty dollars for it. Not nearly enough but it kept us going. Michael drank most of the money away, of course. I wonder if it was still in Mostel's office and it burned in the fire.'

'No, it's safe,' I said, 'and I may be able to get it back for you.'

Her face lit up. 'Really?'

'I can't promise anything, but I'll try.'

She jumped up and hugged me. 'Molly, you are a miracle worker.'

'I must go home now,' I said. 'Keep out of sight and let my two trusty friends take care of you. You'll be quite safe with them.'

'I'm sure I shall.' Katherine looked around her. 'In fact I shall be so comfortable here that I may never want to leave.'

I smiled as I walked to the front door. I had the same warm feelings about 9 Patchin Place. I hadn't wanted to leave either. My little home across the street still felt like a bleak substitute, but at least I didn't have to worry that Shamey and Bridie were living in an unbearable slum.

I stepped out into the night and pulled my wrap around me as I crossed the street. As I went to open my front door a figure stepped out of the shadows and an arm grabbed me.

I opened my mouth to scream, but no sound came out.

'It's only me,' Daniel's voice said.

'Holy Mother of God! My heart nearly jumped right out of my chest,' I said.

Daniel stepped out of the shadows into the light of the street lamp. 'I had to see you. I've just called at your house but they said you weren't home.'

'I was across the street with Sid and Gus,' I said. 'What do you mean by scaring me half to death?'

'I heard about the fire. I got there just in time to see you in the arms of that Singer fellow. Before I could reach you, you went off in a cab with him.'

'I was naturally upset, having just escaped from being burned to death. Jacob comforted me.'

'Ah, so that's all it was. That's fine then.' The lines of concern had melted from his face. Anger welled up inside me.

'No, that's not all it was. I think you should know that he's asked me to marry him.'

He looked at me for a second, then laughed. 'Of course you're not going to marry him.'

'Oh, and why not, pray? Does the New York police force have jurisdiction over marriages these days?'

'You're not going to marry him because you don't love him.'

'How do you know that I don't love him?'

'Because you love me and you can't love two people at once.'

'I *loved* you,' I corrected. 'But I grew tired of waiting. Almost a year has gone by, Daniel, and still you haven't told Miss Norton of my existence.'

The flickering light of the gas lamp lit his face. He was wearing his greatcoat with the collar turned up and the wind tugged at his unruly curls. As usual the physical attraction of the man was overwhelming. I fought it.

'The time has never been right, Molly. I work so darned hard that I barely have time to sleep. I have hardly seen Miss Norton for months and, when I do see her, the time just goes before I can pluck up courage. I told you it has to be done properly. If I make her feel betrayed, she will stop at nothing until she has ruined me completely and utterly. She might appear sweet but she has a ruthless streak in her nature.'

'If you chose such a person to marry – your advancement must indeed mean a lot to you.'

'I was a young man when I first proposed to her. She seemed sweet and delicate and all that a man could want in a wife.'

'Rich too, of course. And influential.'

'That was taken into consideration. But I didn't have a chance to see any of her faults until later.'

'And now it seems you would rather live with her faults than risk her wrath. That doesn't say much for your character.'

'I agree. I have been a hopeless coward where this is

concerned. I just beg you, do not do anything rash to spite me.'

'If I marry Jacob, it will not be to spite you. It will be because he is kind and caring and honorable and will take good care of me.'

'When did you ever need anyone to take care of you?' That roguish smile crossed his lips.

'Maybe I have had enough of trying to fend for myself. And I can help him with his work too. He is making a difference, Daniel.'

'And I am not?'

'Of course you are, but Jacob does his work for love, and you do yours for ambition. He could make a lot of money from his photographs but chooses to take pictures to arouse the public conscience. He is actively seeking to better the lot of those poor people who have no voice of their own. It's a noble cause.'

'But not your cause. I don't see you as a rabid socialist by nature,' Daniel said. 'When your enthusiasm wanes, what will you have left then?'

'Mutual respect and affection.'

'Is that enough, Molly?'

'It may have to be, Daniel. If you came to me tomorrow and told me that you were free of your engagement and asked me to marry you, I might well consider it, but I do not intend to become an elderly spinster while I sit at home waiting.'

'You could always have written to Miss Norton yourself. That would have brought matters to a head.'

I shook my head. 'Oh no, Daniel. Either you come to me willingly, freely, and with your whole heart, or not at all. It has to be your choice and yours alone. You should go now. The night is cold to be standing outside.'

'You could ask me in.'

'That wouldn't be proper, would it? Word might get back to my fiancé.'

As I went to walk past him he grabbed my arm and swung me around to face him. 'Don't do this to me, Molly. Don't taunt me this way.'

'I assure you, sir, that I take matters of the heart very earnestly. If you think my decision to marry Jacob is merely to taunt you, then you are wrong. If I commit to him, I commit wholeheartedly, and with full knowledge of what I am giving up.'

He grasped at my shoulders, his fingers digging into my flesh. 'Don't give up on me, Molly, please.'

'Let go of me.' I shook myself free. 'You're not going to soften me up with your sweet-talking blarney anymore. I'm getting on with my own life without you and I'm doing just fine.'

'Apart from almost getting yourself burned to death in a fire, shot at, captured by gangsters, and arrested for prostitution?'

'Apart from those, yes.'

I looked at him and he started to laugh. I had to smile too.

'I love you, Molly Murphy,' he said softly, then he reached out to stroke my cheek.

'Good night, Daniel,' I said somewhat shakily, then I fled inside the door before I could weaken. Once inside I stood in the doorway with my hand to that cheek where his hand had been.

Twenty-seven

It was an unaccustomed luxury to rise with the sun the next morning, to dress and breakfast in leisure, and to get a kiss from the children as they went off to school.

'I'm glad you're not going to that horrid place anymore, Molly,' Bridie said, wrapping her little arms around my neck. 'It was no fun when you weren't here. All we had to eat was dripping toast and Shamey bullied me.'

'Well, I'm going to bully you now,' I said, stroking her hair fondly. 'And my first command is to bring me your hairbrush. You have a knot the size of Galway Bay in the back of your hair. And you, Shamey, haven't washed your neck in a week. Go and do it now.'

'Tough guys don't need to wash their necks,' he muttered as he made for the scullery.

I waved as they ran off to school.

'They're turning out just grand, aren't they?' I asked Seamus, who had come into the room.

'Thanks to your help. Who knows where they'd have been if we had stayed with Nuala in the tenement? I wish there was some way to repay you, Molly. I'm doing my best to find a job, really I am. I'm seeing a man today at the department store called Macy's. Do you know of it? They say it's very

285

grand. They take on extra help for the Christmas season – carrying packages for ladies and the like.'

'You'll be back on your feet soon enough.'

He nodded as if he didn't really believe this. 'I've only ever been a laborer, you see, and now I don't think I've the strength to swing a pick and shovel.'

'You'll find something, Seamus. Don't worry about it. I've just concluded two cases, so I'll have money coming in.'

As I said that, a smile spread across my face. Two cases solved. I had become a real detective. I would go and collect my fee today. I thought it only fair to confront Sarah first and verify the truth about those papers I had seen. I had been wrong about things before – just occasionally.

I had no idea where Sarah lived, or Mr Mostel either. I headed for the garment factory because I couldn't think of any other sensible starting point. As I approached along Canal Street I saw that a small crowd was still gathered around the burned-out shell of the building. Men were dragging out sorry-looking pieces of furniture from the cabinetmaker on the ground floor. On the sidewalk were stacked bolts of waterlogged, singed cloth. It was a sorry sight. I noticed that several of my fellow workers were standing among the crowd, staring at the building as if they couldn't believe what they saw. Then Seedy Sam emerged from the ruined doorway, shaking his head. He spotted me and pointed his finger accusingly.

'It was you, wasn't it? You and that Sadie girl – you started the fire deliberately because I locked you in. I knew you were trouble from the first day.'

I marched right up to him. 'We started the fire?' I demanded 'Is that what your addled brain has been thinking? We were almost burned alive in that firetrap. It was only sheer luck that we got out.'

'You probably didn't mean it to burn up the whole building – just drawing attention to yourselves.'

'The fire started because one of the little girls panicked at the thought of being locked in and she knocked over one of those unsafe oil stoves. You'll be lucky that you're not arrested after we've told the police how you locked us in.'

'Me – arrested?' He stepped away, his eyes darting around the crowd. 'I didn't do anything against the law.'

'I'd say holding people prisoner against their will might be grounds for arrest,' I said, looking at the other girls in the crowd. 'What do you think?'

The crowd made angry murmurs.

'I was just doing my duty, doing right by Mr Mostel.'

'I hope that's how he sees it, because I'm on my way to visit him now, and you can be sure I'll let him know how you locked us in – just as we'll be letting the newspapers know all the details too.'

He seemed to deflate like a balloon. 'I'm just the foreman,' he said. 'They can't pin anything on me.' And he hurried off. The girls looked at me and laughed.

'Are you really going to tell the police and the news-papers?' one of them asked.

'I might. In fact I probably should, shouldn't I? It would make people aware of how badly we've been treated. Maybe some good will come of it.' I decided to visit Jacob as soon as I'd settled the matter with Sarah.

'Do any of you know where Sarah lives? The frail-looking girl from Russia – quiet as a mouse?'

'Oh that one.' One of the girls nodded. 'She lives on Hester. Two buildings from us.'

I noted the address in my little book. 'And what about Mr Mostel?' I asked.

'You're going to see him too?'

'I might – just to tell him what I think of him and his fire-trap,' I said. 'Does anyone know where he lives?'

'Oh sure. We go to supper there every Shabbat,' one of the girls said with a laugh.

'He lives on the Upper East Side,' someone else said. 'Right by the park. Fancy schmancy. I saw him when I went uptown to the zoo once. He came out of a side street, right across from the zoo. He was riding in his carriage with his family. Very grand.'

'Thanks,' I said.

'Are you really going to see him? You sure have *chutz-pah*, Molly. I bet he throws you out.' I heard them calling after me as I made my way toward Hester Street. Of all the Lower East Side, Hester Street was the most bustling street of commerce. Pushcarts made through traffic impossible. It was hard enough for a pedestrian to squeeze between them. Everything from fish to old clothes, from the lyrics to popular Yiddish songs to roasting sweet corn, all crammed in along the sidewalk. I picked up my skirts and stepped daintily through the debris. Sarah's building was above a kosher butcher shop and the dead animal smell accompanied me up the stairs. I knocked on the front door. It was Sarah's narrow little face that peeped through the crack in the opened door.

'Molly! What are you doing here?'

'Just come to pay you a visit, Sarah.'

She opened the door wide. 'Come in, please. This is so nice of you.' She led me into a small room, that clearly comprised their living space. On one wall was a shelf of pots and dishes. There was a crude bench and table. Possessions were stacked in orange crates and blankets and quilts were folded in a corner. A pale woman sat in the one good chair, a rug over her knees. In the poor light her skin looked almost gray and was so shrunk around her bones that she looked like a marble statue sitting there. Sarah's sister Fanny sat on an upturned crate at her feet. The place was damp and cold, the wallpaper peeling to show black holes in the walls. It was about the most sorry sight I had seen since coming to America.

'Mama, this is Molly who works with me,' Sarah said, then repeated it in Yiddish in case her mother hadn't understood. 'She was wonderful. She jumped across the roof, like in a circus.'

Sarah's mother said something. Sarah nodded. 'Mama says you must have some tea with us. She is sorry we have no cake or sugar.'

'Oh no, don't make tea specially for me . . .'

'Of course you must have tea.' Sarah filled a pan from a jug, then put it onto a little spirit stove.

I sat on the bench and looked around again. On the shelf and the walls were some fine little charcoal sketches – street scenes and street urchins.

'You must be the artist, Sarah,' I said.

'My sister Fanny also draws well,' Sarah said. 'We had a tutor in Russia who had studied in Paris. He taught us well. He said we both had a gift.'

'That must have made copying Mostel's designs easy for you then.'

The girls both jumped as if they had been burned.

'What do you mean?' Sarah asked.

'I saw those pages that floated away yesterday. They were Mr Mostel's new designs. You were going to hand them to your sister to take to Lowenstein's, weren't you?'

Sarah glanced swiftly around the room. 'Please. Not here. Mama doesn't know. She doesn't understand much English, but – step outside, please.'

I followed her out of the front door. 'So I copied his

designs,' she said, lifting her little chin defiantly. 'Serve him right, mean old man.'

'But Sarah, he was employing you.'

'I was slaving for him,' she said venomously. Quite a transformation from the meek little mouse who had worked beside me. 'He deserves what he gets. He wouldn't let my sister work with me. He said no families, bad for business, so she had to find work with Lowenstein. Then Mr Lowenstein found out I was working for Mostel and he tell us he pay good money if we find out what Mostel's new designs look like.'

'You must have known that was wrong?'

'Wrong? Ha! I tell you something – I wasn't going to do it. I say to Fanny we are from good family. We do not resort to stealing like common peasants. And that very next day my mother is taken bad. We have to send for the doctor. The doctor wants paying right away. I come in to work an hour late and the foreman says to me, "If you're gonna come in late again, don't bother showing up." He wouldn't even listen. So I thought – why not? We did it last season and Lowenstein give us fifty dollars. Fifty dollars – can you imagine? We could buy Mama good food, we could pay the rent and the doctor bills.'

'But you were cheating your employer.'

'Oh, and he never cheated us? Ten cents for sneezing. Ten cents for going to the washroom, for coming back one minute late from lunch. And don't think we didn't know about turning back the clock hands to get extra minutes out of us. We were cheated every single day, so don't preach to me about cheating.' She looked at me, suddenly suspicious. 'Why do you want to know this? Are you some kind of church lady preacher?'

I shook my head. 'No, I was hired by Mr Mostel to find out who was stealing his designs.'

'So you're going to go and tell him you've found out?'

'I have to.'

'And then what? We get arrested and go to jail and our mother will die. That's good American justice. They killed my father and brothers in Russia, you know. We came here with nothing – we left everything in Russia: clothes, jewelry, books, all left behind. Our mother has been sick ever since.'

'I'm really sorry,' I said. 'I'll do what I can for you. I'll make Mostel agree not to press charges, if you promise me you won't do it again.'

'Won't do it again?' She laughed bitterly. 'I won't be stealing Mostel's designs again because there is no Mostel's. We'll be trying to live on Fanny's six dollars a week and we're going to starve and Mama's going to die.'

'I really am sorry. If I could do something, I would. Perhaps another shop will take you on.'

'Me and fifty other girls. Oh sure.'

'I should go,' I said. 'Give my respects to your mother. I hope her health improves.'

Without saying a word she turned and went back into the room. I heard her telling them in Yiddish that I didn't want any tea.

I felt really sick as I descended the stairs to busy Hester Street. Here, down below that one room, life was going on merrily – housewives bargaining over herrings and chickens, little boys throwing mud balls at each other, a monkey dancing on an organ grinder's shoulder. Should I just forget the whole thing and let Mostel think that I hadn't found his spy? If I made personal judgements about each case that I undertook, I wouldn't be making much money in my chosen profession. I had to learn to keep myself remote. I had been hired to do a job. I had done that job and now my duty was to report my findings to my employer.

I couldn't help feeling like a heel as I rode the Third Avenue El north to the Upper East Side where I had been told Mr Mostel lived. It was always a shock going from the Lower East Side to another part of the city. The sensation was like Alice falling down a rabbit hole and finding herself in another world. There were mansions facing the park with the occasional horse and carriage waiting patiently outside a front door. A maid was scrubbing front steps. A nanny walked past pushing a high English perambulator. On a street across from the zoo I found a mailman delivering letters. Luckily he was an observant mailman and directed me to East Sixty-third.

I found the house easily enough – an elegant brownstone, four floors high. This was what the sweat of his laborers had bought for Mr Mostel and his family. It was hard to feel too sorry for his current disaster.

I pulled back my shoulders with resolution and went up the front steps. The door was opened by a stiffly starched maid.

'Miss Murphy to see Mr Mostel.'

'Mr Mostel senior or junior?' she asked, trying to size me up with a haughty stare.

'Senior. I have been carrying out a commission from him.'

'I'm afraid he is not at home at present, but he is expected shortly. If you would care to wait?'

'Thank you.' I stepped into the welcoming warmth of the front hall. I wasn't sure that my nerves would hold up to waiting, but it seemed stupid to have come all this way for nothing. I was shown into a small sitting room, obviously a front parlor for visitors as the fire wasn't lit. I sat on a brocade chair and waited. A clock ticked loudly on the mantelpiece, otherwise there was no sound, no hint that a family lived in this house. I wondered about Mrs Mostel and what she might be doing.

Then, after what seemed an eternity, I heard footsteps on

the stairs. The footsteps came toward me and Ben Mostel came into the room. He froze when he saw who was sitting there.

'You. What are you doing here?'

'I'm here to see your father.'

Another look of pure terror. 'You're not going to tell him, are you? About the checks, I mean. Because I don't make a habit of it and—'

'I'm not here to tell him about what I saw,' I said. In midsentence I saw my opportunity. 'If you can do me a favor,' I added.

'A favor? It's no good asking me for cash. As you have observed, I am constantly hard up.'

'It's not cash I want. It's the return of that locket to its rightful owner. It belonged to her grandmother and it means a lot to her.'

'But I can't ask Letitia for it back.'

'If you could maybe substitute another piece of jewelry and explain the locket's history, I'm sure she could be persuaded.'

Ben sucked in air through his teeth. 'Another piece of jewelry. That means money, which I don't seem to have at the moment.'

'Then the promise of another piece. You gave her something which was not yours to give. You helped yourself to what you found in your father's drawer. The piece was only being pawned with the expectation of being retrieved.'

'I just don't see how—'

'Then I shall be forced to tell your father what you did. I may also be forced to mention the checks.'

He paced nervously. 'All right. I'll do what I can. Where can I find you?'

'My card.' I handed it to him.

He glanced at it. 'Discreet investigations? You're actually a

293

professional dick? So that's why you were snooping around. Detecting what, may one ask?'

'Something I have come to share with your father, as soon as he returns.'

As if on cue the front door opened. 'Millie – my hat and gloves!' a voice boomed. He spied us through the half-opened door and came through, his hat and gloves still in his hand. 'Miss Murphy.' He looked surprised.

'Mr Mostel.'

'I'm sorry I wasn't home to receive you.'

'Your son was keeping me well amused, thank you.' I glanced at Ben whose eyes were riveted to my face.

'At least the boy is good for something then,' Mostel said. 'Off you go then, boy. With your father out of work, it will be up to you to support the family from now on.' Then he laughed at Ben's stricken face.

'Very droll, Papa,' Ben said. 'Now if you will excuse me. A pleasure talking to you, Miss Murphy.'

'And you too, Mr Mostel. I look forward to hearing your future – news.'

Ben nodded and beat a hasty retreat.

'If we really did have to rely on the boy, we'd all starve,' Mostel said genially as he pulled up a chair. 'Now to what do I owe the pleasure of this visit?'

I took a deep breath, was about to tell him, and changed my mind at the last moment. 'I came to express my condolences at the loss of your factory.'

He nodded. 'A sad business, Miss Murphy.'

'It is indeed. I hope you were insured.'

'Naturally, but what use is insurance money? I'll have lost the profits from the holiday season by the time I'm up and running again.'

'And your workers will have lost their income for the whole

holiday season too, which for them will mean going without food and heat.'

'That is naturally regrettable. Let us hope they find jobs with other shops.'

'You will be rebuilding again, surely?'

'I was only renting space so that decision is not mine to make. I rather think that I will reopen across the bridge in Brooklyn. Plenty of room to expand over there and a work-force ready and waiting.'

'And your old workforce?'

'Is welcome to reapply if they care to ride the trolley across the bridge. But I rather think I'll take Mrs Mostel to Florida for the winter before we make any plans. New York doesn't agree with her delicate constitution.'

I studied him sitting there relaxed and smiling, with his tailored suit and its velvet collar and his gold watch chain strung across his vest and I thought of Sarah's one room. My conscience whispered that I should just keep quiet about what I had found out. On the other hand, I was damned if he'd get away without paying me.

I took a deep breath and plunged right in. 'I came today because I found out which of your girls was spying for Lowenstein.'

A broad shrug of his hands. 'As if that's any use to me now, Miss Murphy. Lowenstein will have the Christmas market to himself and *mazeltov* to him.'

'I also came to collect my fee.'

This jolted him from his complacency. 'Your fee? You expect me to pay you now when I have become a penniless beggar out on the street with no income?'

'Enough income to take Mrs Mostel to Florida for the winter.'

'But, Miss Murphy, surely you must see that—'

'Mr Mostel,' I interrupted. 'Did you or did you not hire me to find the spy in your midst? Did we not shake hands over the deal?'

'We did, Miss Murphy, but circumstances have changed.'

'The deal, as I remember it, was for me to ferret out the spy. I have done so.'

'Give me the girl's name then, Miss Murphy and I will hand it over to the police.'

'You'd have a hard time proving anything, Mr Mostel. The evidence went up in flames in the fire – the fire started by your inadequate and ancient heating system, I might add.'

He spread his hands again, a little happier now. 'With no evidence, you expect me to pay you?'

I nodded. 'Because I can guarantee that it will never happen to you again.'

'Of course it will never happen to me again. I'll be over in Brooklyn.'

'And I can tell you how it was done, so that you'll know what to look out for next time.'

'Ah.' He paused.

'And I think you would like your family to consider you a man of his word,' I added for good measure.

Another pause then a heavy sigh. 'Very well, Miss Murphy. If you wish to take the last penny from my starving children, go ahead. Ruin me. I'll be sending you a check if you care to present your bill.'

'If you'd be good enough to provide paper and ink, I'll be happy to write you a bill on the spot, Mr Mostel, and then you won't have the inconvenience of having to mail me a check.'

He got to his feet reluctantly. 'Very well, Miss Murphy. If you'll wait one moment.'

I waited and he returned with a portable lap desk on which were paper and ink. I wrote, 'To Molly Murphy of J. P. Riley and Associates. For services to unmask a spy at Mostel's garment factory $100.'

Mostel stared at it. 'Did we agree on one hundred, Miss Murphy?'

'We did, Mr Mostel, as I think you very well remember.'

'Since you say yourself you have no evidence, the job is only half finished, wouldn't you say? Shall we settle on fifty?'

'One hundred, Mr Mostel.'

'You'll be the ruin of me, Miss Murphy.' He took out a checkbook then froze with his hand held about the check.

'So how did she do it, Miss Murphy?'

'She was a girl nobody would have suspected – quiet, unobtrusive, so well behaved that when she asked to go to the washroom your foreman never objected. She had a sister who worked for Lowenstein, and she had studied art. It only took her a second or two to copy your sketches. She's a very competent artist, in fact you could do worse than employ her to help you with your designs.'

'I'd never employ someone I couldn't trust,' he said. 'In fact I'm shocked that one of my girls could betray me so easily, after I treated them like a father. It goes straight to my heart, Miss Murphy.'

I struggled with wanting to tell him the truth about his factory and ensuring that I received my payment. 'If you're going to reopen your factory, Mr Mostel,' I said at last, 'may I suggest that you make the conditions bearable for your employees. And relax your rule about not hiring members of the same family. Then they won't be tempted to betray you.' Then, as his hand was still poised above that check, 'It was one hundred dollars, Mr Mostel.'

I watched as he filled in the check with bold, black strokes. He blotted it then handed it to me. 'Don't let it be said that Max Mostel doesn't keep his word.'

'Thank you.' I put the check into my purse and rose from my seat.

'Good-bye, Mr Mostel.' I held out my hand to him. 'It was a pleasure doing business with you.'

'Good-bye, Miss Murphy.'

He escorted me personally to the door.

Twenty-eight

With a light heart and one hundred dollars in my purse I jumped on the trolley back to the Lower East Side and presented myself at Jacob's apartment on Rivington Street.

'Is everything all right?' he asked in a worried voice.

'Couldn't be better. Look at this – a check for one hundred dollars. You can come to the bank with me and watch me deposit it and then I'm going to take you out to lunch. But I also have an ulterior motive—' I laughed at Jacob's expression. 'I've come for help.' I breezed past him into the apartment. 'I think I should tell my story to the newspapers – how we escaped from the fire, as told by a garment worker. It might help raise public awareness of the abuses in the garment industry. It was a pity you didn't bring your camera with you that day.'

He gave an embarrassed smile. 'I did have my little Kodak in my pocket but I was too concerned about you to remember to use it.'

'Oh, Jacob. You are so sweet.' I wrapped my arms around his neck.

'So when shall we get married?' His hands tightened around my waist.

'Why rush into something so important? Let's enjoy each

other's company for a while and get to know each other better.'

'Very well, although I made up my mind the moment I saw you.'

'You were desperate to beat the matchmaker who would have saddled you with a boring, respectable, religious girl,' I teased.

He shook his head. 'I've never felt this way about a girl before you. I never believed this happiness was possible, Molly. Would it be highly improper to try to kiss you?'

'It would completely wreck my reputation, as you very well know,' I said. 'But since my reputation is already wrecked by coming here alone, I'll allow you a quick peck on the cheek.'

His lips brushed my cheek and I was disturbed by the still strange sensation of his beard scratching me. I moved away, laughing. 'Your beard. It tickles.'

'Then I'll shave it off for you.'

'You'll do no such thing. I think it looks grand. I'll learn to like it.' I moved away from him. 'Now enough frivolity. I want you to help me write this newspaper article and then you'll know the right people to take it to.'

We spent a pleasant hour composing the piece and then walked together to Herald Square and presented it to one of Jacob's contacts at the *Herald*. He seemed excited to get the scoop and asked me more questions and asked Jacob to take my picture.

'I prefer to remain anonymous, if you don't mind,' I said. 'It's the conditions I wanted to feature, not me.'

After that we visited the bank to deposit the check, then had the promised lunch at a nice restaurant. I suggested Delmonico's, but steady and sensible Jacob steered me in the direction of a French café just below Union Square. I insisted on paying, much to Jacob's embarrassment. On the way home we walked around Wanamaker's department store, looking in wonder at the items on the food counter – cans and bottles from all over the world, foodstuffs I had never even heard of – as well as the silk stockings from France and varieties of face makeup. I finally arrived home, tired but content, about five o'clock, having left Jacob to hurry off to a union meeting somewhere.

'Hello, all.' I hung my cape on the peg in the hall. No answer. Shamey was often out playing with his friends or earning dimes by running errands, but Bridie and Seamus were always around. I lit the gas in the kitchen then checked around the house. Nobody.

Then I noticed a piece of paper had been pushed through the letter slot. I picked it up and carried it close to the gas mantle to read. It was scrawled in poor penmanship:

If you want to see the little girl again Katherine must meet me at the end of Delancey Street at eight o'clock tonight. Tell her to come alone or no trade.

I stared at the paper, willing the words to say something different. Think, Molly, I commanded myself, trying to slow down my racing brain. The simplest thing to do would be to let Katherine go and trade herself for Bridie. Michael wouldn't harm his wife, would he? But then she wouldn't want to go with him either. If I told the police I would be risking Bridie's life. Michael might kill her as soon as he spotted a police helmet. Or, I could say nothing to Katherine and go in her place. In the dark, with a shawl over my head, I could get close enough to snatch Bridie away, close enough to appeal to his better nature. I'd give him a chance to escape, promise to say nothing until he was safely far away, even give him money for a train ticket.

I wandered around the kitchen in a panic, straightening out the tablecloth, putting a jug back on the shelf, trying to come up with something better. But I couldn't. Nothing really mattered at this point apart from saving Bridie. This man had killed at least twice before. He wouldn't hesitate to kill a child, or to drag her with him as a hostage. And I didn't want Katherine to be a hostage either. But then I didn't want to be a hostage myself – or a dead body, for that matter.

Would I really be in danger? I asked myself. Delancey Street, from what I remembered, was full of life. If I cried out, someone would come to my aid. Shops would still be open at eight o'clock. Workers would be returning from work, saloons would be full. In fact it was a strange place to choose for such a meeting – unless Michael had decided that he could melt into the crowds of the Lower East Side and make it hard for anyone to follow him.

I took my shawl off the peg and wrapped it over my head, hiding that telltale red hair. Apart from that we were about the same stature. If I couldn't get close enough, I'd yell for help. Passersby would grab the child for me. Thus reassured that I was doing the right thing I wrote a hurried note to Seamus and the boy. 'Out with Bridie. Don't worry. Back soon. Love, Molly.' No sense in worrying them too.

Then I let myself out and closed the front door behind me. It was a damp, cold, wintery night. Fog would be swirling in from the East River, which might aid my cause. As I set off down Patchin Place I heard footsteps behind me. I spun around. Katherine was running down Patchin Place after me, wrapping a shawl around her as she ran.

'Wait, Molly. Where are you going?'

'Nowhere. Just out for a stroll.'

She caught up to me, her face anguished. 'He came here. I saw him. He put something through your letterbox. I've been

302

waiting for you to come home. What did he say? Please tell me the truth.'

'I wasn't going to tell you,' I said, and handed her the note, 'but for once I can't come up with a good lie.'

She held it up under the gas lamp to read it and gasped. 'He's taken a little girl?'

'Yes, young Bridie who lives with me.'

'He had a big sack with him. I never thought – never imagined – what were you going to do? Not the police. He'd kill her.'

'If you really must know, I was going in your place. I was going to try and snatch the child and then find safety in the crowds on Delancey Street. It's sure to be busy at this time of night.'

'You'll do no such thing,' Katherine said, with that commanding look I remembered so well from the photograph. 'I'll go and make the trade. If Michael wants to take me with him, so be it. It's my fault. I chose to run away with him. I made my own bed. Now I must lie in it.'

'But you didn't know his true nature then, Katherine.'

She gave a rueful smile. 'He could be very charming when he wanted to. I'd never met anyone like him.'

'But you don't want to go with him now, do you?'

'Of course not. Knowing that he killed a woman in cold blood, and that he felt nothing at all for our lost child, I could never love him again.'

'Then let me go in your place.'

'Absolutely not. He won't hurt me. I'll be all right, I'm sure.'

'I'll come with you then,' I said. 'I'll be in the crowd behind you and if I get a chance I'll dart out and snatch Bridie. If Michael tries to grab you, scream and make a fuss.'

She nodded solemnly. 'Yes. All right. In fact I'd be very glad if you'd come with me. I have been living in fear for weeks

with no one to turn to. Those awful men Michael latched onto
– those Eastman brutes – it was like being plunged into hell.'

'I'm sure it was,' I said. I slipped my arm through hers.
'We escaped from the fire together, didn't we? We can come
through this. He'll find out we're not soft and frightened little
women—'

'We are Amazons, not to be trifled with.' Katherine threw
back her head defiantly.

We strode out, matching steps, in the direction of Delancey
Street. As I had expected, Delancey was bustling with life as
we entered it from the Bowery.

'This is the end of Delancey Street,' I said.

'Or the beginning,' Katherine pointed out.

We stood on the street corner, scanning the crowds who
hurried past, eager to be home and out of the damp chill. The
fog was indeed rolling in, clinging to lampposts and awnings.
It muffled the sound of a clock chiming the three quarters.
Maybe he hadn't arrived yet.

'We should walk to the other end of the street,' Katherine
suggested. 'That would be more logical. He could make an
easier escape down on the docks and there would be fewer
people around to witness too.'

In my confusion I hadn't paused to consider that Delancey
did indeed end in the dockland. It would be easy to hide a
small child on the wharf among piles of cargo. It would also
be easy to throw a small child into the river without being
seen.

'Then let us hurry,' I said. 'Maybe we can intercept him
before he reaches the docks.'

We pushed our way along the crowded street, dodging carts,
horses, children, and piles of rubbish. The street seemed twice
as long as I remembered it. I wished that Jacob had not gone
to an unknown meeting tonight. I wished that I had asked

for Daniel's help. I wished we weren't so very alone. As we approached the far end, the traffic thinned. There were fewer open stores, fewer lights, fewer people. And thicker fog. A mournful foghorn sounded from out on the river. Then the fog swirled, parted, and closed again and I caught a glimpse of a giant structure rising up in front of me – a giant monster from childhood nightmares, reaching out cruel arms. I stared at the fog as if the thing might be a figment of my imagination. Then I remembered, with a cold sinking feeling that clutched at my gut. That was why he had chosen Delancey over any other street. I was looking at the tower being built for the new East River Bridge.

Katherine must have echoed my thoughts. 'It's not built all the way across the river yet, is it?' she asked.

'Just the towers and the cables. No roadway yet.'

'No way to get across then. That's good. Perhaps Michael thinks it's finished and he can get out of New York that way.'

'Only if he's a tightrope walker.'

As we came closer the giant tower loomed above us, the steel girders, ringed with scaffolding, rising into the fog.

'Let's wait here,' Katherine said. 'I'll stand out in the middle of the street, where I can be seen and where I can see him coming. You wait in a doorway where he can't see you.'

I nodded and moved across the street to a darkened doorway. Katherine walked boldly out into the street. I drew my cape around me to stop myself from shivering. The fog had muffled the sounds of Delancey Street so that they came as a distant murmur. It was amazing how remote and deserted it felt here, only a block away from all that life and gaiety.

Katherine walked up and down, stamping her feet against the chill. Then she stopped, her head cocked to one side, listening.

I stepped out from my doorway and heard it too.

'Help me. Somebody help me, please.' The little voice floated out of the fog above our heads.

I came out of my hiding place and stood beside Katherine, who was staring upward.

'It's Bridie,' I whispered. 'Where can she be?'

'Up there, somewhere.' Katherine pointed. 'It sounds like it's coming from the tower.'

'But how—?' I ran around it, peering up at the scaffolding. How could he have taken a small child up there? Then I saw it – a crude staircase made of wood going up between the scaffolding and the tower. It had a gate across it to keep people out but the lock had been forced and the gate flapped open.

'I'll go up,' Katherine said. 'If Michael's up there, he's expecting me.'

'If he's left the child up there, she won't come to you,' I said. 'We'll go together. Come on.'

We held hands and shrank together, taking those makeshift steps side by side. After one flight there was no more light coming up from the street, only an eerie orange glow coming from the city streets beyond. We felt our way up. Eight steps in one direction then eight in the other, back and forth zigzagging up the side of the tower. My legs started to tremble at the exertion. Would these steps never end?

I sensed rather than saw that we had come to an opening. Cold air rushed into my face and I felt nothingness on one side of me. My hand gripped at the cold metal of the scaffolding as wind swirled around me.

Then the voice came again – a small whimper of a terrified child. 'Somebody get me down, please.'

'She's out there,' I whispered to Katherine. But how could she be? I had seen for myself in daylight that there were only cables strung across the river. Then the fog swirled and through the mist I saw that a narrow walkway of planks, about a foot wide, was strung out from the tower, running beside the bottom cable – a fine path for the workmen, I've no doubt, but then they were used to the height. I could only see a few feet in front of me but I could make out the shape of a small person, out there on that path in the fog.

I didn't stop to think. 'It's all right, darling. Molly's here. I'm coming for you,' I called. I turned back to Katherine. 'You stay here and keep watch. Let me know if you hear him coming.'

Then I took a deep breath and stepped out onto the catwalk. It bucked and swayed under my feet like a live thing and I clung onto the thin cables that ran beside it, waist high – the only means of support. The wire seemed as frail and ethereal as gossamer. Cold damp air rushed up from the invisible river. I peered into the gloom, trying to make out the bigger shape of a man, but Bridie appeared to be quite alone. Had he lost his nerve and abandoned her then?

'Molly,' she whimpered. 'I'm frightened. I can't move. The man said he'd be back, but he hasn't come.'

'It's going to be just fine, my darling,' I said, trying to keep my voice calm and even. 'I'll get you down and we'll go home.'

Inch by inch I moved closer to her. She was standing sideways, clinging onto that support cable with both hands. I reached her and let go with one hand to put my arm around her and give her a kiss. 'See, it's really me and you're safe now,' I said. 'Now all we have to do is move back slowly toward the tower then we can go home.'

'I can't,' she whispered. 'I can't move.'

For a horrible moment I thought he might have tied her in some way, but then she added, 'I'm scared I'll fall.'

'You won't fall. Look, we'll take tiny steps, holding on, just like this. One foot. Two foot. Do it just like me.'

I started to move. I felt the walkway vibrate and sway again under my feet. I was so intent on watching her progress that I didn't look up until Bridie screamed.

Michael Kelly was standing a few feet away between us and the tower. His arm was around Katherine's neck and one big hand was over her mouth.

'There you are, Katherine,' he said pleasantly. 'What did I tell you? They were as easy to trap as the rats on your father's estate, weren't they now?'

Katherine struggled as he shoved her forward. 'I couldn't believe that my own wife would turn traitor on me. What sort of wife is that? You promised to love, honor, and obey.'

He had released her mouth or she had broken free. 'It was a sham, Michael. You were a sham. You used me.'

'You should have come alone like I told you, Kathy, then the child would have been safe. We'd have been off, across the bridge to Brooklyn before anyone came looking for us. Now we have to take care of them first.'

It didn't take much intelligence to know what he had in mind. Would it be possible to survive a fall into water from this height? I wasn't sure how high we were, but surely too high to survive a fall. I wasn't even sure if we were over water yet.

'Why do you want me with you?' she demanded 'You don't really love me. I'll slow you down.'

'Insurance, me darlin'. You're my insurance.'

He pushed her closer to Bridie and me. The catwalk swayed and shuddered. Bridie whimpered again. Then, for the first time in my life I found myself face-to-face with Michael Kelly in the flesh. He was watching me with an arrogant smile at that handsome mouth. Cocky. Sure of himself. Delighted that I had been so stupidly naive. I tried to make my brain work in an orderly fashion. Maybe I could protect myself, but how could I possibly defend myself and a small child on this gossamer thread so high above the world?

'How did you find us?' I asked, stalling for time.

'Easy.' Again that cocky grin. Enjoying this almost. 'You think the Eastmans don't run this city? They know all about you.'

I felt Bridie's little body brush against me and was terrified that she'd cling onto me, sealing our doom.

'Bridie,' I whispered to her. 'Hold on very tight to that wire and don't move or let go until I tell you to.'

Michael had released Katherine from his grip. 'Wait there,' he said as he moved past her. 'I don't need your help, but don't think of moving. I don't want to get rid of you too, but I will if I have to.'

'Just let us go, please,' I said in my most submissive voice. 'We can't do you any harm. At least let me take the little girl back to the tower.'

'You've already done me harm,' he said. Then he came at me. The one thing in my favor was that I was ready for him. While I talked I had released one hand quickly to hitch up my skirts enough to move my legs. As he came toward me I held on grimly with both hands and kicked out backward, like a mule. I heard the grunt of air escaping, letting me know that my kick had been high enough to do damage. I had brought one of my brothers to his knees once with a similar move. He teetered for a moment, fought to regain his balance, then as he teetered backward he made a grab for the foot that had kicked him. His hands fastened around my ankle, almost jerking me off the catwalk. I clutched at the wire as his full weight tugged at me. Bridie screamed, the catwalk swung wildly, and then there we were, poised at the edge of eternity, Michael hanging over nothingness and about to pull me with him.

'Let me up again,' he shouted. 'If I go, I'll make damned sure you all go with me.'

My brain was racing, trying to work out how I could pry his hand loose without sacrificing my own balance. In the short seconds that I hesitated Michael grabbed at the planks with his other hand and hauled himself back onto the catwalk.

'You've made enough trouble,' he gasped, clambering to his feet. 'Why couldn't you have left us alone? I might have spared the child, but not now.' He looked past me to Katherine. 'When I give you the nod, we throw her down. Ready?'

'No,' Katherine said. 'No, Michael, I'm not doing it. I'm not helping you again.'

'Don't be a fool, Katherine. Don't think you'll get off free. You won't. I'll tell them you begged me to kill that woman. I'll tell them it was you who made me do it.'

'Thank you for making up my mind for me,' Katherine said. 'I would have done anything for you once, Michael, but not now. But then I really loved you once. This proves that you never loved me. Why don't you go, while you still have time? I'll grant you that much.'

'You'll grant me? You are not in a position to grant me anything, Katherine. If you won't help me, I can do it alone. I don't need your stinking help to get rid of a couple of scrawny females. But, by God, you're going to be sorry.'

Katherine stuck out her chin defiantly. 'I'll help her. It will be two against one and likely enough we'll all go down.'

At that moment a light shone out from the tower, cutting an eerie swath through the mist.

'You out there,' a big voice shouted. 'Police! We know you're there, Kelly.'

'Take one step out here and I throw them down – all of them,' Michael shouted back.

'We've got sharpshooters aiming at you. We don't need to

take a step,' the voice shouted back. 'Come quietly or you're a dead man.'

Michael grasped at Katherine.

'Come with me, Katherine,' he pleaded. 'We'll get away. We'll escape. If they catch you, they'll send you to jail. They'll send you home.'

'You'd better run if you don't want to be caught,' Katherine said evenly.

'Katherine!' He reached out to her.

She knocked away his hand. 'Go, Michael.'

Michael glanced back at the light, then forced his way past me and Bridie, pushing us aside. I held onto her grimly, thinking he might try to throw us over as he passed, or take Bridie hostage again, but I need not have worried. He was anxious to get away and hardly noticed our presence.

'Hold it right there, Kelly,' the voice behind us shouted.

Michael had started to run away, teetering, staggering out along the catwalk that disappeared into the fog.

'Duck down, ladies,' the voice commanded. A shot whizzed over our heads, then another. Michael teetered, then, as if in slow motion, he fell and was swallowed up into the night. We didn't even hear a splash.

Twenty-nine

Strong arms helped us back to the safety of the stairway. Even as I stood on the solid wood of the landing again I felt myself swaying.

'You're all right now, ladies,' the helmeted figure said. 'You're lucky that we got here when we did, and that Higgins is such a crack shot.'

Another constable reached out to scoop up Bridie into his arms. She cried out in fear.

'It's all right, darling. These nice policemen are here to help us,' I said. 'They'll take you down to the ground again. We're following right behind.'

'Just a minute,' Katherine said. 'I'm feeling faint. I have to sit down for a moment.'

'That's what comes of wearing corsets,' I said, helping her to the step.

'You mean you don't?'

'Never have,' I said.

'But don't your insides rattle around? That's what Mother said would happen if I didn't.'

'I've never felt them rattling around yet,' I said. 'Put your head down until you feel better.'

'Thank you, Molly.'

I perched on the step beside her and put my hand on her shoulder.

'It was all so horrible, wasn't it?' she whispered.

'Very horrible,' I said. 'Especially for you.'

'For me? It was you he was trying to kill.'

'But you loved him once,' I said. 'I had no second thoughts about fighting for my life.'

'I still can't believe . . .' she began and put her hand over her mouth. 'I thought I was so strong and brave but . . .'

'You were, very strong and brave. You had to make some horrible choices out there. Your parents would be proud of you.'

'I'm not going back to them,' she said, looking up suddenly. She got to her feet. 'I'm recovered now, thank you. Let's go down.'

As we made our way down the steps a man came up toward us, taking the steps two at a time. In the dim light of the flashlight behind us I took in the unruly curls, the square jaw, and for a horrible moment I thought that it was Michael, and he had somehow survived the shooting and the fall. Then as he came closer to the light I recognized him.

'Daniel!'

'Thank God you're safe,' he gasped as he saw me, and he grasped my shoulders as he fought to regain his breath. 'I came as soon as I heard.' His gaze went past me to Katherine. 'You must be Miss Faversham. I'm Captain Sullivan of the New York police. I'm glad to see you safe and sound. What happened to Kelly?'

'Higgins shot him, sir. Fell into the drink,' one of the constables said.

'Good work, boys. I passed the little girl at the bottom of the tower. She's with her brother.'

'Her brother? What's he doing here?' I asked.

'He was the one who came to find me,' Daniel said. 'Smart lad, that one. He came home and found the note that Kelly left for you and came to tell me right away. I was out on a case unfortunately, so they sent a constable to fetch me and dispatched sharpshooters straight to the bridge.'

'We could have handled it without your men, you know,' I said. 'Katherine and I had the situation under control.'

'Oh, you did, did you?' Daniel gave me a quizzical look.

'Absolutely.' I picked up my skirts and pushed past him to descend the final flight of steps.

When we reached the bottom of the tower and came out onto the dockside we found that a crowd had gathered. It took me a while to pick out Bridie, standing to one side, holding Shamey's hand.

'Molly!' they cried and ran to me.

I knelt to hug them both, and couldn't stop the tears from streaming down my cheeks. 'You see,' I said to Shamey through my tears. 'You see how good it is to go to school now? You might not have been able to read the note.'

We were laughing and crying at the same time. I looked up to see Daniel watching us. I got to my feet.

'I'd better get these children home now. It's past their bedtime.'

'I've a carriage waiting,' Daniel said. He took my elbow and steered us though the crowd.

'Don't we need a statement first, sir?' one of the constables asked.

'The morning will do, Higgins. You get back to HQ and make your report. I'll join you as soon as I can.'

Daniel handed us into the carriage, then climbed in himself. It was a tight squeeze. I took Bridie on my lap and Katherine balanced Shamey on hers. Daniel was beside me. I was aware of the pressure of his body against mine. Would I never get over these stupid feelings when he was near me? I stroked Bridie's hair and pretended I didn't notice him.

'I suppose it's a waste of time to ask, but what in God's name made you decide to climb a half-built tower with a man like Kelly?' he demanded.

'The answer to that is simple,' I said. 'He took Bridie.'

'You could have come to me for help, as young Seamus here so properly did.'

'And when he spotted the first police uniform, what do you think he would have done with her?' I demanded. 'Anyway, we had no idea we were going up to a place like that. The note said the end of Delancey Street. I didn't think about the half-built bridge.'

'That's one more of your nine lives gone,' Daniel said. 'I hope it gave you enough of a scare up there to seek a more sensible occupation in the future.'

'Something like a companion, had you in mind?' I said, turning away from him. 'I find such jobs to be more of a strain on the heart.'

'You did very well, Seamus, my boy,' Daniel said, leaning past me to ruffle Shamey's hair. 'Your father will be proud of you. If you go on like this, I might be able to use you as a messenger when you get a little older.'

'Really?' Seamus leaned forward to look at Daniel. 'How old do I have to be?'

'You have to have enough schooling so that you can read longer notes with harder words,' I said and saw Daniel's smile.

The bright lights of the Bowery flashed past us. A theater performance had just ended and the crowd spilled off the sidewalk forcing our horse to slow to a walk.

'Where can we take you, Miss Faversham?' Daniel asked Katherine.

'She's staying across the street from me, with my friends,' I said.

'Ah. Across the street. A good thought,' Daniel said. 'And may I say, Miss Faversham, or rather Mrs Kelly, that I commend your bravery tonight. I can only tell you that you've had a narrow escape in more ways than one. The man you married was a dangerous thug, wanted by police both here and in Ireland. Had you stayed with him, you would soon have become part of one of the most violent criminal elements in the city, from which there would have been no escape.'

'I realize that,' she said, 'and I suppose I should be grateful, but it's all been rather a shock. I did love him, you know. You can't just stop loving someone, just like that.'

I could feel Daniel looking at me.

'No,' he said. 'You can't.'

Katherine sighed. 'I expect I'll get over him with time. I come from tough stock, you know. My father fought in the Khyber Pass.' She gave a sad little chuckle. 'I'll be all right.'

The carriage slowed and came to a halt.

'We're here,' Daniel said and lifted the children down, then assisted Katherine and myself from the carriage. His hand lingered against mine. When I tried to pull mine away he was looking at me again.

'Are you going to invite me in tonight?' he asked.

'I think not. The children are tired. But thank you for escorting us home.' I gave a correct little nod of the head, equal to anything Miss Arabella Norton could produce.

The children had run ahead to the front door. Seamus opened it and the worried look melted instantly from his face. 'Oh, so there you are. I wondered where on God's earth you'd all got to. I've been worrying about you.'

'We're all just fine, Seamus. And these children are ready for some bread and milk and bed.'

Seamus looked past me to Katherine and Daniel and the carriage at the end of Patchin Place.

'We had a little excitement. No doubt the children will tell you about it in their own good time,' I said.

'I've had a little excitement of my own,' Seamus said. 'I got a job at last. I've been hired by Macy's department store to carry out packages to carriages and automobiles during the Christmas season. And if that works well, they'll keep me on in the stock room.'

'I'm pleased for you, Seamus,' I said. 'Go inside, children. Say good night to Miss Faversham and thank you to Captain Sullivan.'

'Good night, Miss Faversham. Thank you, Captain Sullivan,' two voices chanted in unison. 'Daddy, you'll never guess what . . .' I heard animated voices as they went into the kitchen.

'I'll be off to bed then,' Katherine said. 'Thank you again, Molly.'

'Do you want me to come with you, Katherine?' I asked.

She glanced at Daniel, then at me. 'No, I think not,' she said, and walked across Patchin Place to Number 9.

Daniel and I were left standing together in the darkness. 'I must go and fix that bread and milk for the children,' I said. 'Thank you for bringing us home and thank your men for coming to our aid.'

'Molly,' he said urgently, 'I'll tell her, I promise. Don't do anything rash.'

'If you mean marry someone else, it wouldn't be rash. It would be a carefully thought through decision. I don't make promises lightly.'

'Promise me that you won't make a commitment to another man until I'm free to ask you myself. If I get down on my knees and you tell me that you choose another man over me, then I'll go away and never bother you again.'

317

I looked up at his earnest face and suddenly laughed. 'Daniel – I've a feeling you're full of blarney. You won't tell her. Oh, you'll have great intentions, but when you see her and you realize what you'd be risking and what you'd be giving up, then you'll suddenly become tongue-tied again.'

'No, Molly. Not this time. I swear to you. I love you. I can't live without you. I beg you, don't rush into a marriage you'd regret. A lifetime is a lot of years to live with someone you don't love.'

'And a lot of years to wait for something that may never happen,' I said.

'Just tell me you do still love me and that, if I come to you free and available, you'll not send me away.'

I looked at him and had to smile. 'Oh, Daniel. Like Katherine said, you can't just stop loving somebody. There will probably be a place in my heart for you for the rest of my life. But that doesn't mean I can't find happiness with someone else.'

'Not the same happiness we two can have together.'

'No, probably not the same kind of passion. But passion often dies, doesn't it? Mutual affection and companionship can last forever.'

'You can get those from a dog,' Daniel said.

'One thing you should understand, Daniel,' I said. 'If I marry Jacob, I won't be settling for second best. I would be marrying him because I believe we could be happy together.'

'No, Molly. I won't let you marry him. I'll burst into the ceremony and carry you off if I have to.'

'Oh, Daniel.' I had to smile again. 'If you come to me on your knees before I've made the trip to the altar, I might listen to what you have to say. Other than that, I'm not promising anything. Good night, now.'

I moved to make my escape but Daniel was quicker. He

grabbed me and crushed his lips against mine. I tried not to respond but my body took over and for just a moment I was one with him, pressed against him, the warmth of his body flowing through me. Then I controlled myself and pushed him away.

'That wasn't fair, Daniel. Go home.'

'Does he set you on fire when he kisses you? Does he make you feel the way I do?' he demanded.

'There's more to life than kisses.' I fled to my front door and slammed it behind me, leaving him standing on the cobblestones outside. Once inside I rested my forehead against the cold oak of the door. Not for the first time I wished I had never met Captain Daniel Sullivan.

The sound of lively children's voices came from the kitchen.

'And then you'll never guess what the policeman did!'

I envied their ability to rebound from tragedy or terror.

The next morning I was awakened by pounding on my front door. I put on my robe and made my way downstairs. Jacob stood outside, a newspaper in his hands.

'I've just seen today's paper,' he said, waving it at me as he came into the house.

The headline in the first column of the *New York Times* read, DANGEROUS RESCUE ON NEW EAST RIVER BRIDGE. I scanned down the text. Two young women attempted daring rescue of a child, taken up there by a madman. Situation resolved by fearless, sharpshooting New York police. It mentioned me by name.

'What were you thinking?' Jacob demanded.

'Michael Kelly had Bridie with him. He wanted to trade her for Katherine. I went along to make sure Bridie got down safely.'

'You're lucky to be alive. I went to take a look for myself

319

this morning. Those few planks along the side of the cable? That's what you were on?'

I nodded. 'And it wasn't very pleasant, I can tell you.'

He put his hands on my shoulders. 'Molly, please listen to me. No more of this reckless behavior. I can't live, worrying about you every time you're out of my sight. The moment I saw this I thought that I should have been there, I should have saved you.'

'I don't intend to make a habit of it, I assure you. In fact I can positively guarantee that I'll never climb up a half-built bridge again.' I attempted a laugh. 'You don't have to worry about me, Jacob.'

'Not worry? Since I've met you a woman was killed by mistake in your place, you were almost burned to death in a fire, and then almost hurled to your death from a bridge. What is there to reassure me that you're not to be worried about?'

'Let's just hope that my future cases are more mundane.'

'Let's just hope there are no future cases,' he said firmly. 'Molly, I want you to give up this absurd idea right now. If you want a job, I can find you one that will challenge you and use your talents. The women's trade union league could use someone fearless and articulate like you. You'd be doing a real service, Molly. Making a difference. What do you say?'

'It's very tempting, Jacob. I will think about it.'

'Just promise me you'll stop trying to be a detective.'

'But I'm not trying to be one,' I said as the realization came to me. 'I *am* a detective. I've just concluded two cases satisfactorily. I'll have earned two hundred dollars – not bad for a month's work, wouldn't you say?'

Jacob shook his head, but he was smiling. 'Molly. What am I going to do with you? I don't want to let you out of my sight for another moment.'

I turned away from him. 'Jacob, I . . .'

'I'm sorry. That was stupid of me,' he said. 'I promised I wouldn't put you in a glass case, didn't I? It's because I care so much that I—'

'Jacob,' I interrupted and looked at him this time. 'This talk of marriage makes me uneasy. There's something you should know. I like you, Jacob. I admire you and respect you, but I'm not sure that I can love you.'

He looked down at his hands. 'I see,' he said. 'Cannot love be learned and grow over time? If our match had been arranged by the matchmaker, we wouldn't even know each other before the ceremony, and yet many such marriages are truly happy ones.'

'I'm sure they are, but that would be a risk I wasn't willing to take. I will only marry for love.'

There was another long pause.

'Is there someone else?'

'Yes, and no.'

'That policeman,' he said sharply. 'The one who shouted at you.' He looked at me for confirmation and I nodded. 'He shouted, as I did, because he'd been worried for you. Do you still love him?'

'I'm not sure, but I have experienced what love feels like, and I'm not ready to settle for less.'

'Then why did you not marry him?'

'Because he wasn't free.'

'Ah,' he said quietly. 'So are you're trying to tell me that you don't want to marry me?'

'I don't know, Jacob. I really don't know what I want. That's the trouble. I want to be fair to you as well as fair to me, so that, if I decide to marry you, it will be because you're my true choice and not because I'm settling for second best. You do understand that, don't you?'

'I understand.' He paused, staring past me out of the

window. 'And I commend you for it. You will let me continue to visit you so that I can woo you and sweep you off your feet?'

I laughed, making him smile too. 'You do not need to woo me. You have nothing to prove to me. It is I who has to decide what I want from life and to shake off the ghosts of the past. But I look forward to continuing our friendship and seeing where it might lead us.'

His face lit up. 'Then I am content.'

'Thank you. You are a very dear person.' I put my hand to his cheek and leaned forward to brush his lips with a kiss. 'I'll have to get used to that beard, someday,' I said.

A week later a letter arrived from Ireland from Major Faversham.

> *Dear Miss Murphy,*
>
> *I can't tell you how relieved my wife and I were to receive the letter from you and from Katherine. To know she is alive and well and to discover that she is no longer married to that bounder has lifted our spirits considerably. Of course, we had hoped that she would return to us immediately, but she has promised that she will keep in touch with us via letters and may be coming home soon. Thank you for your splendid work. Enclosed please find a cheque for twenty-five guineas.*

A little over a hundred dollars! I was on my way to becoming a successful woman. I ran across the street and burst into Sid and Gus's house waving the envelope. I found them all at the kitchen table, enjoying the morning coffee and hot rolls ritual.

'A letter from your parents, Katherine. They were so

thrilled to hear from you.' I stopped. A strange man was sitting at the kitchen table with his back to me. 'Oh,' I said, 'I'm so sorry. I didn't realize you had company.'

The man rose to his feet and turned toward me. 'Company, you call it? It is I, darling Molly, come home to the bosom of my loved ones.' And the dashing, irresponsible, loveable, infuriating Ryan O'Hare stood there, dressed in a black velvet jacket with a large diamond pin in his purple silk cravat.

'Ryan!' I ran to his arms. 'How wonderful to see you. We have missed you so much. Have you finally brought the play to New York?'

'It is due to make its glorious opening at the Victoria Theater next week – don't say anything about bad omen in the name. It was the one theater that was free and willing.'

'Why should it be a bad omen?' Katherine asked.

Ryan made a face. 'I had to leave England in a hurry after the queen was not amused about my satirical play about Her Majesty and Albert.' Then that brilliant smile flashed across his face. 'I must say it was deliciously wicked. I had the both of them to a T, in all their boring glory. I even gave them plaid sheets on the marriage bed.'

'Ryan, you are very naughty, we all know that,' Sid said. 'I hope your American audiences haven't been equally incensed with your new satire of the American lifestyle.'

'My dear, it goes over most of their heads. They laugh uproariously, not realizing they are laughing about themselves. It is too marvelous for words. You'll all come to opening night, of course, as my guests – and to the party afterward. Everyone who is anyone will be there.'

'We wouldn't miss it for the world, would we?' Gus said, looking around the table.

I realized with a great flood of relief that this was my normal life now. I could eat long, luxurious breakfasts and take hot baths and go to plays. I was no longer a sweatshop worker. I was Molly, a member of the artistic set of Greenwich Village.

'Let me have a roll and some coffee, please,' I said. 'I'm positively starving.'

'And I have to haste myself in the direction of the Victoria Theater to see about the scenery,' Ryan said. 'I gather there's an annoying pillar that will have to go. Let us hope it will not bring the house down, literally.' He blew kisses and swept out.

Katherine was looking at me strangely. 'I may have made a mistake,' she said. 'I had thought that Jacob was the man in your life, and then I thought that perhaps it was the policeman, but perhaps I am wrong.'

'Ryan?' I laughed.

'My dear Katherine,' Sid said. 'Everyone loves Ryan. Even Ryan loves Ryan.'

'Especially Ryan loves Ryan,' Gus added. 'No, I think that Jacob might not be such a bad choice for Molly after all.'

'I've just told him I'm not ready to think of marriage yet. I'm not at all sure I want to marry him.'

'Quite right. Too earnest.' Sid set a cup of Turkish coffee in front of me. 'And think what a hindrance it would be to your career if you wanted to marry. You need time to enjoy life first, Molly.'

'You're right,' I said. 'What is the rush? I'm sure husbands are an infernal inconvenience.'

I glanced across at Katherine who was looking pensive, fingering the locket she now wore again at her neck, returned by the repentant Ben Mostel. 'I'm sorry,' I said, flushing. 'How insensitive of us to speak of marriage, after what you've just been through. I expect you never wish to hear the word again.'

'Not for a long while,' Katherine answered. 'But I can assure you I'm not going to be a widow and wear black. As a matter of fact, I am excited about starting life on my own, although I have no idea what I'll find to do with myself.'

'We've told you that you're welcome to stay here as long as you want,' Sid said. 'You can fill the empty nest left by Molly.'

Katherine smiled. 'You are most kind, but I have to leave New York, just in case my father comes looking for me. He can be very forceful, as I've told you. I will stay in touch with my parents, but I really don't want to go home again.'

'Then you must go to Boston, of course,' Gus said. 'I'm sure we can find something for you there. My family owns half the city. I'll write some letters for you.'

'But I don't want to go back to the upper-class life,' Katherine said. 'Now I've seen how much needs to be done for poor working women, I'm anxious to do more for them.'

'Not back to a terrible sweatshop, surely?' I asked.

'Preferably not a terrible sweatshop,' Katherine agreed, 'but I have to do something useful to give my life a meaning.'

Her words struck at my conscience. Was I being selfish if I didn't continue to work for the union? As Jacob had said there was a lot of good I could do. Then Sid sat at the table between us, brandishing the silver coffeepot.

'I commend you, Katherine,' she said, 'but I have to confess that my morning coffee and hot rolls and my friends, and Gus here of course, are what give my life meaning. I couldn't exist without them.'

'Amen to that,' Gus said, and raised her coffee cup in salute. I did the same.

Just before Christmas I received a letter from Katherine.

I have settled in Boston. There is a thriving garment industry here as well as a large Irish population, so I feel well at home. Thanks to Gus's connections, I am boarding with several other girls of good family who have started a league dedicated to improving the lot of female factory workers. We have started a branch of the garment workers union in several shops. We have just opened a clinic in one of the worst slums and staffed it with volunteer doctors and nurses. It is challenging, but satisfying work.

Thank you for everything. I hope we may meet again and I wish you well.

Katherine